# FLOWERING PLANT FAMILIES

*at the*

# NATIONAL BOTANIC GARDEN OF WALES

*Based on the Classification System of the Angiosperm Phylogeny Group*

*by Dianne Edwards, Priscilla Spears*
*and Alan Channing*

# FLOWERING PLANT FAMILIES
## AT THE NATIONAL BOTANIC GARDEN OF WALES

Based on the Classification System of the Angiosperm Phylogeny Group

Front cover: The Great Glasshouse from the Broadwalk at the National Botanic Garden of Wales
Back cover: Ivy-leaved toadflax
Page iv: A Welsh woodland in spring with bluebells, early purple orchid, violets and celandines
Facing page ix: Thrift (sea pinks) on a Pembrokeshire cliff

ISBN 978-0-9546409-3-4

Chairman: Rupert Goodman
Chief Operating Officer: Eamonn Daly
Head of Design and Production: Helen Eida

FIRST
56 Haymarket
London SW1Y 4RN
All rights reserved
Printed in the UK
www.firstmagazine.com

LONDON • WASHINGTON

THE QUEEN'S AWARDS
FOR ENTERPRISE
2010

National Botanic
Garden of Wales
Gardd Fotaneg
Genedlaethol Cymru

CARDIFF
UNIVERSITY

PRIFYSGOL
CAERDYⱢD

MISSOURI
BOTANICAL
GARDEN

# FLOWERING PLANT FAMILIES

*at the*

# NATIONAL BOTANIC GARDEN OF WALES

*Based on the Classification System of the Angiosperm Phylogeny Group*

Based on the original text and photographs of
*A Tour of the Flowering Plants* by Priscilla Spears
with modifications written by Dianne Edwards
and coordinated by Alan Channing for the
National Botanic Garden of Wales.

CLARENCE HOUSE

It gives me the greatest pleasure to contribute the foreword to this important book "Flowering Plant Families at the National Botanic Garden of Wales". Wales is still home to an exquisite variety of wild plants and this remarkable book is not only a reference work for all those who study plants and their role in the wider ecosystem, but is a celebration of the richness of Wales's plant heritage.

Conservation of plant species for the long-term is the passion and purpose of Professor Dianne Edwards and the dedicated scientists who work at the National Botanic Gardens of Wales, which will benefit from the sale of this book and where many of the plants featured can be seen. The beauty and knowledge captured in this volume will, I hope, encourage readers to reflect on the beauty as well as the utility of plants, and the importance for the future of our planet of conserving them and their habitats.

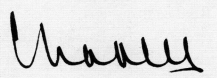

# CONTENTS

# PREFACE AND ACKNOWLEDGEMENTS

When I first saw *A Tour of the Flowering Plants* by Priscilla Spears, I immediately knew it was exactly the kind of publication that would help visitors understand and appreciate the systematic beds in the Double Walled Garden at the National Botanic Garden of Wales (NBGW). Her book was written to demonstrate a new classification of flowering plants (angiosperms) developed by a team of scientists named the Angiosperm Phylogeny Group. Its guiding principle is monophyly, "that taxonomic groups should hold all the descendants of a single ancestor, and only its decendants," as Priscilla Spears explained. This new classification, reflecting the phylogeny (history) of flowering plants, is now used in textbooks, floras, arrangements in herbaria and even in botanic gardens as has been attempted at the National Botanic Garden of Wales. Priscilla's book is at once both beautiful and accessible. Its abundant images include wonderfully detailed botanical photographs of flowering plants. In addition its use of a branching tree diagram to illustrate our current understanding of those plants' evolution and classification is consistent with the design of the Double Walled Garden. This was created to illustrate millions of years of botanic history that ranges from the ancient water-lilies at the garden's centre to the latest cultivars along its outer walls. This publication follows the format devised by Priscilla, but concentrates on the families cultivated at the National Botanic Garden and includes some additional information on always fascinating plants. It would not have been possible without her generosity, advice and forbearance. I am grateful to Priscilla and to the Missouri Botanical Garden Press for releasing permission to reproduce text and photos from *A Tour of the Flowering Plants*.

Although *A Tour of the Flowering Plants* was originally written with North America in mind, many of the plants illustrated in Priscilla's book are also in the Double Walled Garden, and the text here retains a very strong North American flavour, thus reflecting the popularity of trans-Atlantic plants in our gardens. To cover more fully a flowering garden in Wales and the local flora, some of her photographs of North American plants have been replaced. These new images have been provided by many patient and generous colleagues to whom I am most grateful. Those who supplied images are listed in Appendix C. Particularly helpful were Laura Davies and the horticultural team at the National Botanic Garden and two expert photographers Sue Parker and Pat O'Reilly of Ceredigion (First Nature) who all responded cheerfully to numerous requests. I thank all these colleagues effusively. Their assistance has been indispensable.

As a Palaeozoic palaeobotanist, it was with some trepidation that I approached the revision of a book on the phylogeny of flowering plants. I learned a great deal from Priscilla's original text, and am absolutely indebted to Dr M. Fay and Prof M. Chase at Kew who spotted so many errors in my earlier draft. Professor Terry Turner, formerly of Cardiff University, checked the information on medicinal properties. Dr Tim Rich at the National Museum of Wales and Dr David Cutler, Kew, very kindly checked the whole manuscript. Dr David Mabberley has been particularly helpful in bringing me up to date on plant name changes and those resulting from the latest publications of the Angiosperm Phylogeny Group. Ivor Stokes and Mrs Rose Clay provided assistance on horticultural aspects. I thank them all.

The suggestions of Tammy Charron at the Missouri Botanical Garden Press for making this book more relevant for visitors to the National Botanic Garden and her editorial comments have been invaluable and are very gratefully acknowledged.

I am also indebted to Liesbeth Diaz who very skilfully typed up my notes and has been a staunch supporter of the Garden since "grass-roots" days. Alun Rogers is thanked for preparing the line drawings.

The printing of this modified edition of *A Tour of the Flowering Plants* has been made possible through the generosity of Rupert Goodman, who is also a former Trustee of the NBGW.

Despite all this help, there will be mistakes and I would appreciate knowing about them so that they can be corrected. Please send comments to me at Cardiff University.

*by Dianne Edwards*

*The Great Glasshouse at the National Botanic Garden of Wales viewed from Llyn Uchaf, one of the three restored lakes.*

# INTRODUCTION

*Welcome to the Flowering Plant Families at the National Botanic Garden of Wales*

## Why read this guide?

Do you enjoy attractive colour and beautiful form? How about interesting life stories? Do you want to know more about the plants around you? Do you want to know more about what makes our planet and its life work? This guide has something for you. Even better, you can experience some of the plants themselves at the National Botanic Garden of Wales.

Life on Earth depends heavily on the flowering plants, the angiosperms, as primary producers and the foundation of most ecosystems. Angiosperms play important roles in aquatic ecosystems as well. Beyond their vital ecological roles, flowering plants are beautiful and visually interesting, with a wide variety of forms and life stories. Many people, however, are able to name only a few plants around them. Many cannot see the amazing diversity of flowers because they have never learned to look. We hope this guide will open many eyes to the beauty and wonderful stories of the flowering plants and, at the same time, increase understanding of the diversity of this vital part of the living world.

This book, like a physical tour of the botanic garden, will give you a quick look at a wide spectrum of its subject area, the flowering plants in mostly temperate areas of the world and particularly the British flora. It provides an overview of their families and evolutionary relationships, and introduces an up-to-date system of classification. At the end, we hope you will be inspired to observe more plants around you and find their place in the flowering plants. For more in-depth information about flowering plant families, see the Selected References section at the end of the book.

## What families are included?

The families of flowering plants that are illustrated here are well-known or common families, ones that are used for food or medicine, grow in our gardens or contain familiar wild flowers. Some families are shown here because they form important branches on the "family tree" of flowering plants. Because the flower itself is the major distinguishing feature of the families, most illustrations are of flowers, with photos of fruits and other plant parts as supplements. For a more extensive outline of flowering plant families, refer to Appendix A. This listing will also help you to see the structure of the Angiosperm Phylogeny Group classification system.

## Why this guide uses a recent classification system:

The science that studies the diversity of life, systematics, has advanced greatly in the past two decades. We have traditionally placed organisms that resemble one another in groups, but now we are also concerned with the relationships among these groups. Current scientific thought maintains that taxonomic groups should contain all the descendants of a single ancestor, and only its descendants. Recent systematics studies use all the information we had previously on the structure of plants, and add additional information about the DNA and the development of plants. The result is similar to traditional classification, but with important differences. The remodelled system reflects the evolutionary history of the organisms.

The revised classification for flowering plants, also known as the angiosperms, has been and continues to be developed by a team of scientists called the Angiosperm Phylogeny Group (APG). Members of this large, worldwide team have pooled their data and efforts to produce a new picture of flowering plant relationships. The result is a phylogenetic classification. "Phylogeny" refers to the evolutionary history of a group of organisms. Phylogenetic classifications show the branching of the tree of life and reflect the evolutionary history of life.

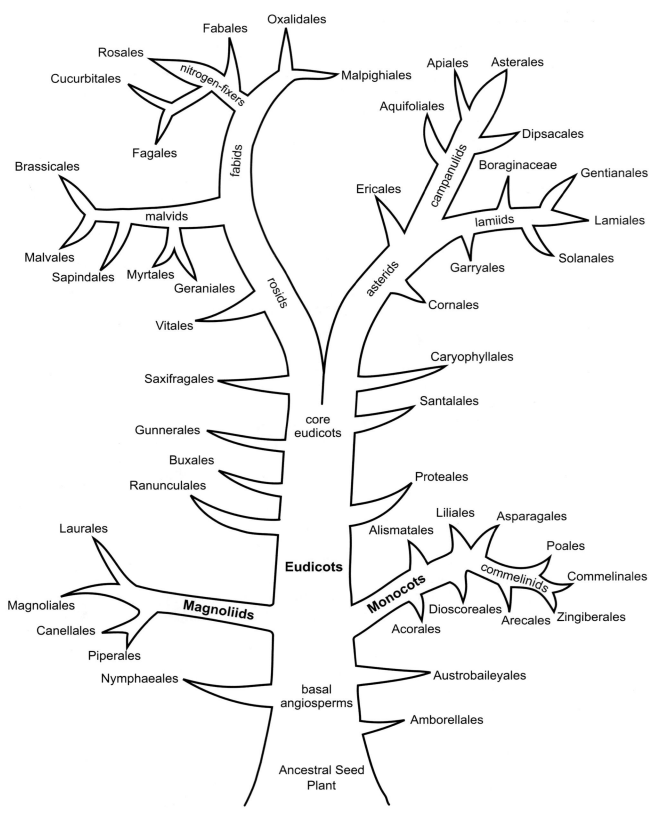

**A map to help you find your way around the flowering plants.**

The tree diagram above is our framework for the guide. It shows the basic relationships among the orders of flowering plants. You will see this map again at the introduction to certain groups, with highlighting to show the upcoming sections.

**The real maps of the flowering plants** used by botanists are much more complex and quantitative. These diagrams are called phylograms or cladograms. An example, redrawn from APGIII (2009), is given on the facing page. See the Selected References section if you are interested in this and further explorations of branching diagrams.

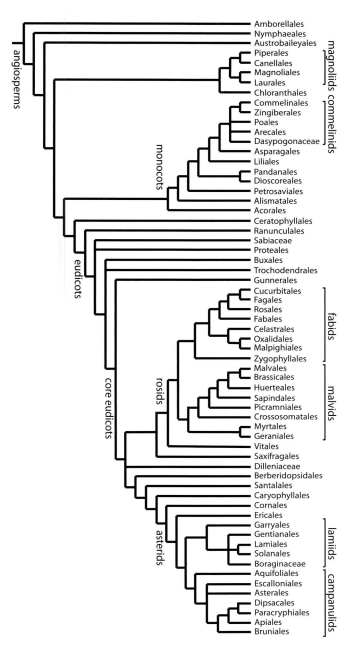

The tree diagram labels (read top to bottom) are:

Amborellales
Nymphaeales
Austrobaileyales
Piperales
Canellales
Magnoliales — magnoliids
Laurales
Chloranthales
Commelinales
Zingiberales
Poales
Arecales — commelinids
Dasypogonaceae
Asparagales
Liliales
Pandanales — monocots
Dioscoreales
Petrosaviales
Alismatales
Acorales
Ceratophyllales
Ranunculales
Sabiaceae
Proteales
Buxales
Trochodendrales
Gunnerales — eudicots
Cucurbitales
Fagales
Rosales
Fabales
Celastrales — fabids
Oxalidales
Malpighiales
Zygophyllales
Malvales
Brassicales
Huerteales
Sapindales — malvids — rosids
Picramniales
Crossosomatales
Myrtales
Geraniales
Vitales
Saxifragales — core eudicots
Dilleniaceae
Berberidopsidales
Santalales
Caryophyllales
Cornales
Ericales
Garryales
Gentianales — lamiids
Lamiales
Solanales
Boraginaceae
Aquifoliales — asterids
Escalloniales
Asterales
Dipsacales — campanulids
Paracryphiales
Apiales
Bruniales

(angiosperms labels the whole tree)

## How our guide operates

The coloured labels on the right side of the page will help you navigate this book. The top label and the colour divide the flowering plants into three parts – basal angiosperms, monocots and eudicots. The second label gives a subgrouping, such as campanulids or core eudicots. These lineages are not given a traditional hierarchical category such as subclass or superorder. You can see the middle label subgroups on our tree diagram. From these subgroups down, our classification looks much like traditional systems, which have orders, families, genera, and species. The bottom label on the page lists the order shown. The label across the top of the page lists the family, as well as subfamily or tribe as needed. You will be able to recognise plant order names, because they always end in -ales. Family names end in -aceae.

The flowering plant orders are presented according to their place on the tree diagram. Within each order, the families are placed in phylogenetic order. For more information on the phylogeny of families within the orders, see the Selected References section at the end of the book.

For each family, we have listed the classification on the left page across from its pictures. This includes major genera in the family, along with common names. We have given the approximate number of genera and species for that family as it occurs worldwide.

### The basal angiosperms have green labels

This group makes up about only 3% of the flowering plants, but it includes some intriguing lines of descent. The term "basal" means "at the base" and commonly refers to a group or groups that diverge early from a lineage. Basal lineages, like any other lineage, are not static – they continue on their own evolutionary path. On our tree diagram of flowering plant orders, the basal angiosperms are the magnoliid branch and the three lowest branches. Plants of this group have some features in common with monocots and eudicots, but they belong to neither group. For now, we place them in their own "miscellaneous drawer."

### The monocots have purple labels.

Monocots are all one related group, i.e. members of a single lineage. Their subgroups are the basal monocots, the lilioid or petaloid monocots, and the commelinid monocots. Monocots make up about a quarter of the flowering plants.

### The eudicots have blue labels.

The traditional class for dicots included the basal angiosperms. With the basal groups excluded, the remainder are called the eudicots, meaning "true dicots" (pronounced "U-dicots"). They are the largest group of flowering plants, making up over 70% of the quarter-million-plus species. They are divided further into basal eudicots and core eudicots. Within core eudicots, there are five main groups – Caryophyllales, Santalales, Saxifragales, the rosids, and the asterids. The largest of these groups are the rosids and asterids, each of which have two main branches. The subgroups are called fabids and malvids, and lamiids and campanulids.

## Changes of note in the classification of flowering plants:

For those familiar with previous classifications, the following notes may help explain some of the changes. The recognition of basal angiosperms makes the class Magnoliopsida, the dicotyledons or dicots, obsolete. There are no longer two classes of angiosperms. The magnoliids and the water-lilies are not closely related to the eudicots, and therefore cannot share their class. This situation, like so much of life, is not simple. Our map, the tree diagram, shows this. This diagram is simplified; it mainly shows orders that are featured in this guide. The full tree for flowering plants particularly when tropical ones are included would have many more branches.

**Recent changes in the monocots** include placing sweet flag, *Acorus*, as the most basal monocot. The main groups of monocots are the basal monocots, the lilioid or petaloid monocots (botanists use both terms) and the commelinid monocots. On the family level, the break-up of the lily family is a big change. Field guides and gardening books still place most monocots with six similar "petals" into the lily family. Currently, the traditional lilies are divided into two orders and several other families.

**Major changes in the eudicots** include the creation of the order Saxifragales. Many of the orders from older plant classifications are no longer recognised or include different families. Some families of eudicots have been combined, while others have been split apart. These changes include:

- The amaranth and goosefoot families have been combined under the name of Amaranthaceae. Chenopodiaceae is no longer recognised as a family.

- The peonies, family Paeoniaceae, are now placed in the order Saxifragales.

- The mallow or hollyhock family, Malvaceae, has several new subfamilies that were formerly independent families. They include the former lime family, Tiliaceae, and the former family Sterculiaceae.

- The sycamore or maple family, Aceraceae, is no longer recognised on its own. It is now a subfamily of the soapberry family, Sapindaceae.

- The borage family and the waterleaf family are combined; they are called Boraginaceae.

- The milkweed family, Asclepiadaceae, is no longer recognised. It is now a subfamily of the dogbane family, Apocynaceae.

- Most members of the family Scrophulariaceae have been moved to other families, which include Orobanchaceae and Plantaginaceae. Relationships in the former Scrophulariaceae have been difficult to resolve and their investigation is on-going.

What you will not see in this guide are the many biochemical and microscopic features that help botanists classify plants. The DNA sequences of selected genes are vital in determining relationships. Features such as how the ovules are attached inside the ovary and the cellular structure of the vascular tissues are examples of some of the additional data used. Bear in mind that you cannot see everything that went into this system of classification. If you would like further details, see Selected References at the book's end.

## Before we start

A brief review of the language of botany and flower structure

Foreign language notes: For botanists, words such as "nut" and "numerous" have special meanings, apart from their common usage. In botany, a fruit is not something we eat for dessert. It is a mature, ripened ovary of a flower. It can be hard and dry, or soft and juicy. Botany has many terms, because of the need to describe the huge diversity of plants. As you encounter terms or usages that are foreign to you, consult the glossary for help.

## Citation of plant names

Following each Latin name, be it of an order, family or genus, you will find the surname of the person (or persons) who first erected it. L. stands for Linnaeus who was responsible for so many names. A son is indicated by f. Thus the son of Linnaeus is L.f.

## By the way, what IS a flower?

A flower is the reproductive organ of a flowering plant. (Note: Pine trees don't have flowers; neither do ferns nor mosses.) Each flower is a puzzle for us to solve, because it has certain basic parts, but they may be greatly modified. We will be seeing and describing many flowers, so you will need some basic terms. A generalised flower is described here, but bear in mind that there are many variations. The flower starts with its stem, sometimes called a floral shoot. The end of the stem, where the flower attaches, is called the receptacle. There are four basic levels of parts attached above this. The first is the calyx, which is made up of sepals. Sepals usually cover the flower when it is in bud. The next is the corolla, which is made up of all the petals. The term for the calyx and corolla together is the perianth, which literally means "surrounds the flower." If the perianth segments are both coloured and look similar, they are neither sepals nor petals, but instead are called tepals. Flowers such as tulips and daylilies have tepals, not petals and sepals.

## So what is the real flower?

That comes next. Above the petals there are stamens, the male structures, which typically have a stalk-like filament with a pollen-bearing anther at the end. In the centre, there are carpels (the female part), where the seeds develop. There can be a single carpel, several independent ones, or a pistil that is made of two or more carpels fused together. Carpels and pistils can have three sections-the ovary, the style, and the stigma. The ovary holds the ovules, the structures that become seeds if they are fertilised. The ovary matures into the fruit of the plant. The style is a connecting structure that ties the ovary to the stigma, the pollen-receiving surface.

These flower parts may not seem exceptionally complicated, but the variations are enormous. Floral parts can be fused either to like or different parts. Parts can be reduced in size, altered to something with a different function, or be missing altogether. The calyx and corolla, which together make up the perianth, can be large and showy, tiny and hard to see, or not there at all. To be a flower, a structure has to have some part that functions in the plant's reproduction. It can be as simple as a single stamen or a single pistil.

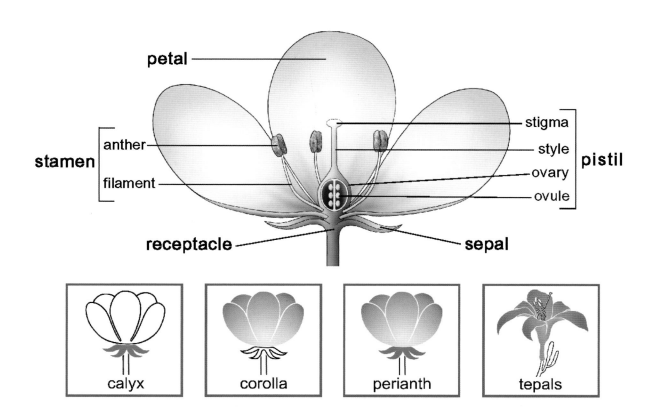

5

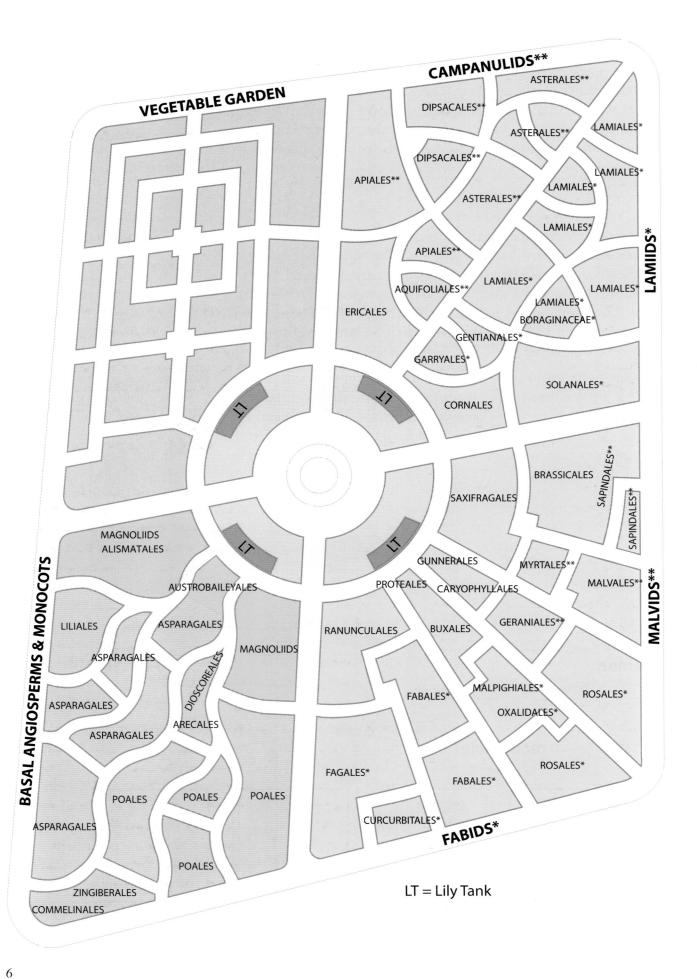

# Diagram of the layout in the inner part of the Double Walled Garden at the National Botanic Garden of Wales

LT = Lily Tank

# THE NATIONAL BOTANIC GARDEN OF WALES

A visit to the National Botanic Garden of Wales offers an opportunity for a tour in person of flowering plants. The botanic garden is a new institution dedicated to conserving threatened plant species, particularly those native to Wales, Britain and the western seaboard of Europe. As a centre for research, life-long education and pleasure, it aims to play a major role in the cultural life of the Principality and contribute to its economy through tourism and employment. It opened in May 2000 on the site of a Regency park, Middleton Hall, following financial support from the Millennium Commission, matched by donations from numerous public and private organisations and individuals. Its vision is based on two elements, the scientific and the aesthetic.

While striving to be a centre for scientific excellence, it has an obligation to attract visitors through imaginative display and innovative interpretation. It seeks to link the ethos and infrastructure of a historic garden with an understanding of new global roles of contemporary botanic gardens in conservation of biodiversity, in demonstrating the relationship and interdependence of plants and society and in promoting sustainable use of plants.

**The Double Walled Garden** as the nucleus of our tour of the flowering plants in the outdoors exemplifies our commitment to inform our public about the classification and evolutionary relationships of plants in a novel and aesthetically pleasing way. It was designed to provide a garden of pleasure, colour and fun for all visitors and show how contemporary materials that are easily obtained could be used to create interesting designs. Thus instead of a series of geometrically similar order beds containing representative families, we attempted to arrange the beds to reflect the position of the orders on the evolutionary tree with its three major branches radiating from the basal group of flowering plants. This was the challenge presented to the design group led by Elizabeth Banks and including landscape architect Tony Jellard, garden historian, Robin Whalley, and the curator, Wolfgang Bopp.

At the start of the project the area was essentially an overgrown field with occasional old fruit trees surrounded by crumbling walls, but after much research and excavation, most of its original structural layout was discovered. Mrs Banks recalls that the original central basin was excavated to reveal the remains of a water feature and the lines of the paths crossing the garden were found. These were so narrow that neither the public nor machinery could use them easily. Nothing was symmetrical; each of the four compartments was a different shape and size. The final design recognised the importance of the original, central stone fountain and created a generous formal circle edged by pleached hornbeams. The four paths were widened to provide a comfortable promenade walk for visitors and to accommodate garden vehicles. To provide year round interest the main paths were edged with long borders framed by espalier fruit trees and filled with colourful shrubs and a wide range of perennials. As the garden was originally laid out to grow vegetables, the northwest quadrant was designed in a simple but formal manner as a vegetable garden growing unusual cultivars.

To show the evolution of plants, each of the remaining compartments was developed as a kind of maze, starting from the large tanks containing water-lilies (the descendants of some of the oldest flowering plants) positioned behind the hornbeam hedge. This enabled paths to wind out from the central area and provided a route to demonstrate the evolutionary progression. In one quadrant that displays the basal angiosperms and monocots, the paths wind through like snakes. In another that shows the basal eudicot and rosid orders, they move in straight lines linked by formal rectangles. In the third that contains the asterid orders, a diagonal path connects all the linking sidewalks. All the paths and the shapes of the beds were designed to be explored by energetic children and to be fun to walk through, especially in the winter when much of the plant material would die down. Each compartment has specially designed seating areas. Different materials were used in the hard landscape of each of the quadrants to reinforce the ways in which the various groups of plants diversified.

Of course it was impossible to map exactly the relationships between orders and the arrangement of the beds; size constraints necessitated the inclusion of more than one order per bed in some cases, while some the larger orders encompass more than one bed. In the latter, members of closely related families have been planted together. Horticultural challenges were numerous, especially as they related to the limitations of gardening in a cool temperate climate and the accommodating of a wide range of growth habits ranging from herbs to trees. Tree dominated orders such as the Fagales, which includes oaks, beeches and birches, were particularly demanding of the skills of our horticulturalists! Nevertheless, the result represents a very innovative approach to the display of the evolutionary relationships among the flowering plants, which is combined with a celebration of their beauty, utility and diversity.

### A Note of Caution

**This book is NOT a handbook on medicinal plants for self-treatment. However, the additional notes do contain information on the past and present medicinal uses of some of the plants. Today the active chemicals are very carefully extracted and purified. The plants themselves should never be eaten raw as these chemicals when untreated can be poisonous or cause severe allergic responses. Neither the authors nor the publishers can be held responsible for their misuse.**

*The Great Glasshouse from the Mediterranean Garden*

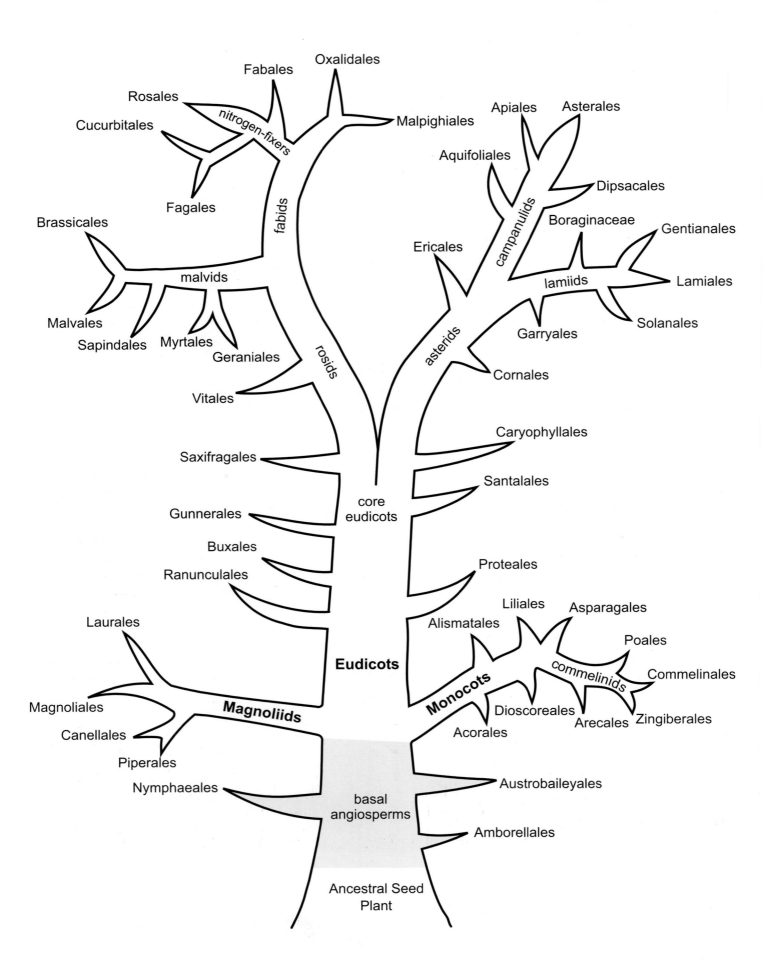

*Amborella trichopoda, female flower*

*Kadsura interior*

*Illicium floridanum*

# INTRODUCING THE FIRST BRANCHES OF THE FLOWERING PLANTS

For many years, botanists have speculated about the oldest lineage of the flowering plants. Magnolias were once thought to be the oldest, based on the fossil record. However, flowering plants did not fossilise very well, probably because they had few hard parts and they grew in environments that led to decay rather than preservation. With further studies of the "second fossil record," the sequences in DNA, a new picture has come into focus.

Of flowering plants that still exist, the plant from the earliest or most basal branch is *Amborella*, a shrub on the island of New Caledonia. That is outside the realm of this tour, which starts with Nymphaeales, on the second oldest lineage of the presently living flowering plants. Nymphaeales includes the family Nymphaeaceae, the water-lilies and pond lilies, and the family Cabombaceae, the fanworts, which are common aquarium plants.

Next to branch was the ancestor of the Austrobaileyales, the order of *Illicium* (star anise), *Schisandra* (star vine and wild sarsaparilla) and *Kadsura* (Japanese kadsura), genera now placed in the Schisandraceae. Most members of Austrobaileyales are found in Australia and New Guinea or Asia.

After these early branches, the flowering plants split into three main lineages, the magnoliids, the monocots, and the eudicots ("true dicots"). It is difficult to tell if one of these came first or if they all emerged more or less at the same time. Because the magnoliids have traditionally been considered among the oldest lineages, they are often grouped with the basal branches as they are in the predominantly monocot quadrant in the Garden. Together, the basal branches and the magnoliids make up about 3% of flowering plants and are termed the basal angiosperms.

The basal angiosperms were once classified as dicots, but it was not a very good fit. They have many characteristics in common with monocots, but do not properly fit on the monocot branch either. Placing them on their own separate branches better reflects flowering plant evolution.

*Schisandra rubriflora flower (left) and fruits (right)*

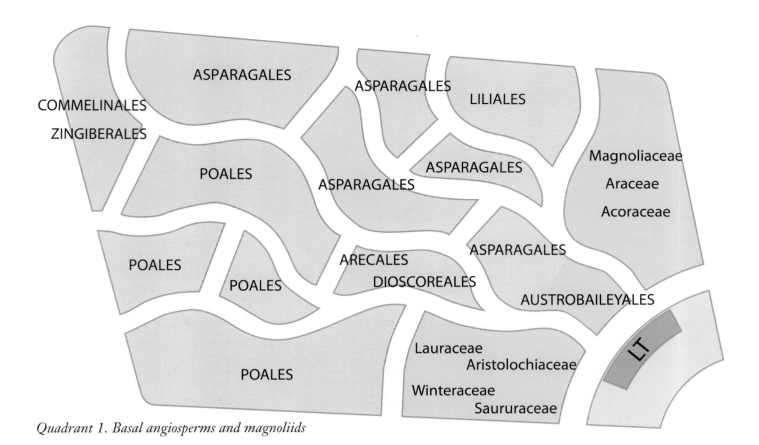

COMMELINALES

ZINGIBERALES

ASPARAGALES

ASPARAGALES

LILIALES

POALES

ASPARAGALES

ASPARAGALES

Magnoliaceae

Araceae

Acoraceae

POALES

ASPARAGALES

POALES

ARECALES

DIOSCOREALES

AUSTROBAILEYALES

LT

Lauraceae

Aristolochiaceae

Winteraceae

POALES

Saururaceae

*Quadrant 1. Basal angiosperms and magnoliids*

*Evergreen foliage of the basal angiosperms in the Austrobaileyales, with Laurales in the background*

*Top: Lauraceae and Saururaceae (left) in Quadrant 1 of the Double Walled Garden. Bottom: Magnoliaceae with underplanting of Araceae and Acoraceae in Quadrant 1 of the Double Walled Garden*

**Basal angiosperms**

**Basal lineages**

**Nymphaeales** Dumortier

    **Nymphaeaceae** Salisbury             5 genera/95 species

      Genera include:

      *Nuphar* Smith (yellow water-lily, brandy bottle, brandy balls)

      *Nymphaea* L. (water-lily)

      *Victoria* Lindley (Victorian water-lily, giant water-lily)

The cosmopolitan family Nymphaeaceae contains plants whose ancestors evolved before the monocotyledons appeared. Water-lilies are aquatic plants with rhizomes that are anchored on the bottom of ponds. The genus *Nymphaea* has flowers with four to six sepals that are sometimes coloured like petals. The petals are numerous; they show gradual transition into stamens, which are arranged in spirals. In more highly evolved (derived) angiosperms, the flower parts have definite numbers and are arranged in whorls. As in monocot pollen, pollen grains of water-lily have one opening. Another ancient feature is pollination by beetles amongst a wide range of other insects. The leaves are rolled in bud and unfurl as they mature. Their long petioles or leaf stalks allow the blades to float on the water's surface. The blades have a deep notch near the petiole attachment. The rhizomes of water-lilies are reported to have aphrodisiac properties.

*Examine the parts near the middle of this water-lily flower, a Nymphaea hybrid. Some parts look something like stamens, but also look something like petals*

# NYMPHAEACEAE, *the water-lily family*

Nymphaea alba (white water-lily) is widespread in England and Wales. It grows in lakes, ponds, canals and slow moving rivers. Its flowers float on the water's surface

Nuphar lutea (yellow water-lily) has smaller, more globular, flowers than the white water-lily and they are held above the water on long flower stalks. Their smell is reminiscent of wine-dregs – but the common names brandy balls or bottles refer to the fruit shape. Lutea means deep or buttercup yellow in Latin. Both genera have declined because of over collecting for garden ponds and to water pollution

The lily ponds at Bosherston, part of the Stackpole estate in Pembrokeshire, provide an ideal environment for water-lilies. These calcareous marl lakes were created between 1780 and 1840 by damming and flooding three small valleys close to the sea from which they were isolated by a sand-dune ridge

15

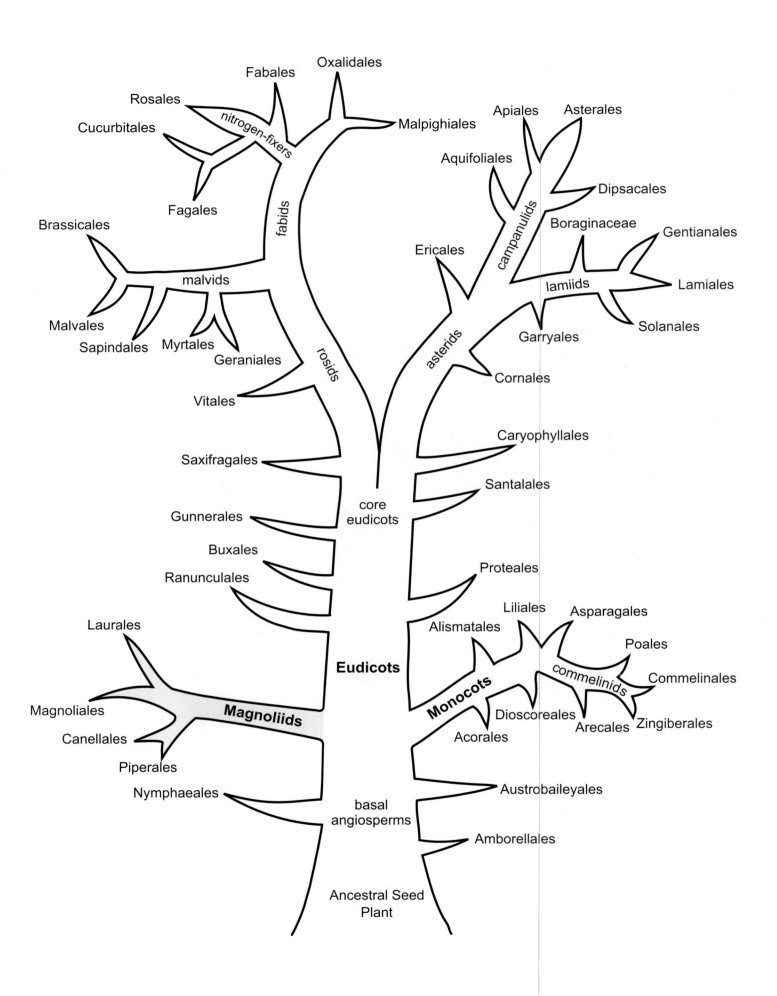

Oxalidales
Fabales
Rosales
Cucurbitales
nitrogen-fixers
Fagales
fabids
Malpighiales
Brassicales
malvids
Malvales
Sapindales
Myrtales
Geraniales
Vitales
rosids
Saxifragales
Gunnerales
core
eudicots
Buxales
Ranunculales

Laurales
Magnoliales
**Magnoliids**
Canellales
Piperales
Nymphaeales

basal
angiosperms

**Eudicots**

Apiales
Asterales
Aquifoliales
campanulids
Dipsacales
Boraginaceae
Gentianales
Ericales
lamiids
Lamiales
Garryales
Solanales
asterids
Cornales
Caryophyllales
Santalales
Proteales
Liliales
Asparagales
Poales
commelinids
Commelinales
Alismatales
**Monocots**
Dioscoreales
Zingiberales
Arecales
Acorales
Austrobaileyales
Amborellales

Ancestral Seed
Plant

16

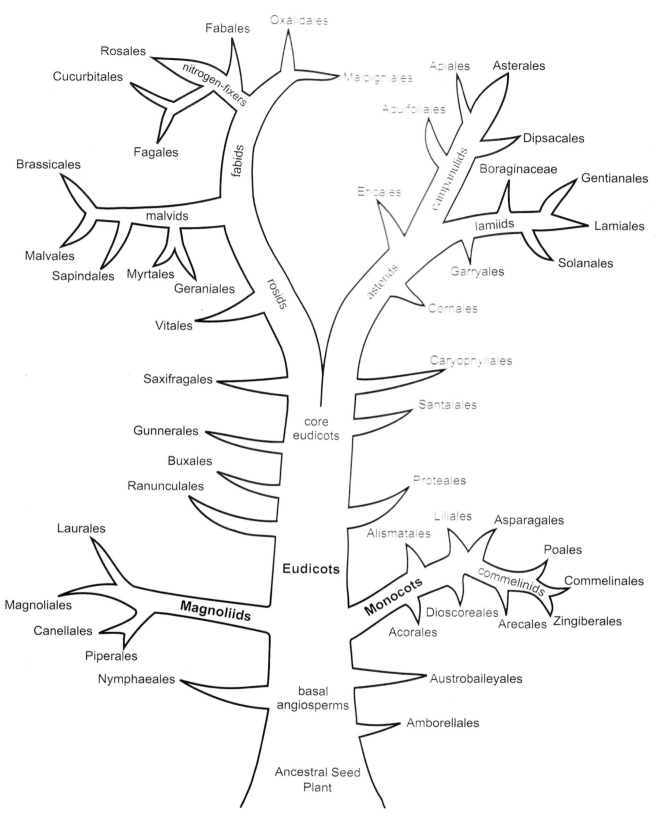

The tree diagram above is our framework for the guide. It shows the basic relationships among the orc of flowering plants. You will see this map again at the introduction to certain groups, with highlight to show the upcoming sections.

The real maps of the flowering plants used by botanists are much more complex and quantitat These diagrams are called phylograms or cladograms. An example, redrawn from APG111 (2009) given on the facing page. See the Selected References section if you are interested in this and furt explorations of branching diagrams.

## How our guide operates

The coloured labels on the right side of the page will help you navigate this book. The top label and the colour divide the flowering plants into three parts – basal angiosperms, monocots and eudicots. The second label gives a subgrouping, such as campanulids or core eudicots. These lineages are not given a traditional hierarchical category such as subclass or superorder. You can see the middle label subgroups on our tree diagram. From these subgroups down, our classification looks much like traditional systems, which have orders, families, genera, and species. The bottom label on the page is the order shown. The label across the top of the page lists the family, as well as subfamily or tribe as needed. You will be able to recognise plant order names, because they always end in -ales. ... family names end in -aceae.

The flowering plant orders are presented according to their place on the tree diagram. Within each order, the families are placed in phylogenetic order. For more information on the phylogeny of families within the orders, see the Selected References section at the end of the book.

For each family, we have listed the classification on the left page across from its pictures. This includes major genera in the family, along with common names. We have given the approximate number of genera and species for that family as it occurs worldwide.

## The basal angiosperms have green labels

This group makes up about 3% of the flowering plants, but it includes some intriguing lines of descent. The term "basal" means "at the base" and commonly refers to a group or groups that diverge early from a lineage. Basal lineages, like any other lineage, are not static – they continue on their own evolutionary path. On our tree diagram of flowering plant orders, the basal angiosperms are the magnoliid branch and the three lowest branches. Plants of this group have some features in common with monocots and eudicots, but they belong to neither group. For now, we place them in their own "miscellaneous drawer."

## The monocots have purple labels

Monocots are all one related group, i.e. members of a single lineage. Their subgroups are the basal monocots, the lilioid or petaloid monocots, and the commelinid monocots. Monocots make up about a quarter of the flowering plants.

## The eudicots have blue labels

The traditional class for dicots included the basal angiosperms. With the basal groups excluded, the remainder are called the eudicots, meaning "true dicots" (pronounced "U-dicots"). They are the largest group of flowering plants, making up over 70% of the quarter-million-plus species. They are divided further into basal eudicots and core eudicots. Within core eudicots, there are five main groups – Caryophyllales, Santalales, Saxifragales, the rosids, and the asterids. The largest of these groups are the rosids and the asterids, each of which have two main branches. The subgroups are called fabids and malvids, and lamiids and campanulids.

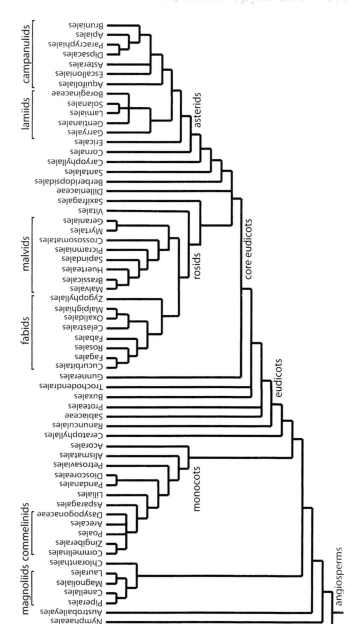

## CHELSEA PHYSIC GARDEN

# Points of Interest – June 2011

Welcome to Chelsea Physic Garden, London's oldest botanic garden, founded in 1673. You will find the plants mentioned in this month's Points of Interest marked by green alphabetical labels in the Garden.

**A.** In the centre of the Garden is an 18th century rock garden, possibly the earliest in Europe. It was built with Icelandic lava rock, given to the Garden by Sir Joseph Banks, and stone from the Tower of London. Today, it contains a collection of Cretan endemics, including *Petromarula pinnata* (Wall Lettuce), a plant which can be seen growing in vertical rock faces and old buildings in Crete. The pond in the centre is an early Victorian addition.

**B.** A specimen of Yew, *Taxus baccata*, can be found on the oncology bed in the Pharmaceutical area. Taxol or Taxoterre, used to treat breast cancer, is derived semi-synthetically from the clippings of this evergreen conifer. The plant on this bed was propagated from a cutting of the Fortinghall Yew, found in the village of Fortinghall in Perthshire, Scotland. The Fortinghall Yew is estimated to be between 2,000 and 5,000 years old.

**C.** The sweetly smelling flowers of *Lilium candidum,* the Madonna Lily (Liliaceae) in the Aromatherapy border are a valuable source of perfume. The tubers are also rich in starch and can be cooked and eaten in a similar way to the potato, *Solanum tuberosum.* The red Lily beetle (*Lilioceris lilii*), which you may see on these plants, is a pest on all lilies. They feed and lay eggs on the underside of the leaves from April to September; the eggs hatch after a week and feed on the leaves and flowers. *Convallaria majalis* (Lily of the Valley), another highly scented plant used in perfume, can be found growing in several other parts of the garden, including the poisons bed in the Pharmaceutical area.

**D.** In the Tropical Corridor are a number of orchids in the genus *Stanhopea*, which grow in Central and South America. They bear spectacular, highly-scented, but short-lived flowers. The house has a particularly fine specimen of *Stanhopea oculata* 'Aurea' whose waxy flowers hang down underneath the container it grows in.

**E.** Outside the shop is *Quercus coccifera*, the Kermes Oak, a spiny leaved evergreen tree from the Mediterranean. It is the host plant of the kermes scale insect, once harvested for a red dye. In Europe it was the most important insect dye before the discovery of cochineal from the Americas. The word crimson is derived from the word kermes.

**F.** Growing up the *Catalpa bignonioides* (Indian Bean Tree) on the Summary Bed is a magnificent specimen of the fragrant *Rosa brunonii* (Himalayan Musk Rose). It is a very vigorous plant which needs the support of a large tree to display it at its best. The Indian Bean Tree itself now has two large props for public safety, as it is nearing the end of its life.

**G.** On the south side of Fortune's Tank Pond is the cornfield annuals display. This area shows plants that were once a common sight in the British countryside, but which have now largely disappeared as a result of changes in agricultural practices. Growing among the more well known flowers such as *Agrostemma githago* (Corncockle) and *Centaurea cyanus* (Cornflower) are *Misopates orontium* (Weasels Snout) and *Silene noctiflora* (Night Flowering Catchfly).

WRITTEN BY THE GARDEN TEAM      Printed on recycled paper.

*Lilium candidum*, the Madonna Lily, much loved by the red Lily beetle.

# Points of Interest Map

Entrance
Exit

66 Royal Hospital Rond

D

WC

Café    WC

no entry

Shop

WC

Tropical Corridor
& Glasshouses

no entry

Education
Room

E

C

History beds

F

Garden
of World
Medicine

Pharmaceutical
beds

B

A

Sloane statue

Pond Rockery

Swan Walk
Entrance

Woodland
Garden

Monocot Beds

Systematic order beds
Dicotyledons

Macaronesian
borders

Fortune's Tank Pond

G British natives

North American beds

Beehives &
Mediterranean
Woodland

no entry

Boatyard

Chelsea Embankment

The Thames

Compost Yard
& Study Centre

---

## YOUR SAFETY – NOTICE TO ALL VISITORS

Chelsea Physic Garden is a historic botanic Garden. It has uneven paths, ponds, beehives, a compost area, poisonous plants and many natural features that could be hazardous if not approached with care. The Garden is not a suitable place for children to play. The following notice is for your safety, the care of the rare and precious plants in the Graden and the peaceful enjoyment of the Garden for everyone.

- **Do not touch or eat any plants**  • No running  • No climbing on trees, fences or the pond rockery  • No ball games
- Children should be kept under close supervision (within physical reach) at all times and must not go near the ponds
- Strictly no wallking, trampling on plant beds or disturbing wildlife

# Chelsea Physic Garden – A Brief History

Founded 1673   Patron: HRH The Prince of Wales KG KT GCB OM

*Chelsea Physic Garden by Walter Burgess (1846–1908)*

## The Garden's founding

In 1673 the Society of Apothecaries of London founded a Physic Garden at Chelsea, so that their apprentices could learn to grow medicinal plants and study their uses. In England, this is unusual because it was not attached to a university. When the Garden was founded the word 'physic' meant 'pertaining to things natural as distinct from the metaphysical'. Now the New Oxford English Dictionary defines physic firstly as 'medicinal drugs', and secondly as 'the art of healing'.

When the Apothecaries chose this four-acre site beside the River Thames, it was already famed for its market gardens, orchards and some great houses belonging to King Henry VIII, his Chancellor Sir Thomas More and Sir John Danvers. In those days they would all have preferred to travel by river, which was both safer and quicker than road.

The riverside position also appealed to the Apothecaries because they needed somewhere to house the gaily painted barge they used for royal pageants and for their celebrated 'herborising' expeditions to collect plants. No doubt the free-draining soil and southerly aspect would have been an added attraction. Even today the special microclimate enables us to cultivate many tender species, including the largest olive tree growing outside in Britain.

For the first ten years the Apothecaries had difficulty in finding a good Gardener, as the Curators were called. Then they appointed John Watts who was also an apothecary. Watts made contact with Paul Hermann, the Professor of Botany at Leiden University, and by 1683 the two men were exchanging plants and seeds, the most notable being four seedlings of *Cedrus libani*, the Cedar of Lebanon, which were amongst the first cultivated in Britain. These distinctive trees feature in many of the old prints and pictures of the Garden and the last was eventually felled in the winter of 1903. You can still see the offspring of the Chelsea Physic Garden cedars in the Cambridge

Botanic Garden and in other old estates in Britain. The Garden continues to publish an *Index Seminum*, and still exchanges seeds with botanic gardens around the world. Glasshouses have always been an important feature of the Garden. As early as 1685, on one of his many visits to the Garden, the celebrated diarist John Evelyn describes the heated glass-house, thought to be the first in Europe.

## The era of Sloane and Miller

When Dr Hans Sloane (1660–1753) bought the Manor of Chelsea from Charles Cheyne in 1712, he also took over the freehold of the Garden. Sloane had studied at the Garden in his youth, and was sympathetic to the Apothecaries who were struggling with its upkeep. Sloane, who was knighted in 1716 and who became President of both the Royal Society and the Royal College of Physicians, granted the Apothecaries a lease on the land for a rent of £5 a year in perpetuity, on condition 'it be for ever kept up and maintained as a physic garden'. This deed of covenant, established in 1722, secured the future of the Garden and required that 50 plant specimens be delivered each year to the Royal Society until 2,000 pressed and mounted species had been received; by 1795 the total had reached 3,700.

When Sloane died, aged almost 93, his collection of curiosities and his vast library became the nucleus of the British Museum, later moving to the Natural History Museum. Sloane's name lives on in local streets such as Hans Crescent and Sloane Square, and the rent of £5 per annum is still paid to his heirs.

Sir Hans Sloane made another great contribution to Chelsea Physic Garden when he appointed Philip Miller as Gardener. Miller (1691–1771) made the Garden world-famous during his fifty-year tenure. He trained William Aiton, who became the first

Gardener at Kew, and William Forsyth, his own successor at Chelsea, and after whom Forsythia is named. Miller's correspondence with the leading botanists of the day generated an exchange of plants and seeds, many of them cultivated in the Garden for the first time in Britain. Miller also wrote eight editions of his famous *Dictionary of Gardening*, which became the standard reference work for gardeners in Britain and America.

Carl von Linné (Linnaeus), the great Swedish botanist, made several visits to the Garden in the 1730s and many species first described by Miller still retain the names he ascribed to them. Between 1731 and 1768 Sloane instructed Miller to arrange for various crops, including cotton, to be sent out from the Garden to the new colony of Georgia in America. Miller also introduced madder, which is used to produce red dye, as an agricultural crop in Britain.

In 1732 Sloane laid the foundation stone for a glorious orangery where Miller lived for a short time with his family; sadly this elegant building had to be pulled down in the mid 19th century when the Garden's fortunes went into decline. In 1899 the Apothecaries finally gave up the management of the Garden. It was taken over by the City Parochial Foundation. During this period, university and college students continued to use the Garden for scientific research, but it remained closed to the general public.

In 1983 the City Parochial Foundation decided that they could no longer maintain the Garden, so a new independent charity was set up, and it was decided that the Garden should be opened to the public for the first time in its 300 year history.

## Chelsea Physic Garden today

Chelsea Physic Garden now covers 3.8 acres with Royal Hospital Road to the north, Swan Walk to the east, and the Embankment to the south. The main buildings – offices, lecture rooms, Curator's house and most of the greenhouses – are at the northern end. The remaining space is divided by gravel paths into quadrants, which are mostly sub-divided into the narrow rectilinear beds which are an original design feature of the Garden.

Many medicinal and other useful plants are grown at the northern end, while the Systematic Order Beds are set out to demonstrate the botanical relationship of plants, most of which have labels detailing their botanical classification and origin. The formal design of the botanical garden is broken by trees which often have a multitude of uses, and include the famous olive and an ancient yew.

A replica of the original statue of Sir Hans Sloane created by Michael Rysbrack in 1733 has pride of place at the centre of the Garden; the original, damaged by pollution, is now in the British Museum. Next to the statue are two carts, one created to celebrate the 250th anniversary of Sloane's death, and the other for Linnaeus' tercentenary in 2007.

Near the statue is the oldest man-made rock garden in Europe, which has Grade II* listed status. The rocks include pieces of carved stone which were once part of the Tower of London and basaltic lava used as ballast on Sir Joseph Banks' ship on a voyage to Iceland in 1772. By Chelsea Embankment is a wider area of flowering shrubs and rare peonies, with plenty of places to sit and absorb the atmosphere. Wildlife flourishes in the Garden, and frogs, toads, and newts have come back to inhabit the Fortune's Tank Pond which was restored in 2004. Rare lichens and insects have also been identified in the Garden.

## What else goes on behind our walls?

Today Chelsea Physic Garden is still dedicated to promoting education, conservation, and scientific research. The Natural History Museum's Botany Department grows a large collection of Asplenium ferns for taxonomic research, and botanists continue to work on species which we hope will explain some of the many mysteries of the plant kingdom. We are involved in a joint initiative, the Ethnomedica Project, with medical herbalists, the Royal Botanic Garden at Kew, the Eden Project, the Botanic Garden at Edinburgh, and the Natural History Museum, which involves collecting data about herbal remedies which have been used over the years in Britain. We welcome contributions from members of the public; if you have a 'remembered remedy' please enter it on one of the index cards in the red box in the foyer. Catering for the increased interest in plant-based medicine, the Garden of World Medicine was laid out in 1993, and shows the use of plants for medicinal purposes by the world's indigenous peoples. You will also find borders with plants employed in the perfumery and cosmetic industries, and others used for the manufacture of fabrics and for dyes. The Pharmaceutical Garden displays plants which are the origins of many of the drugs used in contemporary medicine. In the Historical Walk you can follow the Garden's own history, with plants introduced into cultivation by Curators and notable botanists, such as William Hudson, William Curtis, Sir Joseph Banks and Robert Fortune, who have been connected with the Garden over the centuries.

In 1997 Princess Alexandra opened our custom-built Education Department which is run by staff committed to demonstrating the importance of plants in our everyday lives. Over 2000 children and their teachers visit the Garden each year.

If you would like to find out more about the Garden and its activities, please see www.chelseaphysicgarden.co.uk. The Garden is much in demand for functions and wedding receptions, providing an idyllic setting for events of all kinds. See our website or call 020 7349 6459 for more details.

## Friends Membership

Become a Friend of Chelsea Physic Garden and enjoy the year-round tranquility of this beautiful 330-year-old piece of living history. A self-supporting charity with no government funding, we rely on our members' subscriptions to help fund education, interpretation and research at the Garden. As a Friend you receive privileged free access to the Garden on weekdays throughout the year for yourself and one family member.

To join, go to the entrance kiosk or shop, call 020 7349 6459, email friends@chelseaphysicgarden.co.uk. or visit www.chelseaphysicgarden.co.uk

*The Garden is open to the public until 31 October on Tuesdays to Fridays 12–5pm, Sundays & Bank Holidays 12–6pm. Special Late Openings on Wednesdays from 29 June – 7 September until 10pm. (Last admission 8.30pm).*

Chelsea Physic Garden FOUNDED 1673

**Chelsea Physic Garden   Swan Walk   London SW3 4HS**

Tel. 020 7352 5646   enquiries@chelseaphysicgarden.co.uk   www.chelseaphysicgarden.co.uk

Registered in England, Company Number 1690871    Registered Charity Number 286513

## INTRODUCING THE MAGNOLIIDS

The magnoliid angiosperms were once included with the dicots, but now they are placed on a separate branch of the flowering plants. Many magnoliids have spirally arranged flower parts, more like the spirals of pine cones than the whorls of parts found in monocots and eudicots. Most have pollen with one opening, unlike eudicot pollen, which has three openings.

Four orders make up the magnoliids – Canellales, Piperales, Magnoliales and Laurales. Representatives of all four may be seen at the Garden.

Most magnoliids grow in tropical to mild temperate climates, although some magnolia trees can tolerate colder winters. Several magnoliids, such as the annona or paw-paw family, nutmeg family, and pepper family are characteristic of lowland, moist forests.

There is quite an assortment of flower structure in this group. Some magnoliids have flower parts in multiples of three, as do monocots. The flowers range from the large showy magnolias to the tiny, almost indistinguishable flowers of the pepper family. The leaves have smooth edges, which botanists call entire margins. Magnoliids usually have fragrant oils, and this branch of the flowering plants provides us with the familiar cinnamon, nutmeg, mace, black pepper and bay leaves.

**Basal angiosperms**

**Magnoliids**

**Canellales** Cronquist

   **Winteraceae** R. Brown ex Lindley          4 genera/65 species

         Genera include:

         *Drimys* Forster & Forster f. (winter's bark)

         *Pseudowintera* Dandy (pepper tree)

         *Tasmannia* R. Brown (mountain pepper)

Members of this family are mainly distributed in the Southern Hemisphere with representatives in South America, Australia, Southeast Asia and Madagascar. This distribution is typical of a family that once had its roots in the super palaeocontinent, Gondwana. The family has long been considered primitive because its members contain water-conducting cells composed of tracheids, which are typical of ferns and conifers. Vessels usually characterise flowering plants. In addition, its ovules are not completely sealed in the ovary, a condition described as conduplicate. The familiar garden plant, *Drimys winteri* (winter's bark), has bark thought to have medicinal properties. It was used by sailors against scurvy. *Drimys winteri* and other family members are now best known as evergreen ornamental plants. More recently, the Tasmanian mountain pepper, once *Drimys lanceolata*, has been placed in its own genus, *Tasmannia*, based on floral developmental and molecular studies.

# WINTERACEAE, *the winter's bark family*

*Drimys winteri (winter's bark) has flowers with both male (staminate) and female (pistillate) parts*

*Female flowers of Tasmannia lanceolata*

*Male flowers of Tasmannia lanceolata*

*Tasmannia lanceolata plants are described as dioecious because their flowers are unisexual with males and females borne on different plants. The common name, mountain pepper, comes from the aromatic peppery taste of leaves, bark and berries that burns the mouth, although the black berries are palatable to native Tasmanian birds such as the Black Currawong, Strepera fuliginosa*

**Basal angiosperms**

**Magnoliids**

**Piperales** Dumortier

    **Saururaceae** Martynov                     4 genera/6 species

        Genera include:

        *Anemopsis* Hooker & Arnott (yerba mansa)

        *Houttuynia* Thunberg (houttuynia)

        *Saururus* L. (lizard tail)

This small herbaceous family occurs in North America and East Asia – a distribution described as disjunct. Plants are characterised by heart-shaped leaves and inconspicuous flowers clustered in spikes (inflorescences). Flowers in *Houttuynia cordata* 'Chameleon' are densely packed on a short spike. They have no perianth, but there are four petal-like bracts at the base of the inflorescence. *Houttuynia cordata* is important horticulturally, particularly those cultivars with variegated leaves and even double flowers, but it is also used as a green-leaved vegetable in East Asia.

    **Piperaceae** C.A. Agardh                 5 genera/2,750 species

        Genera include:

        *Peperomia* Ruiz & Pavón (peperomia)

        *Piper* L. (black pepper, white pepper, kava, betel)

This is a family of tropical shrubs, climbers and herbs in which *Piper* and *Peperomia* are two very large genera. *Peperomia* has economic importance in horticulture as a house plant, but this is far outweighed by *Piper*, a genus of about 1000 species. *Piper nigrum*, a native of Madagascar, southern India and Sri Lanka is the source of pepper, which is globally the most widely used spice. It is a liane (climber). Its inflorescences are broadly similar to those of *Peperomia*, but its unripe spherical fruits (peppercorns) produce black pepper, and when their coats are removed, white pepper. A New World species, *P. auritum*, is used culinarily, and is called the root beer plant because of its smell. In Asia, the leaves of *P. betel* are eaten with betel nuts (*Areca catechu*) as a kind of chewing gum. In Central America, the *Piper* fruits are eaten by bats.

    **Aristolochiaceae** Jussieu                4 genera/480 species

        Genera include:

        *Aristolochia* L. (Dutchman's pipe, birthwort)

        *Asarum* L. (wild ginger)

The most familiar member of this tropical to warm temperate family is the climber, *Aristolochia*, which has typical heart-shaped leaves. Its flowers are tubular and have a bulbous base. Flowers sometimes attract beetles and flies as pollinators by producing smells reminiscent of rotting meat. Insects crawl inside the flower, which traps them overnight in the enlarged flower base. The flower releases its pollen and its tube reopens. The pollen-covered insects escape and enter another *Aristolochia* flower and pollinate it.

*Aristolochia clematitis* is naturalised in Britain, mostly in the grounds of ruined churches, monasteries and nunneries, a hint of the once medicinal uses of this highly toxic, southern European native. Its flowers are far less spectacular than in the Dutchman's pipe, *A. littoralis*, and although broadly similar in construction, are thought to resemble a uterus. Hence its common name is birthwort, and its traditional use was in speeding up birth. It is also an abortifacient. *Asarum europaeum*, another rare naturalised plant, was also brought to Britain for medicinal purposes, but this time as an emetic and in snuff. It was thought particularly efficacious for hangovers.

# SAURURACEAE, *the lizard-tail family*

*Houttuynia cordata 'Chameleon'*

# PIPERACEAE, *the pepper family*

*This peperomia plant, a cultivar of Peperomia caperata, is blooming. Its tiny flowers are packed densely on spikes. The flowers have no perianth, so individual ones are hard to see. There are about a thousand species of Peperomia, which grow in the tropics worldwide*

# ARISTOLOCHIACEAE, *the Dutchman's pipe or birthwort family*

*Aristolochia littoralis, Dutchman's pipe*

*Aristolochia clematitis, birthwort*

**Basal angiosperms**

**Magnoliids**

**Magnoliales** Bromhead

    **Magnoliaceae** Jussieu                      2 genera/227 species

        Genera:

        *Liriodendron* L. (tulip tree)

        *Magnolia* L. (magnolia)

        (*Michelia* L.)

The Magnoliaceae, a tropical to warm temperate family of woody plants, has a disjunct Northern Hemisphere distribution extending from the Himalayas, China and Japan to North America.

The features of *Magnolia* flowers include strap-shaped stamens that are not differentiated into distinct filaments and anthers, and spirally arranged flower parts. The tepals of flowers on one tree can vary from six to twelve. Magnolias have many separate carpels. An elongated receptacle holds the spirals of carpels and stamens.

*Liriodendron tulipifera* and *Magnolia virginiana* were seventeenth century (1650, 1688) introductions to the United Kingdom from the United States. The majestic *Magnolia grandiflora* arrived some fifty years later. The first *Magnolia* species to be introduced from China was *M. denudata* by Sir Joseph Banks in 1780 and subsequently so named because it was deciduous. It was followed by *M. liliiflora* again from China. All these magnoliids were much sought after and widely grown in the 'incipient botanic gardens' of stately homes.

Plants formerly assigned to *Michelia* are confined to China and rarely seen in British gardens. Their flowers are so similar to those of *Magnolia* that most botanists now use that name.

The bark and flower buds of a number of Chinese species of *Magnolia* have medicinal uses. The North American tulip tree (*Liriodendron tulipifera*) is much valued for its timber.

A second family in the order, the Myristicaceae, contains *Myristica*, whose seeds when ground produce the spice, nutmeg. The outer layer of the seed coat (the aril) produces another familiar spice, mace.

# MAGNOLIACEAE, *the magnolia family*

*Magnolia grandiflora has white stamens set below green carpels with curled stigmas. The fruit is an aggregate of follicles. The seeds have a red fleshy coat. They dangle out of the follicles on fine fibres and are dispersed by birds*

*Magnolia (Michelia) alba is grown in the tropical house at the National Botanic Garden*

*The Chinese tulip tree, Liriodendron chinense and the North American tulip tree, L. tulipifera, are the last two survivors of a genus that was once widespread in the Northern Hemisphere. Climate changes in the Cenozoic (Tertiary) and Pleistocene (Quaternary) time intervals appear to have caused the extinction of other Liriodendron species*

**Basal angiosperms**

**Magnoliids**

**Laurales** Perleb

    **Lauraceae** Jussieu                      50 genera/2,500 species

        Genera include:

        *Cinnamomum* Schaeffer (cinnamon, camphor tree)

        *Laurus* L. (bay laurel, sweet bay)

        *Lindera* Thunberg (spice bush, wild allspice)

        *Persea* Miller (avocado, red bay tree, silk bay tree)

        *Sassafras* Nees & Ebermaier (sassafras)

The Lauraceae is a tropical to warm temperate family of trees and shrubs that have aromatic oils in their bark and leaves. The common name, laurel, provides an excellent example of the value of a Latin scientific name in avoiding confusion. For example, *Laurus nobilis*, whose leaves provide the indispensible culinary herb, bears the name of the order and is known to us as bay. The cherry laurel, a common garden shrub, is actually *Prunus laurocerasus*, a member of the Rosaceae, while Japanese laurel is *Aucuba japonica*, a member of the Garryaceae. The laurel wreath crown of Caesar was probably made from *Ruscus hypoglossum*, whose close relative, *Ruscus aculeatus*, the butcher's broom, is planted in the bed with daffodils and onions and is a member of the Asparagales.

Other aromatic species of the Lauraceae are: *Cinnamomum verum*, whose inner bark contains the flavouring, cinnamic acid, in its essential oil, is the principal source of cinnamon; *Lindera benzoin* which provides wild all-spice; *S. albidium* (sassafras) which is used for both insecticides and perfumes and *Persea americana* (avocado pear) which is a highly nutritious fruit, full of mono-unsaturated fats and vitamins.

# LAURACEAE, *the laurel family*

*Flowers in this family are typically inconspicuous with six green, yellow or white tepals. The anthers have an unusual way of opening. They have tiny flaps that peel back, pulling out the sticky pollen. The fruit is a berry*

*Flowers (above) and developing fruits (right) of Laurus nobilis. The flower on the left is male with a number of functioning and sterile stamens. The female flower on the right shows a swollen green ovary terminated by a dark warty stigma*

*Cinnamomum verum cinnamon*

*Male (staminate) and female (pistillate) flowers of the spice bush, Lindera benzoin, are on separate plants. This shrub grows in woods and bogs of eastern North America*

*Sassafras trees, Sassafras albidum, have three different leaf shapes, often on the same branch. Sassafras is dioecious. The female flowers shown here have yellow staminodes (reduced non-functional stamens). Flower photo © Lisa L. Gould (used by permission)*

25

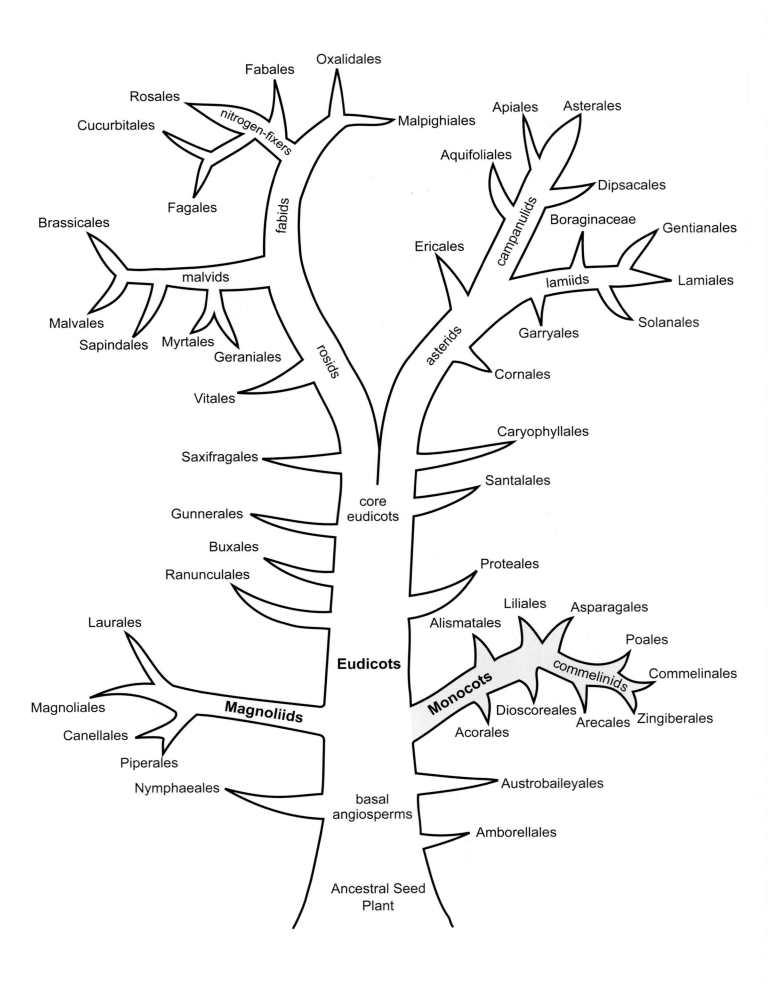

Oxalidales
Fabales
Rosales
Cucurbitales
nitrogen-fixers
Malpighiales
Fagales
Apiales
Asterales
Aquifoliales
Dipsacales
Brassicales
campanulids
Boraginaceae
Gentianales
fabids
Ericales
lamiids
Lamiales
malvids
asterids
Garryales
Solanales
Malvales
Myrtales
Sapindales
Geraniales
Cornales
rosids
Vitales
Caryophyllales
Saxifragales
Santalales
core
eudicots
Gunnerales
Buxales
Proteales
Ranunculales
Liliales
Asparagales
Alismatales
Poales
Laurales
commelinids
Commelinales
Eudicots
Monocots
Dioscoreales
Zingiberales
Magnoliales
Magnoliids
Arecales
Canellales
Acorales
Piperales
Nymphaeales
Austrobaileyales
basal
angiosperms
Amborellales
Ancestral Seed
Plant

# INTRODUCING THE MONOCOTS

The monocots have been recognised as a subgroup of flowering plants ever since the seventeenth century. In many traditional classifications, they were one of the two groups of the angiosperms. With recent intensive study of their nucleic acids and all their other characters, the monocots still stand as a single lineage.

That being said, it is not as easy to define monocots as one might think. The textbook description of monocots often states that their leaves have parallel veins. Many do have parallel veins, but there are some with netted venation. Monocot reversion to netted veins is probably an adaptation to dimly lit forest understorey environments. It is easy to find these netted vein monocots just by looking in the lobbies of office buildings. They make good indoor plants, because they can live in low light. *Monstera*, *Dieffenbachia*, and *Philodendron* are common examples. To find a monocot with parallel veins, look just about anywhere plants grow for one of the ubiquitous grasses.

Monocot leaves seldom have teeth, but when they do, the teeth have spines and are not glandular-tipped like the teeth of some eudicot leaves. Monocot flowers are usually described as having parts in threes. While this is true, there are also magnoliids whose flowers have parts in threes. The seeds of monocots carry the best clue to their identity; they have a single cotyledon (seed leaf), the trait for which monocots are named. As these seeds sprout, the first root that forms, called the primary root, withers and many adventitious roots grow from the sides of the stem, forming a fibrous root system. Fibrous roots are found in other plant groups, so they are not unique to monocots.

Changes to our understanding of monocots in the Angiosperm Phylogeny Group classification include the establishment of *Acorus*, sweet flag, as the basal-most member and sister group to the rest. The next lineage is Alismatales, the order of water plantains and aroids. Other major branches are the lilioid or petaloid monocots and the commelinid monocots.

The lilioid or petaloid monocots include the lily order, Liliales, and the asparagus order, Asparagales. The traditional lily family was a huge miscellaneous box of unrelated species. Many of its members have been moved to the Asparagales. The definition of families within the Asparagales remains a matter for debate and some will probably be combined in the future.

The commelinid monocots include the orders of the palms, the grasses, the dayflowers, and the gingers. Of these, the dayflower order, Commelinales, and the ginger order, Zingiberales, are more closely related to each other than they are to the grasses, Poales, and the palms, Arecales.

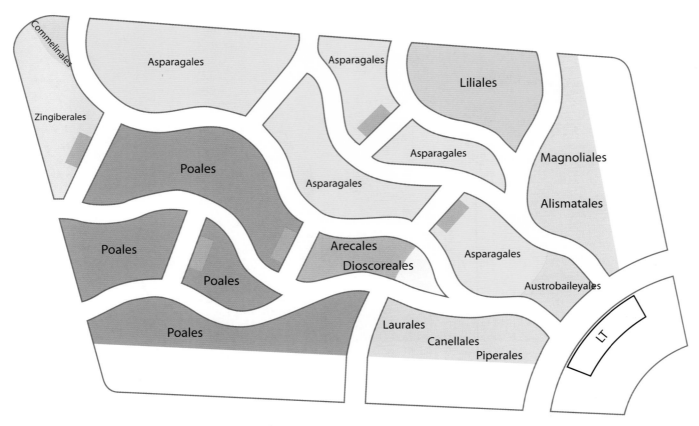

*Quadrant 1 basal angiosperms and monocots*

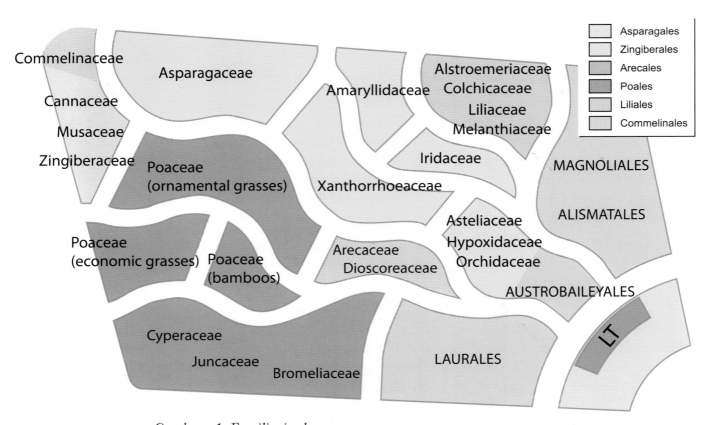

*Quadrant 1. Families in the monocots*

28

*Overview of the Poales in the Double Walled Garden with Tropical House to the left*

*Iridaceae in the monocot quadrant*

**Monocots**

**Basal monocots**

**Acorales** Reveal

**Acoraceae** Martinov                1 genus/2-4 species

Genus:

*Acorus* L. (calamus, sweet flag)

This wetland family occurs in both North America and the Old World. It is considered to be the first branch of the monocots and a sister group to the rest. *Acorus* is the sole genus of this family and its common name comes from the aromatic fragrance of its foliage. Its inflorescence is a pale spike, which arises along the side of a leaf. The flowers have their parts in threes or sixes, although they are so tiny that this is hard to see. Sweet flag has flat leaves, somewhat like those of the iris, but with their midrib set off centre.

*Acorus calamus* (sweet flag or calamus) is a species that extends as far east as India and south to Sulawesi. Its rhizomes produce an oil that was used for anointing altars in the Old Testament times (sweet calamus) and has been used as a medicine for toothache and dysentery since at least 400 BC. The oil is a proven effective insecticide and is also used as a flavouring for the fruit brandy, eaux-de-vie. The rhizomes also produce a compound similar to nutmeg that is used in perfumes.

# ACORACEAE, *the sweet flag family*

*The young spikes of Acorus calamus (sweet flag) are green. They appear cream-coloured as the flowers mature*

*The spike is covered in the tiny flowers, which have six tepals and six stamens. The fruits are berries*

*A general view of sweet flag*

*Fruits are developing on this spike*

**Monocots**

**Basal monocots**

**Alismatales** Dumortier

    **Araceae** Jussieu                             105 genera/3,250 species

        Genera include:

        *Amorphophallus* Blume ex Decaisne (Asian jungle flower)

        *Anthurium* Schott (anthurium)

        *Arisaema* Martius (arisaema, green dragon)

        *Arum* L. (lords & ladies, cuckoo pint etc.)

        *Caladium* Ventenat (Indian kale)

        *Colocasia* Schott (taro)

        *Dieffenbachia* Schott (dieffenbachia, dumb cane)

        *Dracunculus* Miller (dragon arum)

        *Lemna* L. (duckweed)

        *Lysichiton* Schott (skunk cabbage)

        *Monstera* Adanson (Swiss cheese plant, split leaf philodendron)

        *Philodendron* Schott (philodendron)

        *Pistia* L. (water lettuce)

        *Symplocarpus* Salisbury ex Barton (skunk cabbage)

        *Wolffia* Horkel ex Schleiden (water meal)

        *Xanthosoma* Schott (tannia, yautia)

        *Zantedeschia* Sprengel (arum lily)

The Araceae is found mainly in the tropics and subtropics where its members occupy a wide range of habitats. Plants occur as shrubs, climbers with aerial roots, and herbs, including free floating aquatics. The tiny flowers of aroids are embedded on a spike that is called a spadix. The spadix is surrounded by a large bract, the spathe, which is often brightly coloured. In the arum lily, the lower spadix flowers are female (pistillate) and the upper ones are male (staminate). Some aroids have bisexual flowers. The leaf shape and venation vary tremendously in this family, and are particularly evident in the popular house plants *Dieffenbachia* and *Caladium bicolor*. *Dieffenbachia* is native to tropical areas of the Americas. Other horticulturally important genera are *Anthurium*, *Philodendron* and *Monstera*. Of garden plants, *Dracunculus* and *Lysichiton* are renowned for their spectacular flowers and horrendous odours. For example, *D. vulgaris*, originally from the eastern Mediterranean, smells of rotten meat. However the major economic value of the family lies with species with edible tubers (e.g. taro: *Colocasia*) and stems (*Xanthosoma*) that are grown as subsistence crops throughout the tropics. Species of the tuberous Asian jungle flower, *Amorphophallus*, are also eaten, but this genus is remarkable for the production of the world's largest unbranched flower spike (inflorescence) in *A. titanum*.

*Arum maculatum* has more common names than any other British native plant. They include lords and ladies, cuckoo-pint, Jack or parson in the pulpit, devils and angels, willy lilly, cows and bulls, snake's meat etc. Its pollination has been much studied. High respiration rates in the spadix increase the temperature in the basal bulbous region of the flower and heat up the chemicals to produce an appalling smell that makes the chamber an attractive venue for flies. Once inside, their escape route is blocked by downwardly pointing hairs at the mouth of the chamber. By the time the hairs have withered, pollen has been liberated onto the visitors, who then leave to unwittingly pollinate another flower, after literally falling for the same trick. The outcome of such pollination is spikes of vivid orange berries that grace autumn hedgerows. The berries are poisonous, but their toxicity varies with ripeness.

# ARACEAE, *the aroid or arum family*

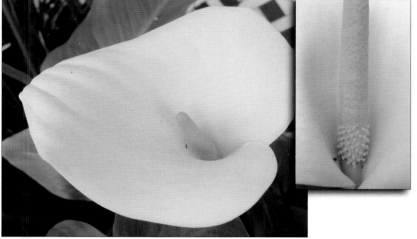

*Zantedeschia aethiopica (arum lily) with a general view of its white spathe (above) and close-up of its golden spadix (inset) with female flowers at the base*

*Caladium bicolor , above, has beautifully patterned leaves, which are examples of netted veins in monocots*

*Arum maculatum flowers and berries, above and above right*

*The tiny duckweed, Lemna minor, (above and right), has minute flowers with single stamens and carpels, but these small aquatic plants typically reproduce vegetatively and may completely cover still water surfaces with a green carpet. The record for the smallest angiosperm is a close relative, Wolffia, which favours warmer waters. Lemnoids are an important food source for some waterfowl, and they have the ability to absorb contaminants from waste water*

MONOCOTS

BASAL MONOCOTS

ALISMATALES

**Monocots**

**Basal monocots**

**Alismatales** Dumortier

    **Alismataceae** Ventenat         12 genera/81 species

        Genera include:

        *Alisma* L. (water plantain)

        *Sagittaria* Rupp ex L. (arrowhead, wapato)

Alismataceae is a cosmopolitan family of water plants, confined for the most part to the Northern Hemisphere. Its members are usually described as emergent aquatics. Plants are rooted in mud at the bottom of lakes, ponds, canals, ditches or slow moving rivers, but their flowers and leaves are lifted above the surface of the water. One of the most striking leaf shapes is seen in the native arrowhead, *Sagittaria sagittifolia*. By contrast, the far more common water plantain, *Alisma plantago-aquatica*, has plantain-shaped, elongate leaves as its species name suggests.

# ALISMATACEAE, *the water plantain family*

The flowers of this family have three sepals and three petals. Alisma has bisexual flowers and Sagittaria, unisexual flowers. The many carpels are separate rather than fused together. The fruits are achenes that float. They are dispersed on water and by waterfowl that eat them

*Alisma (water plantain), above, has bisexual flowers in an inflorescence with many whorled branches. Its flowers are smaller than those of Sagittaria (below)*

*Sagittaria (below) has male and female flowers, usually on the same plant. The flowers form in whorls of three; these whorls are the only branches of the inflorescence. Leaf shape varies a great deal within the genus and even within a species, depending on growing conditions. Some species even have grass-like leaves. The starchy, edible tubers of some species give them the common name of duck potato*

*This Sagittaria has the typical leaf shape from which the common name, arrowhead, is derived. The flowers are male*

*Sagittaria lancifolia has ovate leaves. It is shown with male flowers above the developing fruits*

**Monocots**

**Lilioid (petaloid) monocots**

**Dioscoreales** Hooker f.

**Nartheciaceae** Fries ex Bjurzon         4–5 genera/31 species

Genera include:

*Narthecium* Hudson (bog asphodel)

This small family of perennial herbs was once included in both the Melanthiaceae and Liliaceae. It occurs in temperate regions of the Northern Hemisphere and shows a disjunct distribution in the United States, Europe and Southeast Asia. *Narthecium ossifragum* (bog asphodel) has small spikes of yellow, lily-like flowers and grows in wetlands mainly in western and northern Britain. Its specific name means 'bone breaker', in the belief that brittle bones in sheep resulted from their grazing the plant. However it is most likely that brittle bones in sheep was caused by their grazing the wet, acid, nutrient deficient grasslands. The plants actually contain a type of saponin which is a liver poison and, in Norway, causes a disease in sheep known as 'Alveden'. In Shetland the plants were used as a substitute for saffron and they have also been used as a hair-dye.

**Dioscoreaceae** R. Brown         3 genera/805 species

Genera include:

*Dioscorea* L. (yam)

*Tacca* Forster & Forster f. (arrowroot, bat-flower)

[*Tamus* L. (black bryony) has been transfered to *Dioscorea*]

This family of climbers is found mainly in the tropics but it is represented in the British flora by *Dioscorea* (*Tamus*) *communis* (black bryony). Its glossy, heart-shaped leaves are followed by clusters of bright red berries that garland hedges in Wales in autumn. The aerial shoots of these climbers grow from starchy tubers and rhizomes. The latter have emetic and purgative properties and have been used in the treatment of bruises. Various species of yam, *Dioscorea*, are cultivated for food around the tropics. They are also grown as a source of the saponin, diosgenin, which is the starting material for the partial synthesis of sex hormones, corticosteroids and oral contraceptives.

The taxonomic position of the genus *Tacca* is uncertain as either within the Dioscoreaceae or in a family of its own. Equally perplexing as its taxonomic position is the construction of its fly-pollinated flowers.

# DIOSCOREACEAE, *the yam family*

*Dioscorea sp. foliage, above left, Dioscorea communis (black bryony) flowers, left and fruit, above*

*Tacca chantrieri flowers (right and above)*

# NARTHECIACEAE, *the bog asphodel family*

*Narthecium ossifragum (bog asphodel)*

37

## Monocots
## Lilioid (petaloid) monocots
## Liliales Perleb

### Melanthiaceae Batsch ex Borkhausen      16 genera/170 species

Genera include:

*Paris* L. (herb paris)

*Trillium* L. (wake robin, trinity flower)

The death camus family is so named because it contains many genera that are extremely poisonous, although they may also have medical properties. The family includes *Paris quadrifolia* (herb paris) which is one of Britain's most unusual flowers. It occurs in shady woods on limestone or calcareous marls and silts. Both generic and specific names relate to the four wide leaves (*pars* = Latin for part) attached at the same level some distance below the flower. The flower itself has four green/yellow sepals and similarly coloured but narrower petals. A dark red ovary with four styles sits at the junction of eight elongate stamens. Some plants have five or more leaves. In contrast, in *Trillium* the floral parts are conspicuously in threes.

### Alstroemeriaceae Dumortier      3 genera/165 species

Genera include:

*Alstroemeria* L. (alstroemeria, Chilean lily, Peruvian lily)

*Bomarea* de Mirbel (climbing alstroemeria, bomarea)

This family grows in Central and South America in both tropical and temperate areas. *Alstroemeria* hybrids are favourites of florists, much valued for their long-lasting cut flowers. When the *Alstroemeria* flower first opens, the anthers split and release their yellow pollen, but the stigma is still closed. In older flowers, the three branches of the stigma open and the anthers may fall off.

### Colchicaceae de Candolle      15 genera/225 species

Genera include:

*Colchicum* L. (autumn crocus, meadow saffron)

*Gloriosa* L. (gloriosa lily)

*Sandersonia* Hooker (Christmas bells)

With a few exceptions, genera in this family grow in areas with Mediterranean climates in Europe, Africa and Asia. Its members usually have crocus-like flowers, but they often flower in the late summer and autumn, and are therefore treasured garden plants. All parts of the plant of *Colchicum* are poisonous, but the ground-up corms and seeds can be judiciously used in pain relief particularly for gout. *Colchicum* is best known to scientists as the source of the alkaloid, colchicine, which is used in plant breeding because it causes a doubling of chromosomes. *Colchicum autumnalis* grows in the wild on limestones in the Welsh Borderland and there are records in Montgomeryshire of cattle being paralysed by it. Rather different are the African climbing genera *Gloriosa* and *Sandersonia*. These have long brittle tubers which, like other Colchicaceae, are highly toxic if eaten. The leaves are simple. Flowers are lantern-like in *Sandersonia* and rather lily-like in *Gloriosa*.

# MELANTHIACEAE, *the death camus family*

*Trillium chloropetalum*

*Trillium ovatum*

*Paris quadrifolia (herb paris)*

# ALSTROEMERIACEAE, *the Alstroemeria family*

*Bomarea sp. flowers and fruit*

*Note the inferior ovary and twisted leaf base of Alstroemeria sp., which are characteristic of this family*

# COLCHICACEAE, *the Colchicum family*

*Colchicum autumnale flowers before its leaves appear. Crocus has similar flowers but three, not six, stamens*

*Gloriosa superba with tendrils at its leaf tips*

**Monocots**
**Lilioid (petaloid) monocots**
**Liliales** Perleb

    **Philesiaceae** Dumortier               2 genera/2 species
        Genera:
        *Lapageria* Ruiz & Pavón (Chilean bell flower)
        *Philesia* Commerson ex Jussieu (philesia)

The Philesiaceae is confined to the forests of Chile. *Lapageria rosea*, the Chilean bell flower and the national flower of that country, has beautiful, pendent, typically liliaceous, flowers (see Chilean section of the Great Glasshouse).

    **Smilacaceae** Ventenat            2 genera/360 species
        Genera include:
        *Smilax* L. (greenbrier, sarsaparilla)

Unusual among the Liliales, Smilaceae (and also Philesiaceae) is a small family of lianas. It is found in tropical and warm temperate climates around the world. *Smilax* climbs by means of tendrils and recurved hooks, and is used by florists as a foliage plant. The dried rhizomes of some tropical American species produce the vital ingredient in sarsaparilla. They have also been used in digestive tonics and as medicines for fevers, arthritis, syphilis and, historically, for the treatment of leprosy.

    **Liliaceae** Jussieu           16 genera/600 species
        Genera include:
        *Cardiocrinum* Lindley (giant lily)
        *Clintonia* Rafinesque (bluebeard, yellow bead lily)
        *Erythronium* L. (trout lily, dog tooth violet)
        *Fritillaria* L. (fritillary, snake's head lily, crown imperial lily)
        *Lilium* L. (lily, tiger lily, Easter lily, Turk's cap lily)
        *Nomocharis* Franchet (nomocharis)
        *Tricyrtis* Wallich (toad lily)
        *Tulipa* L. (tulip)

Once the lily family held nearly all the lilioid monocots with six tepals. When botanists studied the plants further, they moved many species to other families. True lilies usually grow from bulbs with contractile roots. Their nectaries are located at the base of their tepals. Many lilies have spotted tepals, and their tepals are distinct, not fused. The ovary is superior. The fruit is usually a capsule, but may also be a berry. Lily pollen is large, often brightly coloured, and can be seen with only a little magnification. Within the genus *Lilium* are some of our most graceful garden flowers, and in *Tulipa*, especially cultivars or hybrids of *T. gesneriana*, are some of the most splendidly flamboyant. Their histories from countries of origin to appearances in gardens across Europe can be traced via various works of arts. The Madonna lily, *L. candidum*, for example was probably introduced into Britain by the Romans, and was first recorded in the 9th century miniature of Queen Ethelreda in an illustrated manuscript and later in many paintings of the Virgin Mary. Lilies and tulips also feature in many of the Dutch still-life Renaissance paintings. The role of *Tulipa* in the economic history of the Netherlands in the 17th century has been comprehensively encompassed by Anna Pavord in *"The Tulip"*.

A British representative of the family, *Fritillaria meleagris* (the fritillary or snake's head lily) has less obvious beauty, which is apparent only on close examination of its nodding, checked perianth. Its credentials as a native are not impeccable. It seems likely to have been an escape from 16th century gardens, since it has no older records in the wild. Another possible British native is the Martagon lily (*L. martagon*), which is found mainly in English woods, e.g. in the Wye Valley. This species has pretty Turk's cap shaped flowers that are pale purple in colour with some dark or white spots.

# LILIACEAE, *the lily family*

*Lilium hybrid (Asian lily)*

*Fritillaria imperialis (crown imperial lily)*

*Tricyrtis formosana (toad lily)*

*Tulipa hybrids have a superior ovary that develops into a three-part capsule*

*Fritillaria meleagris (snake's head lily)*

# PHILESIACEAE, *the Chilean Bell family*

*Lapageria rosea (Chilean bell flower)*

**Monocots**
**Lilioid (petaloid) monocots**
**Asparagales** Bromhead

### Orchidaceae Jussieu                              779 genera/22,500 species

Genera include:

*Anacamptis* Richard (pyramidal orchid)

*Bletilla* Reichenbach f. (urn orchid, ground orchid, bletilla)

*Calanthe* R. Brown (calanthe)

*Cattleya* Lindley (cattleya)

*Cypripedium* L. (lady's slipper orchid)

*Dactylorhiza* Necker ex Nevski (common spotted orchid, marsh orchid)

*Dendrobium* Swartz (dendrobium)

*Epidendrum* L. (star orchid)

*Epipactis* Zinn (helleborines)

*Ophrys* L. (bee orchid, fly orchid)

*Paphiopedilum* Pfitzer (slipper orchid)

*Phalaenopsis* Blume (moth orchid)

*Platanthera* Richard (fringed orchid, green orchid, lesser butterfly orchid)

*Spiranthes* Richard (lady's tresses)

*Vanda* W. Jones ex R. Brown (vanda, lei orchid)

*Vanilla* Miller (vanilla orchid)

The orchid family is one of the largest flowering plant families. Its nearly 25,000 members are mostly tropical, although there are more than fifty species in the British flora. Many of the orchids in Britain such as lady's tresses and twayblades have insignificant but intricate flowers. Magnificent exceptions include the much rarer lady's slipper orchid, which provides an excellent example of a tepal modified into a pouch. Such floral modifications are usually associated with specialised pollinating mechanisms and make orchid flowers some of the most remarkable among the angiosperms. Some flowers evoke miniatures of frogs, soldiers or monkeys, but more obviously useful shapes are those that mimic pollinators such as wasps and flies. In some genera such as *Ophrys*, the flowers also produce a pheromone-like scent to encourage pseudocopulation. Even pollen transfer is unusual in that the pollen is most commonly produced, usually from a single anther, in two adhesive masses (pollinia) that readily become attached to the pollinator. Upon successful pollination, very large numbers of small seeds are produced. A fungus is essential for supporting subsequent germination and growth of the seedling.

Traditionally, classification within the family has been based on features of the flower, and in particular on those of the gynoecium (ovary) and androecium (stamens). Following extensive DNA studies, the family is now divided into five subfamilies: Apostasioideae, Vanilloideae, Cypripedioideae, Orchidoideae and Epidendroideae, which are further divided into tribes. Orchidoideae contains the Orchideae, Cranichideae and Diurideae: Epidendroideae includes tribes Arethuseae, Epidendreae, Vandeae and Cymbidieae.

Orchids have always been treasured as ornamental plants, and hence are constantly under threat in the wild, despite extensive regulations. Recent years have seen an enormous explosion in the commercial market and is the result of hybridisation and new methods of cultivation (e.g. tissue culture). Also of economic importance are two species of *Vanilla* (*V. planifolia*, illustrated here, and *V. tahitensis*) whose seeds, produced in long pods, are the source of the flavouring named after the genus.

# ORCHIDACEAE, *the orchid family*

*Anacamptis pyramidales common on Welsh dune systems [Orchideae]*

*Platanthera species are found in unimproved meadows in Wales. Close up of Platanthera biofolia (lesser butterfly orchid) [Orchideae]*

*Ophrys apifera (bee orchid) common in coastal dune slacks in S. Wales [Orchideae]*

*Epipactis palustris (marsh heleborine) – coastal dune slacks with ephemeral pools [Epidendroideae]*

*Spiranthes spirales (autumn lady's tresses) - cliff and meadows [Cranichideae]*

*Paphiopedilum hybrid [Cypripedioideae]*

*Phalaenopsis hybrid (moth orchid) [Epidendroideae]*

*Vanilla planifolia [Vanilloideae]*

**Monocots**
**Lilioid (petaloid) monocots**
**Asparagales** Bromhead

**Asteliaceae** Dumort             4 genera/35 species

Genera include:

*Astelia* Banks & Solander ex R. Brown (bush flax)

*Milligania* Hooker f.

The family occurs in the southwest Pacific, Australia, New Zealand and Chile. In New Zealand, *Astelia* berries are eaten by Maoris.

**Hypoxidaceae** R. Brown           9 genera/120 species

Genera include:

*Hypoxis* L. (hypoxis)

*Rhodohypoxis* Nel (rhodohypoxis)

The family occurs predominantly in warm temperate to tropical Southern Hemisphere countries, but a few genera extend into Asia and North America. *Rhodohypoxis* is confined to eastern South Africa and Swaziland, and because it is tolerant of colder temperatures, it has become a garden favourite in lime-free, wet soils. *Hypoxis* is native to warmer to tropical parts of the Southern Hemisphere.

**Iridaceae** Jussieu            70 genera/2,000 species

Genera include:

*Crocosmia* Planchon (crocosmia)

*Crocus* L. (crocus)

*Dierama* K. Koch (fairy wand)

*Freesia* Ecklon ex Klatt (freesia)

*Gladiolus* L. (gladiolus)

*Iris* L. (iris)

*Ixia* L. (African corn lily)

*Sisyrinchium* L. (blue-eyed grass)

*Sparaxis* Ker-Gawler (harlequin flower)

*Tigridia* Jussieu (tiger flower)

Iridaceae is a cosmopolitan family, particularly associated with Mediterranean climates. Plants grow from rhizomes (*Iris*), corms (*Gladiolus*) and bulbs (*Tigridia*) and are frequently evergreen. There are three stamens. The perianth may be simple as in *Freesia* or highly modified as in *Iris*, whose often brilliant colours truly justify its name after the Greek goddess of the rainbow. Although relatively undifferentiated, the *Crocus* flower has brightly coloured tepals, stamens and even stigmas that attract insects. The stigmas are most conspicuous in the saffron crocus, and are probably the most valuable stigmas in the world, as several thousand flowers are required to produce a kilo of the spice, saffron, used as a colourant and flavouring.

*Iris* has a unique flower structure. Generally there are three petalloid segments (tepals) that hang down (falls) and three erect tepals (flags). This arrangement is most conspicuous in hybrid bearded irises. In the flag iris, the pistil has three styles that also look like petals and each is pressed against an almost horizontal fall. A single stamen is located in the space between them. The stigma is a small rigid flap on the underside of the style. The weight of a specialist pollinator, often a bee, forces down the fall. The visitor enters and either deposits pollen from its back onto the stigma, or leaves the plant with a load of pollen.

## ASTELIACEAE, *the astelia family*

*Astelia chathamica at the National Botanic Garden of Wales*

## HYPOXIDACEAE

*Rhodohypoxis sp.*

*Hypoxis parvula var. abliflora*

## IRIDACEAE, *the iris family*

*Note that three tepals are erect (flags) and three tepals are reflexed (falls) in the bearded iris (right)*

*Iris missouriensis (left) has three styles that look like petals*

*Tigridia pavonia (above)*
*Gladiolus sp. (left)*

*Note the three stamens that distinguish Crocus (right) from Colchicum*

45

**Monocots**

**Lilioid (petaloid) monocots**

**Asparagales** Bromhead

    **Xanthorrhoeaceae** Dumortier               1 genus/30 species

      **Subfamily Xanthorrhoeoideae** M.W. Chase, J.L. Reveal & M.F. Fay

        Genus:

        *Xanthorrhoea* E. Smith (grass tree)

This small subfamily is confined to Australia, New Guinea and New Caledonia. Some members, e.g. *Xanthorrhoea*, the grass tree, look like a small palm, but with a tuft of long needle-like leaves replacing the palm leaves. The stems of these plants are thick and often pithy and these characters, combined with the crown of leaves, are characteristic of the pachycaul habit. *Xanthorrhoea* from Western Australia can be seen in the Great Glass House. Its inflorescence is an impressive spike whose production, in most species, is stimulated by the fires that frequently rage through its very dry habitats.

      **Subfamily Hemerocallidoideae** Lindley        19 genera/60 species

        Genera include:

        *Dianella* Lamark ex Jussieu (flax lily)

        *Hemerocallis* L. (daylily)

        *Phormium* Forster & Forster f. (New Zealand flax)

The Hemerocallidoideae has a widespread distribution in both tropical and temperate regions, but is not found in Africa nor in North America.

Japanese and Chinese species of *Hemerocallis* were already sought after plants in English gardens in Shakespeare's time. *Hemerocallis lilioasphodelus* (syn. *H. flava*) is cultivated as a food plant in China – its flowers for people and leaves for cows. New Zealand flax, *Phormium tenax*, is not related to the European flax, *Linum*, that has been used to make linen cloth since prehistoric times. The first settlers of New Zealand, the Maori, used the fibres from *Phormium* leaves to make clothing and cordage. Europeans called the plant New Zealand flax because it was a good source of fibre. Horticulturalists have bred variegated and coloured-leaf cultivars of *Phormium* for garden landscape use around the world. While *Phormium* is confined to New Zealand, *Dianella* has a wider distribution in the Southern Hemisphere from east Africa to the West Pacific. Its somewhat insignificant flowers, which open for less than a day, are outshone by brilliant blue berries.

# XANTHORRHOEOIDEAE, *the grass tree subfamily*

*This broken trunk of Xanthorrhoea, which is often blackened by fire in the wild, here shows the remains of the bases of the numerous leaves. The brown acaroid resin extracted from these bases by the Aborigines was used as a lacquer or varnish and to glue spear heads to shafts*

*Xanthorrhoea sp. (grass tree, left)*

# HEMEROCALLIDOIDEAE, *the daylily subfamily*

*Phormium tenax (New Zealand flax) flowers*

*Hemerocallis hybrids (above and left), are popular garden flowers. They have been bred in many colours, including yellow, orange, pink, and red. Their foliage is a basal clump of long, narrow leaves. Their flowers last only one day, hence their common name, day lily*

*Dianella tasmanica fruit (below left) and flower (below right)*

47

**Monocots**
**Lilioid (petaloid) monocots**
**Asparagales** Bromhead
    **Xanthorrhoeaceae** Dumort
      **Subfamily Asphodeloideae** Burnett      15 genera/785 species
        Genera include:
        *Aloe* L. (aloe)
        *Asphodelus* L. (asphodel)
        *Bulbine* Wolf (onion weed)
        *Eremurus* Marschall von Bieberstein (foxtail lily)
        *Haworthia* Duval (haworthia)
        *Kniphofia* Moench (red hot poker, torch lily)

This small subfamily is confined to temperate to tropical regions of the Old World and shows a wide range of habits. Species of *Aloe* produce rosettes of succulent leaves, which are unusual in monocots in that spines are present on their edges. Succulence is an indication of the tolerance of many family members to arid habitats, particularly in South Africa. Others range from mat-forming ground dwellers to tall, branched trees. All have variously coloured spikes of tubular flowers. Sap from the fleshy leaves is the basis of the economic importance of the aloes. When bitter it is used to flavour drinks and as a purgative. It contains anthraquinones which are used in the treatment of Type 2 diabetes. The sap from the centre of the leaves lacks bitterness and is used in cosmetics and health products. Mucilaginous material produced on compressing leaves has anti-inflammatory properties and was used to treat burns (including radiation burns). In British gardens, genera such as *Kniphofia* and *Eremurus* are familiar ornamentals. In Mediterranean areas, a sign of overgrazing is the abundance of asphodel, because of its unpalatability to animals.

# ASPHODELOIDEAE, *the aloe subfamily*

*Aloe distans, foliage and flowers (ablove). Aloe arborescens (below)*

*Aloe dichotoma*

*Kniphofia 'Wrexham Buttercup'*

*Asphodelus lusitanicus*

**Monocots**
**Lilioids (petaloid) monocots**
**Asparagales** Bromhead
    **Amaryllidaceae** J. Saint-Hilaire
      **Subfamily Amaryllidoideae** J. Saint-Hilaire        59 genera/800 species
          Genera include:
          *Amaryllis* L. (Cape belladonna, belladonna lily)
          *Clivia* Lindley (clivia, kaffir lily)
          *Crinum* L. (swamp lily, Cape lily, crinum)
          *Galanthus* L. (snowdrop)
          *Hippeastrum* Herbert (amaryllis)
          *Hymenocallis* Salisbury (spider lily)
          *Leucojum* L. (snowflake)
          *Narcissus* L. (jonquil, daffodil)
          *Sprekelia* Heister (Jacobean lily, Aztec lily)
          *Zephyranthes* Herbert (zephyr lily, atamasco)

In contrast to the Allioideae (p. 52), all flowers of the Amaryllidoideae have inferior ovaries. Flowers are usually solitary, but occasionally grow in clusters as in *Clivia*. All grow from bulbs. The family is of major economic importance, with *Narcissus* hybrids at the heart of the horticultural industry. The daffodil, characterised by a trumpet-shaped outgrowth of the tepals, is also much cherished in Wales as a national emblem often substituted for the rather smelly leek (see p. 52). Indeed the distinction between the daffodil and the leek is much smaller in Welsh than in English as regards the names, because, in Welsh, leek is Cennin and daffodil is Cennin Aur (golden leek). It seems likely that the national flower is the native *Narcissus pseudonarcissus* (the wild Lent lily). However there are daffodils possibly unique to Wales that may stake a claim to the title. One is the Tenby daffodil (*N. pseudonarcissus* ssp. *obvallaris*), now widely cultivated, and another is the Derwydd daffodil, which flourishes at the National Botanic Garden. The name *Narcissus* stems from the Greek *narke* meaning stupor, from which narcotic is derived, and is also the name of the egocentric Greek youth, Narcissus. Today *Narcissus* and its relative *Galanthus* (snowdrop) are being intensively analysed as the natural producers of gallactin, a drug with promise for the treatment of Alzheimer's disease. Similar research is carried out in South Africa on the medicinal uses of *Crinum*.

      **Subfamily Agapanthoideae** Endlicher        1 genus/9 species

Agapanthoideae contains one genus *Agapanthus* L'Héritier that is endemic to South Africa, but is considered a weed in parts of Australia. Its showy flowers impose some economic importance. They are widely cultivated in gardens.

# AMARYLLIDOIDEAE, *the daffodil subfamily*

*Narcissus hybrid (daffodil)*

*Derwydd daffodil*

*Clivia miniata (kaffir lilly)*

The Tenby daffodil (left)

The flowers of Amaryllidoideae have inferior ovaries (white arrows). Daffodils have a corona, which is an extension of the perianth

*Galanthus nivalis (snowdrop) right*

The amaryllis (below), a hybrid of genus Hippeastrum, grows from a large bulb. It is often grown indoors in the winter. The bloom stalk is usually a foot or more tall. Several flowers form at its end, with their buds initially enclosed in a large, green bract. When the tepals first open, the stamens and gynoecium are immature (a). The stamens mature first. Their anthers start as long, pale lavender or cream-coloured structures, which split and fold back to reveal the yellow, pollen-bearing surface. The style grows longer, but the stigma is still closed when the anthers first split (b). Finally, the style bends upward (c) and the three lobes of the stigma open, preparing the flower to receive pollen

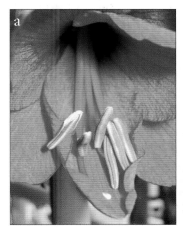

**Monocots**

**Lilioids (petaloid) monocots**

**Asparagales** Bromhead

    **Amaryllidaceae** J. Saint-Hilaire

        **Subfamily Allioideae** Herbich        13 genera/795 species

        Genera include:

        *Allium* L. (onion, leek, garlic, shallot, allium, chives)

        *Ipheion* Rafinesque (spring star flower)

        *Nothoscordum* Kunth (false garlic, crow poison)

        *Tulbaghia* L. (society garlic)

The Allioideae is a north temperate subfamily of mostly perennial bulbs or rhizomatous herbs that smell when crushed because they possess sulphur-containing molecules that also irritate people's eyes. The flowers have six tepals and grow in often globular umbels with scaly bracts at their base. They have a superior ovary. Their bulbs are structures composed of leaves modified for storage. Some species such as chives and onions have tubular leaves. Although primarily known as flavoursome foods (e.g. the onion, *A. cepa*), members of the genus *Allium* have more recently become fashionable as garden plants including the large flowered *A. giganteum* and nodding headed *A. cernuum*, a native of woodlands across the United States. *Allium sativum* (garlic) also has bactericidal and medicinal properties. Wild garlic or ramsons (*A. ursinum*) has particular associations in Wales, where it grows prolifically in woods and even in coastal areas, as is evidenced in place names such as in Snowdonia, Crafnant, the valley of the garlic (Welsh root = *cra*) and Ramsey Island off Pembrokeshire (Old English root = *hramsa*). Also native in Wales at St David's Head and on rocky river banks in the Wye Valley is *A. schoenoprasum* (chives). For the National Botanic Garden of Wales, it is appropriate to mention the cultivar of *A. ampeloprasum* var. *porrum*, the leek, which became the national emblem of Wales following the victory of Cadwallader over the Saxons (640 AD) when the vegetable was worn to distinguish the Welsh soldiers.

# ALLIOIDEAE, *the onion subfamily*

*Ipheion uniflorum (spring star flower) has three yellow stamens that are clearly visible and three that attach further down in the narrow tube formed by the fused bases of its six tepals*

*Allium schoenoprasum (chives), above*

*Allium giganteum (giant allium, above right). Note the fruits split into three segments revealing seeds (above)*

*Allium cernuum, the nodding onion*

*Allium ursinum (wild garlic)*

*Tulbaghia sp. (society garlic)*

**Monocots**

**Lilioids (petaloid) monocots**

**Asparagales** Bromhead

    **Asparagaceae** Jussieu

      **Subfamily Asparagoideae** Burmeister   2 genera/165-295 species

        Genera:

        *Asparagus* L. (asparagus, asparagus fern)

        *Hemiphylacus* S. Watson (hemiphylacus)

This small subfamily, characterised by a lack of well developed green leaves, has two genera: *Asparagus* is confined to an area of the Old World with arid to Mediterranean climates and *Hemiphylacus* to Mexico.

Wild asparagus, *A. prostratus*, is a very rare native found on grassy cliff tops in south-west England and South Wales. Its close relative that provides the luxury vegetable, comprising succulent emergent shoots, is *A. officinalis*, native to southern Europe. The asparagus fern, *A. setaceous*, used by florists is not a fern (i.e. a spore-bearing plant). It is a true asparagus and a flowering plant.

      **Subfamily Nolinoideae** Burnett                26 genera/475 species

        Genera include:

        *Convallaria* L. (lily-of-the-valley)

        *Dracaena* Vandelli ex L. (dragon's blood tree)

        *Liriope* Loureiro (lily turf)

        *Polygonatum* Miller (Solomon's seal)

        *Ruscus* L. (butcher's broom)

        *Sansevieria* Thunberg (mother-in-law's tongue)

This subfamily shows a wide range of growth forms ranging from climbers to herbs to small trees (*Dracaena*).

The butcher's broom (*Ruscus aculeatus*) is an unusual member of the Asparagales being a small, prickly evergreen shrub confined to old woods and hedges in limited areas of England and Wales, but with a wider distribution in the Mediterranean area. Its common name possibly derives from its putative use to clean wood blocks (by butchers); it is still used to decorate meat . Butcher's broom is a remarkably deceptive plant. It appears to have small flowers growing out of the middle of its leaves. The trick is that these are not leaves. They are broad, flattened stems, known botanically as phylloclades. After the butcher's broom blooms, the fruit, which is a red berry, forms in the middle of the phylloclade. *Ruscus* has unisexual flowers growing on separate male and female plants. In contrast Solomon's seal, *Polygonatum multiflorum*, a herb whose arching leaf-bearing stems grow from underground rhizomes, has bisexual flowers. The hexagonal leaf scars on the rhizomes are said to look like the star of David and hence give the plant its common name. It occurs rarely in limestone woods in South Wales, and should not be confused with the more robust garden escape – a hybrid between *P. multiflorum* and *P. odoratum*. The latter is a very rare plant on limestone substrates in the Severn Valley and Brecon Beacons. *Sansevieria trifasiata*, a popular houseplant, possesses yet another growth habit, its strap-shaped leaves bestowing the common name 'mother-in-law's tongue'.

> Subfamilies **Asparagoideae** and **Nolinoideae** share some interesting characteristics. Members from both subfamilies have phylloclades, also called cladophylls, which are stems that are modified in form and perform the photosynthesis that leaves usually do. The short, narrow phylloclades of *Asparagus* do not look a great deal like the broad ones of *Ruscus*, but they are derived from the same plant part and do the same job.

# ASPARAGOIDEAE, *the asparagus subfamily*

*Flowers (left), fruits (above) and emergent shoot (spear) of Asparagus officinalis (garden asparagus) right*

# NOLINOIDEAE, *the butcher's broom subfamily*

*Ruscus hypoglossum, flower*

*R. aculeatus in fruit*

*The tree-like habit of Dracaena (dragon tree), above, is unusual in the the Nolinoideae. Its trunk has a very different construction from those of palms and dicot trees such as oak. Resins (sometimes called dragon's blood) produced by the trunk are used in varnishes*

*Polygonatum hybrid (Solomon's seal), far left*

*Convallaria (lily of the valley) berries, left*

**Monocots**
**Lilioids (petaloid) monocots**
**Asparagales** Bromhead
    **Asparagaceae** Jussieu
      **Subfamily Agavoideae** Herbich             23 genera/637 species
        Genera include:
        *Agave* L. (century plant, sisal)
        *Camassia* Lindley (camass)
        *Hesperocallis* Engelmann (desert lily)
        *Hosta* Trattinick (hosta, plantain lily)
        *Yucca* L. (yucca, Joshua tree)

The subfamily shows a very wide range in growth habits. These include the tree-like yuccas, rosettes in *Agave*, herbaceous rhizomatous in *Hosta* and the bulbous *Camassia*, but all plants have a basal rosette of leaves. Many members occur in both temperate and tropical areas of the New World. The seeds are flat, with a black outer layer. The subfamily includes many plants that are adapted for life in arid environments as well as for moist shady woodlands. The latter includes *Hosta* which originated in China, Korea, Japan and eastern Russia and was first introduced to British gardens at the end of the eighteenth century. The most successful and varied cultivars derive from mid-19th century hybridisation of *H. sieboldii* and *H. plantaginea*. Yuccas have a special pollination partnership with yucca moths. Their coevolution is a classic example of the symbiotic relationship, mutualism. *Camassia quamash* is unusual in that both names come from the North American Nootka Chinook tribe. The specific name describes the sweetness of the edible starchy bulb. *Agave* (tropical and warm temperate Americas but now widespread in the Mediterranean areas) was used by native Americans for a variety of fibres and foods, but is perhaps best appreciated as a source of pulque (fermented sap) that, when distilled, produces mescal or tequila. *Agave sisalana* (sisal) contains hecogenin, a sapogenin used in the production of cortisone and steroids. Similar compounds have been isolated from *Yucca*.

      **Subfamily Scilloideae** Burnett          22 genera/637 species
        Genera include:
        *Eucomis* L'Héritier (pineapple lily, eucomis)
        *Galtonia* Decaisne (galton lily, summer hyacinth)
        *Hyacinthoides* Heister ex Fabricius (wood hyacinth, bluebell)
        *Hyacinthus* L. (hyacinth)
        *Muscari* Miller (grape hyacinth)
        *Ornithogalum* L. (star of Bethlehem)
        *Puschkinia* Adams (puschkinia)
        *Scilla* L. (squill)
        *Chionodoxa* is now placed in *Scilla*

This subfamily of predominantly spring-flowering bulbs is found in the Mediterranean region, the Middle East and Africa, where a wet season is followed by a dry summer. *Muscari* and *Hyacinthus* are important as ornamentals, and also in perfume production. The British speciality is undoubtedly the bluebell, whose Latin name, currently *Hyacinthoides non-scripta*, seems to change regularly. Under threat from plant collectors and interbreeding with the garden escape, the Spanish bluebell (*H. hispanica*), drifts of the nodding blue flowers of *H. non-scripta* remain one of the most evocative and unique aspects of British woodlands in spring.

# AGAVOIDEAE, *the agave subfamily*

*Agave (century plant)*

*Hosta hybrid (plantain lily) overview of plant and close-up of flowers*

*Yuccas bloom many times during their lifetime, but they may not bloom every year. Most agaves bloom only once. The basal rosette of leaves accumulates food for years, then blooms and dies. Some agaves are called century plants, but it usually takes just a few decades for them to build enough resources to bloom*

*Yucca rigida, left*

*Camassia (camass) flower details (right) and overview of the inflorescence.*

# SCILLOIDEAE, *the hyacinth subfamily*

*Scilla verna (spring squill)*

*Muscari sp. (grape hyacinth)*

*Hyacinthoides non-scripta (bluebell)*

**Monocots**

**Commelinid monocots**

**Arecales** Bromhead

    **Arecaceae** Schultz-Schultzenstein or **Palmae** Jussieu            189 genera/2,400 species

        Genera include:

        *Arenga* de Labillardière (sugar palm)

        *Calamus* L. (rattan palm)

        *Caryota* L. (fishtail palm)

        *Ceroxylon* Bonpland ex de Candolle (wax palm)

        *Chamaerops* L. (dwarf fan palm)

        *Cocos* L. (coconut palm)

        *Copernicia* Martius ex Endlicher (carnuba wax palm, wax palm)

        *Elaeis* Jacquin (oil palm)

        *Kerriodoxa* Dransfield (white elephant palm)

        *Metroxylon* Rottbøll (sago palm)

        *Phoenix* L. (date palm)

        *Raphia* P. Beauvois (raffia palm)

        *Sabal* Adanson (palmetto palm)

        *Trachycarpus* H. Wendland (chusan palm)

        *Washingtonia* H. Wendland (California fan palm, Mexican fan palm)

The palm family is the sole family of its order. Palms are trees and shrubs of tropical and subtropical climates. They form a large family of about 2,500 species. Only *Trachycarpus fortunei*, the chusan palm, is hardy in Britain. Palm leaves may be fan-shaped (palmate) and hence be fan-folded, or possess two rows of leaflets (pinnate). They may be simple or compound. The petiole base has a large fibrous sheath. Palms usually have an unbranched trunk, and unlike magnoliid and eudicot trees, possess no dense wood.

Palms have great economic importance. *Cocus nucifera*, the coconut palm, originally from eastern Malaysia but now cultivated, is a good example. Its fruits provide food (for people and stock), drink (coconut milk) and oil (for soap and margarine), while their husks (coir), originally used for matting, cord and rope, are now used for mulching and a peat substitute. Leaves provide shelter, and trunks provide soft timber. Other palms are grown for dates (*Phoenix dactylifera*), oil (*Elaeis guineensis*), fibre (*Raphia farinifera*), sago (*Metroxylon sagu*), wax for polish and candles (*Copernicia prunifera*, *Ceroxylon alpinium*) and sugar syrup (*Arenga saccharifera*).

# ARECACEAE, THE PALM FAMILY

*Trachycarpus fortunei (chusan palm) in flower at the NBGW*

*Kerriodoxa elegans has fan-shaped leaves (top right). Palms may have bisexual or unisexual flowers. They may be pollinated either by wind or insects. Male flowers (middle right), female flowers (below right)*

*Phoenix (date palm) with pinnate leaves*

*Cocos (coconut palm)*

**Monocots**

**Commelinid monocots**

**Commelinales** Dumortier

**Commelinaceae** Mirbel                40 genera/600 species

Genera include:

*Callisia* Loefling (inch plant, basket plant)

*Commelina* L. (dayflower)

*Tradescantia* L. (spiderwort, wandering Jew)

Commelinaceae is a small tropical to warm temperate family of herbs and climbers, best known in Britain from the garden plant, *Tradescantia*. The spiderwort family has sheathing leaves and flower clusters at the ends of the stems. The stamens often have fringed filaments. The flowers have a calyx of three sepals and a corolla of three petals, one of which may be much smaller than the others. The flowers last for only one day.

John Tradescant the Elder and his son, John the Younger, were very successful plant hunters in the 17th century, both enjoying royal patronage. John the Elder collected in Europe and Africa, but his son visited eastern South America, and among the numerous plants he introduced to British gardens was the spider-wort, subsequently named *Tradescantia virginiana* (now known to be the hybrid *T.* x *andersoniana*), but in pre-Linnean times was known as *Phalangium Ephemerum Virginiana Joanna tradescantium* [Phalangium refers to the spider against whose bite the plant was supposed to be an antedote]. Linnaeus, the Swedish botanist, provided a great service to the scientific community, when he introduced the binomial system in which the Latin phrase was reduced to just two names representing the genus and species, in this case, *Tradescantia virginiana*.

**Pontederiaceae** Kunth                9 genera/35 species

Genera include:

*Eichhornia* Kunth (water hyacinth)

*Heteranthera* Ruiz & Pavón (mudplantain)

*Pontederia* L. (pickerel weed)

Pontederiaceae is mainly a tropical family of aquatic plants. Although not grown outside in our garden (visit the tropical house!), it is included here because the water hyacinth *Eichhornia crassipes* is a major obstructing weed of waterways. More recently it has been harvested for use as a biofuel and fodder. *Eichhornia natans* is a noxious weed in African rice-fields. The leaves have petioles that are enlarged, hollow, air-filled tubes, which keep the plant afloat. *Pontederia cordata* is a hardy pond margin plant. It has arrow-shaped leaves and spikes of blue flowers. In its native home in eastern North America, it is known as pickerel weed. It has an amazing system of breeding named heterostyly. The flowers can have long, medium, or short styles and they have stamens that are different lengths from the styles. Pollen from any flower is thus less likely to reach its own stigma, which promotes cross pollination and genetic diversity.

# COMMELINACEAE, *the spiderwort family*

*Tradescantia occidentalis (western or prairie spiderwort)*

*Tradescantia sp. in the Andersoniana group of hybrids*

*Tradescantia pallida (below)*

*Tradescantia zebrina (right)*
*(wandering Jew)*

# PONTEDERIACEAE, *the water hyacinth/pickerel weed family*

*Eichhornia crassipes, common water hyacinth (left and middle)*

*Pontederia cordata, pickerel weed*

# Monocots
## Commelinid monocots
### Zingiberales

**Introducing Zingiberales, the ginger order**

The families of the ginger order have leaves that look very similar, so much so that they can be mistaken for one another. The typical leaf has a strong midrib. The secondary veins are not parallel to the midrib, but are parallel to each other. They leave the midrib at an angle, from acute to about 90°. This pattern of veining is sometimes called pinnate-parallel. The leaves are rolled into a tube when they form; they uncoil as they mature. One sometimes sees leaves with a row of holes going across the blade, where an insect chewed through all the layers while the leaf was rolled. The flowers have inferior ovaries and no more than five functional stamens. The prayer plant and canna families have only a single functional stamen. The remaining stamens are staminodes (modified stamens that often look and function like petals). Most of the families produce aerial stems only when they bloom. The one tropical family that is not in this guide, Costaceae, grows a spiraling aerial stem with one row of leaves.

**Strelitziaceae** Hutchinson                    3 genera/7 species

Genera:

*Phenakospermum* Endlicher

*Ravenala* Adanson (traveler's palm)

*Strelitzia* Banks ex Aiton (bird-of-paradise)

Strelitziaceae is a small family with three genera, one each in tropical South America, South Africa and Madagascar. It has large, simple leaves, rolled in bud that, in common with those of *Musa*, may split in the wind, and that may be borne on erect stems up to 10m tall. The traveller's palm (*Ravenala madagascariensis*) is so named because the two rows of leaves were believed to be aligned in a north-south direction, and hence could be used as a compass! An alternative explanation is that the leaf bases hold rainwater suitable for drinking.

**Heliconiaceae**                              1 genus/100-200 species

Genus:

*Heliconia* L. (heliconia, lobster claw, parrot flower)

The family with its single genus, *Heliconia*, occurs in the tropics of Central America and south-east Asia. *Heliconia* is grown in the tropics for its cut flowers and in hothouses as an ornamental. Heliconias have groups of flowers borne inside large, very long, coloured bracts arranged in two rows, some of which resemble lobster claws or parrot beaks. The flowers themselves are smaller and much less showy than the bracts.

# STRELITZIACEAE, *the bird-of-paradise family*

*Strelitzia reginae (bird-of-paradise)*

*Strelitzia nicolai (the giant bird-of-paradise) inflorescence above, general overview below*

The flowers of this family are so modified that finding their parts is not easy. A series of flowers grow along the top of a large horizontal bract. The sepals of *Strelitzia reginae* (bird-of-paradise) are bright orange. The petals are blue. One petal is separate; it is the small blue structure that stands near the base of the sepals. The rest of the petals are fused together and wrap around the long, pointed style and the five stamens. The stamens are fused inside a groove in the long, blue petals, forming an arrow in which the pollen lies. The ovary has three chambers, each of which holds numerous ovules. The flowers produce copious nectar and are pollinated by insects and birds.

# HELICONIACEAE, *the heliconia family*

*Bracts of this parrot heliconia, left, H. psittacorum, are red. Flowers have tubular yellow tepals with dark green tips. Heliconia rostrata, middle, and H. orthotricha, right, are ornamentals in many tropical or subtropical areas*

**Monocots**

**Commelinid monocots**

**Zingiberales**

    **Musaceae** Jussieu                         3 genera/35 species

        Genera are:

        *Ensete* Horaninow (Abyssinian banana)

        *Musa* L. (banana, plantain)

The larger and most important economic genus in this tropical family is *Musa* which occurs in the Himalayas, southern China, northern Australia and the Philippines. The familiar dessert fruit is derived from sterile triploid forms of *M. acuminata* that originated in the Indomalay area. Such cultivated bananas contain no seeds and so are propagated from suckers. The most important cooking bananas (plantains: *M.* x *paradisiaca*), which are a major source of carbohydrate in the tropics, are hybrids of *Musa balbisiana* and *paradisiaca*. The gigantic leaves of a number of species contain fibres used for cables, cordage (*M. textilis*), paper (in Japanese homes) and tea-bags.

    **Cannaceae** Jussieu                        1 genus/8-10 species

        Genus:

        *Canna* L. (canna, Indian shot)

Cannaceae is a tropical to warm temperate family in the Americas with just one genus characterised by rhizomes full of starch. The latter is edible (*Canna edulis*) and the source of purple or Queensland arrowroot, but the major use of the plant is as an ornamental, both in gardens and conservatories. Its seeds are very hard, hence the name Indian shot, and they are used as beads.

# MUSACEAE, *the banana family*

Musa ornata (ornamental banana)

Musa ornata, male inflorescence

Musa sp. female inflorescence

The banana, genus Musa, has large red or purple bracts that surround its small, tubular flowers. The flowers have yellow or cream-coloured tepals. The female flowers bloom first in the inflorescence. Female flowers have inferior ovaries, which are green in this example. Later flowers are male. This produces a bunch of bananas and a long section of bare stem where the male flowers once bloomed. The banana's leaves spiral around the stem.

# CANNACEAE, *the canna family*

Canna hybrid

Canna indica fruit

Canna indica flower

It is not easy to figure out the structure of a canna flower, but the parts show up more clearly on the species, Canna indica. There are typically three or four modified stamens that look like petals, and which are called staminodes. The one functional stamen has half an anther and is also petal-like. On the gynoecium, the style is flattened. The three true petals are slender and pointed. Their bases are fused, along with the stamens and the style, and form a tube at the base of the flower. The fruit is a three-sided capsule that is covered with pointed projections.

## Monocots
## Commelinid monocots
## Zingiberales

**Marantaceae** R. Brown                      30 genera/630 species

Genera include:

*Calathea* G. Meyer (peacock plant)

*Ctenanthe* Eichler (ctenanthe)

*Maranta* L. (prayer plant, arrow root)

*Stromanthe* Sonder (stromanthe)

*Thalia* L. (water canna)

Marantaceae is a pantropical family (except Australia) of perennial rhizomatous herbs. The junction between the blade and petiole acts as a joint allowing changes of position of the leaves. They fold upward at night, resulting in the common name of the plant. The leaves themselves display beautiful markings such that the plants are popular home ornamentals. *Maranta arundinacea* is an important crop plant in the Caribbean because its rhizomes contain arrowroot, a very high quality, easily digestible starch. Tubers of *Calathea allouia* are eaten as potatoes. Leaves of other species are used in roofing and basket making.

**Zingiberaceae** Martinov                   48 genera/1,275 species

Genera include:

*Alpinia* Roxburgh (shell ginger)

*Curcuma* L. (turmeric)

*Elettaria* Maton (cardamom)

*Etlingera* Giseke (torch ginger)

*Hedychium* Koenig (ginger lily)

*Kaempferia* L. (peacock ginger)

*Roscoea* J. Smith (roscoea)

*Zingiber* P. Miller (ginger)

The Zingiberaceae is a tropical family centred in the humid Indomalay lowlands and extending into south-east Asia and Australia. It is the source of several important spices. The fruits of cardamom, *Elettaria cardamomum*, are picked slightly green and then dried. The seeds are used to flavour baked goods, Indian foods, coffee, tea and liqueurs. The pungent rhizomes of ginger, *Zingiber officinale*, are used as a spice and in medicines as carminatives, stimulants and in the prevention of motion sickness. Ginger has been cultivated in Asia from prehistoric times. Rhizomes of *Curcuma longa* yield turmeric, which is used as a flavouring in curries, as a preservative, and a yellow dye. Rhizomes of *C. angustifolium* yield Bombay or Indian arrowroot. *Curcuma longa* contains curcumins used in Indian and Chinese medicine as a diuretic and in the treatment of jaundice and hepatitis. Members of the family are also cultivated as greenhouse ornamentals (e.g. *Hedychium* and *Roscoea*).

# MARANTACEAE, *the prayer plant family*

*Maranta leuconeura var. erythroneura (red herringbone plant) left*

*Calathea 'Corona' right*

*Note the conspicuous venation patterns of the leaf*

*Close-up of small flowers (bottom right) and overview of foliage (bottom left) of Maranta sp.*

# ZINGIBERACEAE, *the ginger family*

*This family has irregular flowers with a complicated structure. All but one of the stamens have become petal-like staminodes. An example is the ruffled yellow and red part in the Alpinia flower (centre below). The filament of the single functional stamen (arrow) is broad and folds around the style. The three petals of this shell ginger, the bract at the flower's base and the calyx are all white*

*Curcuma longa has pink bracts that hold small, yellow and white flowers*

*Alpinia zerumbet 'Variegata'*

*Etlingera elatior (torch ginger) is a striking ornamental in tropical gardens. Its flowers are the small red structures with yellow edging*

**Monocots**

**Commelinid monocots**

**Poales** Small

    **Typhaceae** Jussieu                    2 genera/25 species

        Genera:

        *Sparganium* L. (bur reed)

        *Typha* L. (cattail, bulrush)

Typhaceae is a very small cosmopolitan family in which both genera colonise marshy ground and shallow margins of lakes and slow-moving rivers. These aquatic plants have male and female flowers in separate clusters in the same flower head. Their male flowers form above the female flowers on the same stalk. The flowers are so small that it is hard to see any of their details. The male flowers fall off after they bloom, and the ovaries of the female flowers develop into the fruits. In *Typha latifolia* the young flowers are green. When the male flowers mature, they give off large amounts of pollen. The female flowers turn brown and enlarge as the seed develops while the male flowers wither. In the autumn, the seeds are shed and blow away with the aid of attached fluffy fibres. Except for its use as an ornamental, *Typha latifolia*, a British native found in wet areas around lakes and ditches, has no economic importance. By contrast, in North America, the Paiute Indians of Nevada still use it for boat building and its pollen as a kind of flour! Other species are used in weaving and may have edible rhizomes. *Sparganium* has only recently joined the family, again on molecular evidence.

    **Bromeliaceae** Jussieu              57 genera/1,400 species

        Genera include:

        *Aechmea* Ruiz & Pavón (bromeliad)

        *Alcantarea* (Mez) Harms (imperial bromeliad)

        *Ananas* Miller (pineapple)

        *Bromelia* L.(tank plant)

        *Neoregelia* L. B. Smith (heart of flame, blushing bromeliad)

        *Puya* Molina (puya)

        *Tillandsia* L. (tillandsia, Spanish moss)

The Bromeliaceae is a tropical family almost completely confined to the New World. Its members have the property of surviving in a wide range of places often where water is not always available. Some grow as epiphytes on tall trees, others on telegraph wires (*Tillandsia*). Members of the genus *Bromelia* are predominantly rain forest plants where the majority are epiphytes high in the canopy. Water collected in the base of the leaves forms mini-ponds that are homes to insects and frogs. Ground growing examples include *Puya* (see Chile section in Great Glass House). The economic importance of bromeliads in horticulture is far outweighed by that of pineapple (*Ananas comosus*) as a crop plant, where a seedless cultivar is now grown globally in the tropics. Its origin was in Paraguay or south Brazil and even in pre-Columbian Indian times the fruit was already being selected for increasing fleshiness. The 'fruit' is actually a collection of fused individual fruits surrounding the quite tough inflorescence stalk at its core.

# TYPHACEAE, *the bulrush or bur reed family*

*Typha latifolia (bulrush), above and centre*

*Sparganium erectum (bur reed)*

# BROMELIACEAE, *the bromeliad family*

*Alcantarea imperialis with typical cup formed from overlapping leaf bases*

*Ananas comosus var variegatus (ornamental pineapple)*

*Tillandsia usneoides (Spanish moss)*

*Puya berteronia*

*Neoregelia carolinae (heart-of-flame bromeliad) has tiny pink flowers in the central cup composed of red leaves*

**Monocots**
**Commelinid monocots**
**Poales** Small

    **Juncaceae** Jussieu                         7 genera/430 species
           Genera include:
           *Juncus* L. (rush)
           *Luzula* de Candolle (wood rush)
           *Prionium* E. Meyer (prionium)

This is a common temperate family that shows greatest generic diversity in the Southern Hemisphere. Although usually grass-like in appearance, the Southern Hemisphere genus, *Prionium*, is a shrub with palm-like habit. In nature, the soft rush, *Juncus*, is an indicator of poor quality, water-logged grassland, and readily recognised because the floral clusters arise from the sides of a cylindrical, leaf-like stem. Before candles became common, it was the white pith of these stems, very carefully extracted, that was dipped into fat or beeswax and burned for lighting.

    **Cyperaceae** Jussieu                    92 genera/4,450 species
           Genera include:
           *Carex* L. (sedge)
           *Cladium* P. Browne (saw edge sedge)
           *Cyperus* L. (papyrus)
           *Eleocharis* R. Brown (spikerush, Chinese water chestnut)
           *Eriophorum* L. (cotton-grass)
           *Schoenoplectus* Palla (bulrush)
           *Scirpus* L. (bulrush)

Cyperaceae is a cosmopolitan temperate family whose members are usually grass-like in appearance, but compared with the grasses are of very little economic importance. In considering the horticultural 'wow' factor that must characterise botanical themes in the NBGW, the sedge and rush families originally posed the greatest challenge in the systematics garden. However members of the genus *Carex* have ornamental forms, e.g. *Carex pendula*, while the umbrella plant *Cyperus alternifolius* is a good structural plant in water gardens. An even more spectacular, but similar flowering head is seen in *C. papyrus*, the plant that was used by the ancient Egyptians for paper making from the pith of the stem. It is also used in cordage, sandal-making, boat construction and, more rarely, as a source of food (starch in rhizomes). In the Cambridgeshire Fens, *Cladium mariscus*, the saw edge, was used for thatching. Somewhat more versatile is *Schoenoplectus lacustris*, whose common name, bulrush, is sometimes also used for *Typha latifolia* (note here again how the use of Latin names can eliminate confusion). Its flexible stems may grow to 3m in height and can be used in weaving baskets, mats, seats etc. Traditionally they were used to make paper and, when strewn on the floor, were an untidy forerunner of the carpet. On the international front, *Eleocharis tuberosa* (Chinese water chestnut) is the crunchy part of a good chop suey.

    **Restionaceae** R. Brown                 48 genera/460 species
           Genera include:
           *Elegia* L. (restio)
           *Restio* Rottbøll (restio)
           *Rhodocoma* Nees (restio)

Restoniaceae is a Southern Hemisphere family with a high concentration of endemic plants in Western Australia and the Cape region of South Africa. Most Cape species occur in wetlands that are seasonally dry and fire prone. Some are capable of growing at high altitudes where they may dominate vegetation. In addition to their economic importance as ornamentals, restios are used in S. Africa for thatching. They have recently gained prominence in British gardens as an attractive evergreen ornamental. Small flowers, either male or female, are arranged in inflorescences rather like those of grasses, but the leaves are much reduced.

# JUNCACEAE, *the rushes family*

*Juncus sp. in upland marshy habitat, left. Middle, in fruit and showing stem with exposed pith*

*Luzula campestris (common wood rush)*

# CYPERACEAE, *the sedge family*

*Carex sp. male (blackish) and female (greenish) flowers*

*Cyperus alternifolius (umbrella plant)*

# RESTIONACEAE, *the restio family*

*Flowering head of Rhodocoma fruticosa (above)*

*Elegia sp. Window Buttress, Cape Province, South Africa (left)*

**Monocots**
**Commelinid monocots**
**Poales** Small

      **Poaceae** (R. Brown) Barnhart or **Gramineae** Jussieu       715 genera/c. 10,550 species

Note that there are two names for this family, but only one with the familiar ending – aceae. Gramineae is typical of a group of families that have been in use for a long time, e.g. Compositae (Asteraceae), Umbelliferae (Apiaceae). Thus, although it is now necessary under the International Code of Botanical Nomenclature to use the name of an included genus in the family name (e.g. Poa/Poaceae) the use of the alternative name is also sanctioned. The family itself is divided into twelve sub-families.

Genera include:

| | | |
|---|---|---|
| *Agrostis* L. | *Deschampsia* Palisot de Beauvois | *Muhlenbergia* Schreber |
| *Ammophila* Host | *Elymus* L. | *Panicum* L. |
| *Brachypodium* Palisot de Beauvois | *Festuca* L. | *Phalaris* L. |
| *Briza* L. | *Imperata* Cirillo | *Phleum* L. |
| *Bromus* L. | *Lolium* L. | *Phragmites* Adanson |
| *Calamagrostis* Adams | *Miscanthus* Andersson | *Poa* L. |
| *Dactylis* L. | *Molinia* Shrank | *Stipa* L. |

(* planted in the ornamental grasses bed. For genera in the economic grasses bed, see over page).

The grasses form a very large and diverse family which is truly cosmopolitan, with a representative even in Antarctica. Their leaves have a sheathed base and most species have hollow stems. It takes careful observation and a hand lens to see details of grass flowers. They have no obvious perianth and are typically wind-pollinated. Flowers form within several green bracts that make up a spikelet. When the flower blooms, the bracts are pushed apart. The stamens hang out where the wind can blow away their pollen. As in many wind-pollinated plants, the pollen grains (with one pore) are small and very abundant – one of the commonest causes of hay fever. The stigmas have many finely divided branches, so they look like tiny feathers. After the flowers bloom, the bracts of the spikelet close back together and the grass fruit, or grain, grows inside. It is the carbohydrate, starch and, occasionally, oil, which accumulates in the seed to form a nutrient source (endosperm) for the developing embryo, that make grass seeds of various genera such important foods (see p74). Indeed, seeds of wild grasses such as emmer wheat are known to have been collected for at least 20,000 years. Horticulturally grasses are almost synonymous with lawns, but they are also being grown increasingly as ornamentals for their foliage (leaf shape and colour), inflorescences and general architecture.

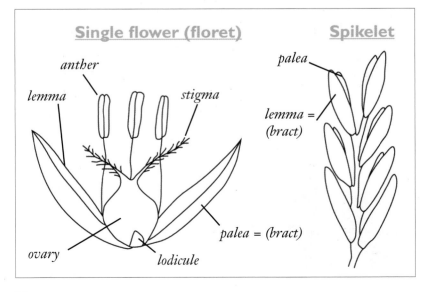

Flowers are aggregated into spikelets that are surrounded by further bracts called glumes. The spikelets with varying numbers of flowers may be closely packed and arranged spirally or in two rows on the inflorescence stalk (spike) or terminate short branches (panicle).

# POACEAE OR GRAMINEAE, *the grass family*

a

b

c

d

e

f

*a) Phleum pratense (foxtail) has very closely arranged florets. Note the dangling stamens. b) Lolium perenne (rye grass) has spikelets with florets in two rows. It is an important fodder and lawn grass. c) Festuca rubra (red fescue grass) with loose panicle of spikelets. Widespread pasture and lawn grass. d) Poa annua (annual meadow grass) displays a loose panicle with small clusters of florets. It is grown in lawns and pastures. e) Dactylis glomerata (cock's foot) is another fodder grass with large clusters of florets that produce numerous stamens, (f) and hence abundant pollen - a major cause of hay fever. Grass leaves have a sheathed base that wraps around the flower stalk (g).*

g

*Ornamental grasses in the Double Walled Garden at the NBGW*

# THE GRASS REVOLUTION

It is hard to imagine a landscape with no grass, but grasses did not appear until late in the Cretaceous period of Earth history, which ended 65 million years ago. It was not until much later that grasses made up large portions of plant communities. About 20 million years ago, the grasslands biome and grass-dominated plant communities appeared. At that time, the climate became cooler and drier, which probably gave grasses a survival advantage. Today, these flowering plants make up a large portion of the terrestrial flora and are a major food source for animal life on land.

Grasses have several traits that helped them dominate plant communities. Many are drought resistant, and they also stand up well to fires and grazing. Their extensive root systems are part of this, but their special meristems the equivalent of stem cells also give them outstanding advantages. Meristems are the growing points of plants. For most plants, the meristems that produce new shoots are at the tips of the branches. Grasses, however, have their meristems inserted at the base of the leaves, sometimes even below ground level. This means that when the leaves are eaten or cut off, the plant continues to grow.

Grazing mammals evolved in concert with grasses and developed teeth with thicker, harder enamel that could withstand the silica deposited in grass leaves. For humans, grasses have a special importance. They provide us with a large portion of our daily food calories. We seldom eat the foliage, since we lack digestive systems to extract nutrients from it, but grass seeds (wheat, barley, oats etc.) are another matter. They provide us with carbohydrates, proteins, vitamins, and other nutrients. Indeed on a global scale, they have traditionally formed the staple diets of the major civilisations, with only root crops such as yam and potato having a similar role.

The cultivation of wheat started at least 9,000 years ago in Anatolia, Iran, (then Persia) and Syria, with unconscious selection leading to the development of plants with intact fruiting heads because primitive farmers had difficulty in collecting heads that broke up easily. As these farmers migrated from the Near East into Europe, Africa and Asia, they took their seeds with them, and probably inadvertently introduced weeds such as rye and oats too. Initially the grains themselves were eaten, but then about 2,500 years ago there is some evidence that the Egyptians begun to grind them up and introduced yeast to make bread. Rice as a food probably had a similar weedy origin, this time some 10,000 years ago in south-east Asia where the Neolithic Hoabinhians were cultivating swampy taro (a starchy tuber of an aroid). In the New World, maize began to be cultivated about 8,000 years ago by Mexican and Andean Indians, and sometime later potatoes and tomatoes were added to their diets. Maize still remains an extremely versatile crop yielding starch, oil, adhesives and silage.

Adding to the pleasures of life are the products of *Hordeum* (barley) and *Saccharum* (sugarcane). Barley has a major use in malting; the simple sugars produced when grains germinate are drained off to provide the medium to be fermented by yeast – the raw ingredient for the brewing of beer and spirits (whisky, gin, vodka).

The sap of the sugarcane produces more than half the world's sugar, and more recently has become an important source of renewable energy because when distilled it produces alcohol for use as a fuel (up to 25% of petrol blend in Brazil). Recent researches suggest that the biomass produced by the elephant grass *Miscanthus* has the potential to become an important carbon-neutral biofuel in the UK.

The bamboos, divided into more than a thousand species, form several subfamilies within the Poaceae and are very versatile economic plants in tropical and subtropical climates around the world. More limited as a food source, they are extensively used in the construction industry as a substitute for scaffolding, houses, bridges, ladders and boats. Bamboo canes can be converted into farm implements and cooking utensils, weapons and even musical instruments. Flowering in some bamboos is remarkable in that it occurs only at long intervals, possibly as much as 120 years. Flowering in a grove is synchronised and followed by the death of plants. A new stand eventually grows from the seeds, but where bamboos are central to local economies as in parts of India, widespread flowering and death can lead to hardship.

| | | |
|---|---|---|
| (i)  Cereals: | *Sorghum* Moench | (iii)  *Bambusa* Schreber (bamboos) |
| *Avena* L. (oats) | *Triticum* L. (wheat) | *Phyllostachys* Siebold & Zuccarini |
| *Hordeum* L. (barley) | *Zea* L. (maize = corn in USA) | *Semiarundinaria* Makino ex Nakai |
| *Oryza* L. (rice) | | |
| *Panicum* L. (millet) | (ii)  *Saccharum* L. (cane sugar, | (iv)  *Miscanthus* Andersson (biofuel) |
| *Secale* L. (rye) | molasses and treacle) | |

# POACEAE OR GRAMINEAE, *the grass family - economic grasses*

a

b

c

d

e

f

*Bambusa textilis
(weaver's bamboo)*

(a) *Avena sativa (oats) fruits are used for porridge and flapjacks.*
*Zea mays (sweet corn or maize) is a monoecious grass. The tassels on the top of the stalk (b) bear the stamens. The ear (c) is the female inflorescence. A kernel (grain) is the ovary of a single flower. Each kernel has its own silk, which is a long style with a stigma at the end. We eat the immature grain as sweet corn.*
(d) *Oryza sativa (rice), grows in tropical to warm temperate climates. Rice produces best when it is cultivated in partly flooded fields, although it can also be grown on dry ground.*
*Triticum aestivum (wheat) grows best in cool, temperate climates. It is shown above late in flowering (e) and as mature, dry fruits (f). The "seeds" are actually the whole fruits - the pericarp adheres closely to the seed. Together, seed and tight pericarp make up the grain. Most cultivated varieties of wheat have grains that are easily threshed and removed from the remains of the bracts that surrounded their flowers.*

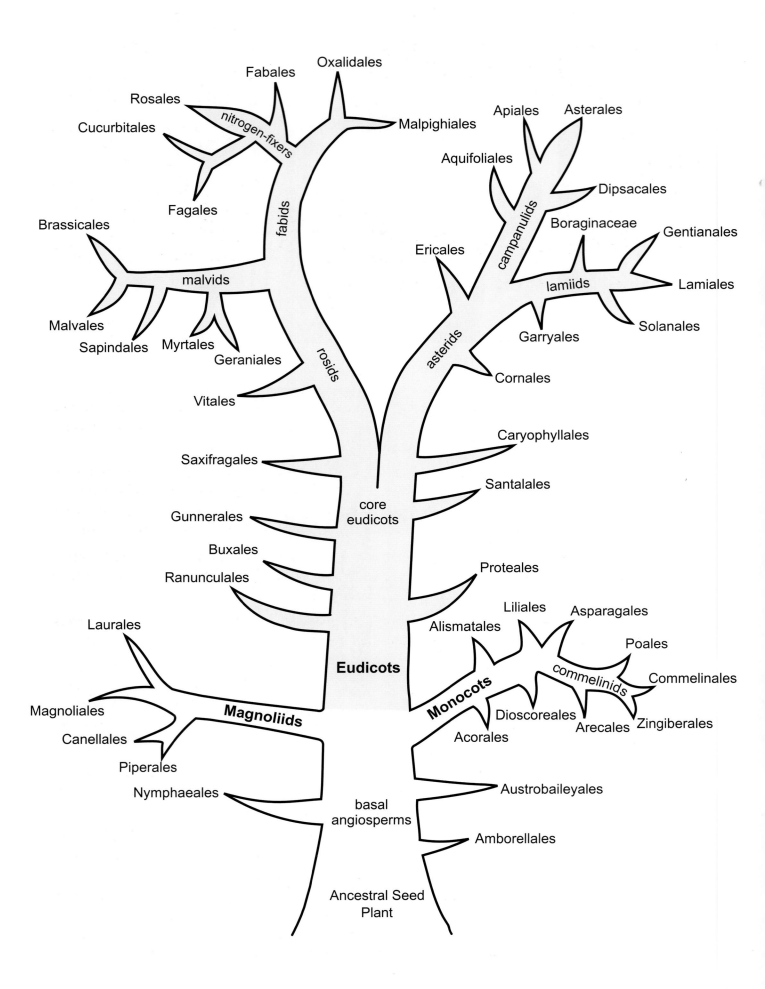

# INTRODUCTION TO THE EUDICOTS

With three quarters of the named species in the angiosperms, eudicots are by far the largest group of the flowering plants.

Traditionally, the dicots were one of two main groups of flowering plants. They were named for their two cotyledons or seed leaves, which can be seen in the photo above of a sunflower seedling. The dicots are now known to be a mixture of plant groups descended from different ancestors. The eudicots are what remain after the magnoliids and other basal angiosperms are removed from the traditional dicots. The name "eudicot" literally means "true dicots."

One characteristic common to eudicots is pollen with three openings. An alternate name for the group is the tricolpates, from the term for pollen grains with three openings. Eudicot flowers typically have parts such as petals and stamens in multiples of four or five. This rule does not apply to the pistils, which may be a single carpel, two-carpellate, or three-carpellate or more.

The leaves of eudicots typically have netted veins; they generally do not have parallel veins. After that, there are many variations, such as simple or compound leaves, with or without stipules, and with a wide diversity of lobes and margins.

Eudicot plant forms and adaptations cover the full diversity of flowering plants, as they include trees, shrubs, vines, herbaceous plants, aquatics, succulents, carnivorous plants, and parasitic plants.

The first branch of the eudicots is the order Ranunculales, which includes the buttercup family (Ranunculaceae), the poppy family (Papaveraceae), and the barberry family (Berberidaceae). The next branch is the Proteales, which includes the lotus family (Nelumbonaceae) and the plane family (Platanaceae). These orders together with the Buxales and Gunnerales are considered basal eudicots.

The rest of the group are called the core eudicots. They split into five main groups—the Caryophyllales, the Santalales, the Saxifragales, and the two biggest branches, the rosids and the asterids. There is more information about these five groups in their sections of this tour.

Eudicots are an ancient group, whose history can be tracked via its characteristic pollen. The first eudicot fossil pollen appears in 125 million-year-old rocks. In comparison, the oldest fossils we have that are clearly flowering plants are just a little older, 135 million years old. Recent datings of branching events within the eudicots, using DNA sequences, suggest a rapid radiation of the major eudicot lineages. The core eudicots may have split off from the basal eudicots as early as 120 million years ago, and rosid and asterids diverged only about 10 million years later. At the end of the Cretaceous, 65 million years ago, most eudicot families were already present.

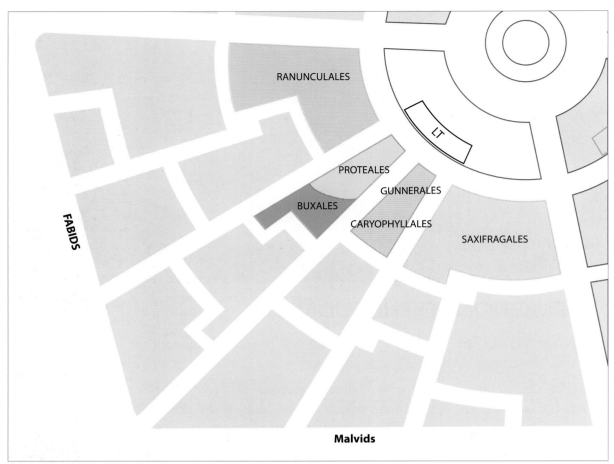

*Quadrant 2. Orders in basal and certain core eudicots*

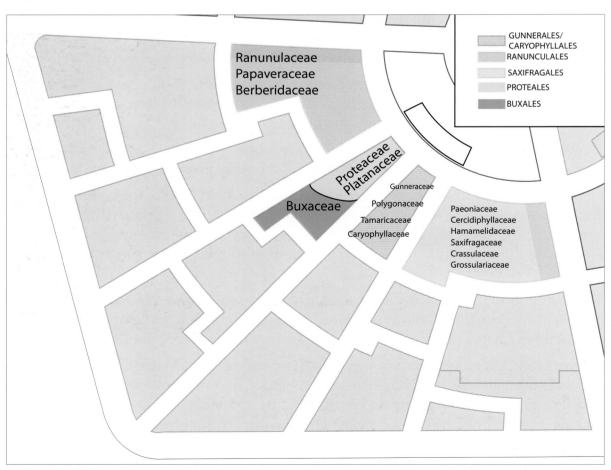

*Quadrant 2. Families in the basal and certain core eudicots*

*Quadrant 2. Bed with families of the Ranunculales and Saxafragales in the background*

*Quadrant 2. Bed with Crassulaceae and Paeoniaceae*

**Eudicots**
**Basal eudicots**
**Ranunculales** Dumortier
    **Papaveraceae** Jussieu                  43 genera/820 species
        Genera of Papaveroidea, the poppy subfamily, include:
        *Argemone* L. (prickly poppy)
        *Chelidonium* L. (greater celandine)
        *Eschscholzia* Chamisso (California poppy)
        *Glaucium* Miller (horned poppy)
        *Meconopsis* Viguier (Himalayan poppy, Welsh poppy)
        *Papaver* L. (poppy, alpine poppy, opium poppy, Shirley poppy)
        *Romneya* Harvey (California tree poppy)
        *Sanguinaria* L. (bloodroot)

        Genera of Fumarioidea, the fumitory subfamily, include:

| | |
|---|---|
| *Adlumia* Rafinesque - Schmaltz ex de Candolle | *Fumaria* L. (fumitory) |
| *Corydalis* de Candolle (corydalis, fumewort) | *Rupicapnos* Pomel |
| *Dicentra* Bentham (bleeding heart) | *Sarcocapnos* de Candolle |

Papaveraceae is predominantly a Northern Hemisphere, temperate family. Common characters in the poppy subfamily are the presence of a milky sap (latex) and petals crumpled in bud. The common or corn poppy (*Papaver rhoeas*) is an iconic flower, a symbol of blood, death, rebirth and fertility from ancient times to our own remembrance ceremonies. The corn poppy is a weed of cereals. Indeed the Romans made it the sacred flower of the goddess of cereals/crops, Ceres. Its seeds, mixed up with cultivated grasses, were probably introduced into Britain by the earliest Neolithic farmers, but it became much scarcer here when crops were intensively sprayed. *Papaver somniferum*, the opium poppy, comes from Asia. Opium resin is the dried latex from the young fruit – later the characteristic "pepper pot". Although the species can be grown in the UK, it does not produce much latex here, and its drug-free seeds are used in cooking. The alkaloids present in the resin can be processed to produce a wide range of drugs including analgesics and antispasmodics, and the source of sleep and pain relief, morphine, whose benefits partially balance the miseries brought to millions by heroin. *Meconopsis cambrica*, the Welsh poppy, is common in Wales, but also present in neighbouring parts of England. Its flowers and latex are yellow. The Chinese *Meconopsis grandis* has striking large blue flowers. Fumitory, a weed, and *Corydalis* were once placed in the family Fumariaceae, now subsumed within the Papaveraceae. Fumitory comes from the Latin *fumus terrae* "smoke of the earth", hence another common name is Earth smoke. Flowers in this group are bilaterally symmetrical and have nectar in spurs or sacs so that they are visited by specialist pollinators. The open flowers of the poppy by contrast are visited by 'promiscuous' pollinators, lots of browsing visitors attracted by the colours.

        **Lardizabalaceae** Decaisne             9 genera/36 species
        Genera include:
        *Akebia* Decaisne (chocolate vine)
        *Decaisnea* Hooker f. & Thomson (decaisnea)
        *Holboellia* Wallich (holboellia)
        *Sinofranchetia* (Diels) Hemsley (sinofranchetia)

Members of this small family of shrubs and climbers from the Himalayas and East Asia, particularly China, are grown in our gardens. The floral parts, as in monocots, are in threes, and the petals and sepals look similar. The semi-evergreen *Akebia quinata* (the chocolate vine) derives its name from the three brownish purple petals. It has edible fruits. *Akebia quinata* illustrated here smells of chocolate when in bloom. *Decaisnea* is a shrub described as pachycaul, because it has a very sparingly branched trunk with terminal crowns of leaves (similar to the palm or tree fern habit). Its fruit are dangling sausage-shaped blue pods, and similar to those on the evergreen liane, *Holboellia*. By contrast, the vine *Sinofranchetia* has large purple berries.

*Papaver nudicaule (Iceland poppy), left. Two green furry sepals fall off when the poppy blooms. Four to six wrinkled petals unfold, revealing many stamens and a compound gynaecium, middle. The stigma sits above the ovary; there is little or no style. The fruit is a capsule, right, often with many holes near the top, like a pepper pot*

*Eschscholzia californica (California poppy)*

*Papaver bracteatum (oriental poppy)*

*Argemone polyanthemos (prickly poppy)*

*The fumitory subfamily has distinctive flowers with bilateral symmetry. The fanciful names include bleeding hearts, squirrel corn, and Dutchman's breeches*

## LARDIZABALACEAE

*Dicentra spectabilis (common bleeding heart)*

*Corydalis aurea (golden corydalis)*

*Akebia quinata (chocolate vine)*

**Eudicots**
**Basal eudicots**
**Ranunculales** Dumortier
    **Berberidaceae** Jussieu                      14 genera/715 species
        Genera include:
        *Berberis* L. (barberry, mahonia, holly grape)
        *Epimedium* L. (epimedium, bishop's hat, barrenwort)
        *Nandina* Thunberg (heavenly bamboo, sacred bamboo)
        *Podophyllum* L. (May apple, American mandrake)
        *Mahonia* (Nuttall) is now included in *Berberis*

Berberidaceae is a widespread, spring flowering, temperate family, whose nectar-containing flowers are brightly coloured. Its flowers have two whorls of perianth, with four to six outer petal-like sepals surrounding six shorter petals. The gynaecium is formed from a single carpel. Fruits are usually berries. The leaves of numerous species are compound and many have spines on the leaf margins. Spines are also common on stems, whose wood is coloured yellow by a substance called berberine. There is one (possibly) British native, *Berberis vulgaris* (barberry). Although a very spiny plant, barberry is no longer used in hedging, because it was found to be the alternate host for the black rust fungus that infects wheat. In teaching, *Berberis* can be used to demonstrate mobile stamens. These normally rest against the petals, but place a pencil tip between them centrally and the anthers spring inwards. If your pencil were to be a bee attracted to the flower for nectar, then pollen would land on its head, and would be carried off to another flower.

    **Ranunculaceae** Jussieu                  56 genera/2,100 species
        Genera include:
        *Aconitum* L. (monkshood, wolf's bane)
        *Actaea* L. (baneberry, [formerly *Cimicifuga*])
        *Anemone* L. (wood anemone, hepatica [formerly *Hepatica*], pasque flower
                [formerly *Pulsatilla*])
        *Aquilegia* L. (columbine)
        *Caltha* L. (king cup, marsh marigold)
        *Clematis* L. (clematis, old man's beard, traveller's joy)
        *Delphinium* L. (delphinium, larkspur)
        *Eranthis* Salisbury (winter aconite)
        *Helleborus* L. (Lenten rose, Christmas rose, hellebore)
        *Nigella* L. (nigella, love-in-a-mist)
        *Ranunculus* L. (buttercup, crowfoot, lesser celandine)
        *Thalictrum* L. (meadow rue)
        *Trollius* L. (globe flower)

This mainly temperate family of herbs and climbers contains some of our most familiar wild flowers (e.g. buttercups and lesser celandine) and, because its flowers are showy, some of our best loved garden plants. Flowers superficially look very different, e.g. *Ranunculus*, *Clematis*, *Delphinium*, *Aquilegia* and *Nigella*, but they usually have many stamens, and their fruits broadly fall into two types – collections of follicles (similar to pea pods) or achenes (single seeded units). This is reflected in the two major subgroups – the hellebores with follicles, e.g. Christmas rose and *Delphinium*, and the anemones with achenes, e.g. buttercups. Variability in flowers is related to insect pollination (colour and nectar). Nectaries (sometimes called honey-leaves) are fascinating – little trumpets in *Helleborus* (modified stamens), little flaps on buttercup petals, spurs in *Delphinium* and *Aconitum*. *Aconitum*, monkshood (see medicinal plants garden), is amongst the most poisonous of our native plants. Its hooded bonnet-like flowers are bright blue. It was used as a poison by hunters (wolf's bane) and as a painkiller and liniment for rheumatism.

# BERBERIDACEAE, *the barberry family*

*Epimedium rubrum*

*Berberis aquifolium*

*Berberis thunbergii var. atropurpurea*

# RANUNCULACEAE, *the buttercup family*

*The many seeded follicles of Colorado columbine*

*Aquilegia caerulea (Colorado columbine)*

*Aconitum carmichaelii (Chinese monkshood)*

*The flower and developing fruits of Anemone x lesseri show a typical aggregate of carpels that are closely grouped, but remain distinct*

*This Clematis hybrid has purple anthers surrounding the white stigmas. The carpels each produce an achene with a long, feathery style*

*Helleborus orientalis (Lenten rose) has red styles and yellow stamens*

**Eudicot**

**Basal eudicots**

**Proteales** Dumortier

    **Nelumbonaceae** Berchtold & J. Presl     1 genus/2 species

        Genus:

        *Nelumbo* Adanson (lotus)

Nelumbonaceae, another aquatic family, occupies marginal habitats in ponds and lakes and contains just one genus, *Nelumbo*. *Nelumbo lutea* has yellow flowers, while in *N. nucifera*, the sacred lotus of the Hindu, they are pink. As with many aquatic plants, flowers are carried above the level of the water. Leaves here are umbrella shaped (peltate) with waxy exposed surfaces held horizontally above the water too. The fruits are used by flower arrangers, being hemispherical with flat tops with holes! Both fruits and rhizomes are used in Asian cooking.

### Relatives do not always look alike and look-alikes may not be related

If you look at older classifications and field guides, you will likely see the lotus, *Nelumbo*, placed in the water-lily family, Nymphaeaceae. Both are aquatics with large showy flowers and rounded leaves. The flowers both have a spiral arrangement of parts. They are not related, however. Their similarities are the result of convergent evolution. They may look the same because of the environment in which they live and the similar adaptations it selects, but they do not share a common ancestor.

The lotus and the water-lily are a good example of the problems of classifying on structures alone. More data, especially the crucial DNA data, show that water-lilies are one of the early branches of the flowering plants.

The lotus is much further up our tree diagram of flowering plants, in the basal eudicots. Its closest relatives are the trees of the family Platanaceae of the Northern Hemisphere and Proteaceae, the *Protea* family, which occurs mainly in the Southern Hemisphere.

A lotus flower may not look much like a plane flower, but they share a common ancestor. Since their relationship was discovered, it has been possible to find traits they have in common. These include details of seed development, the internal structure of their vessels, and the form of the waxes on their leaves. Plants have a myriad of structures. Without DNA evidence, it is very difficult to know which structures indicate close relationships.

The close relationship between the genus *Platanus* and the geographically widespread and diverse family Proteaceae was another very unexpected outcome of molecular DNA studies. Indeed some botanists no longer recognise Platanaceae. The showy flowers of the Proteaceae are in marked contrast to the almost petalless wind-pollinated *Platanus* flowers, but both are actually clusters of quite small, simple flowers. In *Platanus* the globular masses mature into spiky pom-poms.

# NELUMBONACEAE, *the lotus family*

*Nelumbo is the sole genus in this family of aquatic plants. It holds only two species, N. nucifera (sacred lotus) from Asia, and N. lutea (American lotus) which has yellow flowers.*

*The leaves of the sacred lotus have their petioles attached in the middle of the disk-shaped leaf blade, an arrangement that is called a peltate leaf. The leaves are held above the water's surface.*

*The flower of the sacred lotus has two green sepals and numerous petals, some of which are greenish white. Its enlarged receptacle has an inverted cone shape. The numerous stamens and petals attach at the receptacle base. The many ovaries are embedded into the surface of the receptacle. There are no styles; the stigma covers the top of each ovary. The fruits develop in pockets on the receptacle.*

**Eudicots**

**Basal eudicots**

**Proteales** Dumortier

**Platanaceae** T. Lestibudois                1 genus/8-10 species

Genus:

*Platanus* L. (plane, sycamore)


The family contains just one genus of trees whose species occur in the Northern Hemisphere and can be recognised by white, grey or light brown patches on smooth trunks and globular flowers that develop into dangling, prickly balls of achenes.

The London plane, the commonest street tree in many cities, is thought to be a hybrid between *P. orientalis* that extends from the eastern Mediterranean to the eastern Himalayas and *P. occidentalis* from North America. When and where these two came together is uncertain, possibly in Spain and southern France in the 17th century. The hybrid is first recorded in Britain about 1680. Because its seeds are fertile it is sometimes placed in its own species *P. x acerifolia*, reflecting the shape of the leaf which is typical of the maples (genus *Acer*). However, it has never been found in the wild.


**Proteaceae** Jussieu                75 genera/1,775 species

Genera include:

*Banksia* L.f. (banksia)

*Brabejum* L. (wild almond, wild chestnut)

*Embothrium* Forster & Forster f. (Chilean flame tree)

*Grevillea* R. Brown (silky oak)

*Hakea* Schrader (pincushion plant)

*Leucadendron* R. Brown (silver tree)

*Leucospermum* R. Brown (pincushion shrub)

*Macadamia* F. Mueller (macadamia)

*Protea* L. (protea)

*Telopea* R. Brown (waratah)


There are two main divisions, the grevilleoids and proteoids, in this Gondwanan family. The grevilleoids have a fruit called a follicle, which resemble a pea pod, but is often modified to look like a nut. The proteoids have a small nut-like fruit. Both groups were originally inhabitants of rain-forests, but evolved into forms that were adapted to the dry, nutrient-poor and often fire-prone conditions that gradually developed in some Southern Hemisphere continents over the Cenozoic period. The grevilleoid group (e.g. *Banksia, Grevillea, Hakea, Embothrium*) is the more widespread, occurring in Australia, South America, New Zealand, New Caledonia and South Africa, and is considered to be derived from the ancestral form. The main group in South Africa comprises the proteoids, *Protea, Leucadendron* and *Leucospermum*, and there is only a single grevilleoid species (*Brabejum racemosa*).

Commercially the plants are mainly used in horticulture as cut flowers and for minor honey production in southern Australia. The only commercial crop is the 'nut' from the *Macadamia* tree. A number of the rainforest trees and *Grevillea robusta* produce very fine cabinet wood because the wood grain is very attractive.

# PLATANACEAE, *the plane family*

Bark and leaf (inset) of Platanus x acerifolia (London plane)

Young female inflorescence and developing fruit head of California sycamore, P. racemosa. The male flowers are borne on separate inflorescences on the same tree

# PROTEACEAE, *the protea family*

Banksia baueri

Hakea suaveolens

Grevillea hybrid var. 'Robyn Gordon'

Protea cynaroides

Leucadendron tinctum

Embothrium coccineum

Molecular studies have recently had a major role in both defining the families of flowering plants and also their evolutionary relationships. In some cases major problems have been solved – in others they remain for future researchers. Here we illustrate the success stories, the new orders Gunnerales and Buxales.

**Buxales** Takhtajan ex Reveal

    **Buxaceae** Dumort                5 genera/50 species

        Genera include:

        *Buxus* L. (box)

        *Pachysandra* Michaux (Japanese spurge)

        *Sarcococca* Lindley (sweet or Christmas box)

This family now has its own order and might be close, together with *Trochodendron*, to the plants that gave rise to the remaining eudicots. The family, composed of evergreen shrubs to medium-sized trees is found throughout the world in tropical to temperate regions. *Buxus sempervirens* (box) is a native of chalk hills of south-east England, Buckinghamshire and Gloucestershire, and forms the root of many English place-names, having been present since at least Neolithic times. Gardeners have made extensive use of box for hedging and in topiary. The native box can grow into small trees whose exceptionally hard wood is prized for chessmen, pestles, printing blocks and trinkets. The Christmas or sweet box, *Sarcococca*, although superficially similar to *Buxus*, has the advantage as a garden plant of larger leaves with sweetly smelling, if inconspicuous, white flowers and prominent red, purple to bluish black, to black berries.

**Gunnerales** Takhtajan

    **Gunneraceae** Meissner           1 genus/40 species

        Genus:

        *Gunnera* L. (gunnera)

The Gunneraceae is a Gondwanan family, being mostly confined to the Southern Hemisphere. A lover of wet places, it contains both species with massive umbrella-like leaves (up to 2m wide), e.g. *G. manicata* (see also bog garden) and *G. tinctoria* from South America, and minute mat-forming carpets from New Zealand (leaves c. 2cm!). It is of botanical interest because the stems and roots house colonies of the cyanobacterium *Nostoc*, which is able to convert nitrogen in the air into ammonium compounds that form a natural plant fertiliser. This association of plant and bacterium is called a mutualistic symbiosis. The plant benefits from additional nitrogen when growing in nutrient deficient bogs and the bacteria have a protected, moist home.

# BUXACEAE, *the box family*

*Buxus sempervirens (box)*

*Sarcococca confusa (sweet box) flowers (centre) and berries (right)*

# GUNNERACEAE, *the gunnera family*

*Gunnera magellanica, a mat forming plant, with leaves 2cm in diameter*

*Gunnera manicata with leaves c. 1m in diameter, left. Developing inflorescence of G. manicata, top left. Hairs protecting the stem apex in G. manicata, below*

# INTRODUCING SAXIFRAGALES

The order Saxifragales is a new group in the Angiosperm Phylogeny Group scheme. It is not found in previous classifications. This branch of the core eudicots was proposed after DNA analysis revealed the relationships of its members. Its fossil date back to the early branching of the eudicots. There is a wide variety of floral forms in this order, but the flowers usually have separate carpels or carpels that are united only at their bases. Most have a hypanthium, a floral tube or disk, at the base of the flower. The plant forms of this order include trees, shrubs, vines, herbaceous plants, aquatics and succulents.

Just where Saxifragales fits in the core eudicots is not completely clear. Some studies suggest it is a basal group to the rest of the core eudicots, but others put it as a sister group only to the rosids. No study has yet placed this order firmly, so we look forward to further investigations.

Families in the Saxifragales not included here are the east Asian Cercidiphyllaceae Engler and Daphniphyllaceae Mueller, both containing just one genus, and also the cosmopolitan Haloragaceae which includes aquatics such as *Myriophyllum* (water milfoil). The latter is cultivated for aquaria and ponds but can escape to become an invasive weed of waterways.

**Eudicots**
**Core eudicots**
**Saxifragales** Dumortier

    **Paeoniaceae** Rafinesque            1 genus/35 species

        Genus:

        *Paeonia* L. (peony)

Once thought to be part of the Ranunulaceae, *Paeonia* is now placed in its own family following molecular and developmental studies.

Peonies are found either as perennial herbs, the commonest form in British gardens, or as very small trees. The latter are native in remote parts of China and were much prized by the pioneering plant collectors: the first came to Britain at the time of Sir Joseph Banks. Herbaceous peonies have a much wider distribution extending from Japan, through central Asia and around the Mediterranean with two even in America. They were widely cultivated, particularly in monastery gardens, for medicinal compounds from their roots. Escape from a monastery might perhaps explain the presence of *Paeonia mascula* on Steepholm, an island in the Severn Estuary, but it occurs elsewhere in forests around the Mediterranean. The leaves of peonies are compound, usually with three leaflets, and often lobed. The flowers usually have five sepals of unequal sizes, which are persistent. There are five to nine petals, numerous stamens, and two to five separate carpels. Double peonies are cultivated hybrids whose stamens are converted into petal-like staminodes, i.e. derived from stamens but producing no pollen.

    **Hamamelidaceae** R. Brown         27 genera/82 species

        Genera include:

        *Corylopsis* Siebold & Zuccarini (corylopsis)

        *Fothergilla* L. (fothergilla)

        *Hamamelis* L. (witch hazel)

        *Loropetalum* R. Brown ex Reichenbach (Chinese witch hazel)

        *Parrotia* C. Meyer (parrotia, ironwood)

This is a widespread family, largely subtropical in origin, but a number of its genera are grown as ornamental trees or shrubs in our gardens. These include *Corylopsis*, *Hamamelis*, *Fothergilla* and *Parrotia*, all renowned for their autumn colour. The bark and leaves of *Hamamelis* (witch hazel) produce compounds that have been used to treat bruises and haemorrhoids as well as sore eyes.

Altingiaceae is sometimes recognised as a tribe in the Hamamelidaceae.

# PAEONIACEAE, *the peony family*

*The large-flowered peonies shown here are cultivars of Paeonia lactiflora (the Chinese peony). Peony buds have leafy bracts beneath them. The sepals have thin, pointed appendages that vary in length. Sepal size ranges from large, covering half the bud, to small and easily overlooked. Fruits are leathery follicles, which split at maturity revealing the seeds. The seeds that are fertile change from red to black as they mature. The many infertile seeds remain red and may serve to attract birds, which disperse the fertile seeds*

# HAMAMELIDACEAE, *the witch hazel family*

*Flowers and fruits of Hamamelis x intermedia, top*

*Fragrant petalless flowers of Fothergilla with conspicuous long stamens and sweet smell that are produced before the leaves (bottom left)*

*Corylopsis flowers (bottom right) appear in early spring before the leaves*

91

**Eudicots**

**Core eudicots**

**Saxifragales** Dumortier

    **Altingiaceae** Lindley                  2 genera/13 species

        Genera include:

        *Liquidambar* L. (sweet gum)

The genus *Liquidambar* has a disjunct distribution in north-east America and Asia, but was more widely distributed in the Cenozoic (Tertiary) because its fossils are found in Europe. *Liquidambar* produces aromatics: *L. orientalis* is the source of Levant storax, the biblical balm of Gilead, while *L. styraciflua* not only produces an antiseptic, but is used in the preparation of "friar's basalm" and as an inhalant for blocked up noses and lung congestion. It is also a valuable timber tree (satin wood). Some classifications place the Altingiaceae within the Hamamelidaceae.

    **Grossulariaceae** de Candolle          1 genus/200 species

        Genus:

        *Ribes* L. (currant, gooseberry)

Grossulariaceae is a family of shrubs, in which leaves are palmately lobed. The flowers are tubular, but the tube is not just the corolla because the calyx is coloured and forms part of the tube. The whole is called a hypanthium or floral cup. Near the end of the hypanthium, the ends of the five sepals flare out. Five small petals attach to the rim of the tube within the whorl of sepals. The family is economically important because it contains the soft fruits gooseberry (*Ribes uva-crispa*), red currant (*R. rubrum*) and black currant (*R. nigrum*). Note the Latin for red and black in the specific names of the last two. All three are thought to be introduced in the British flora, as many plants are now garden escapes. The familiar red-flowered garden plant, *R. sanguineum*, comes from north-west America. Indeed the genus extends from there through the mountainous backbone of the New World to the Straits of Magellan.

The Escalloniaceae, now separated from Grossulariaceae on molecular evidence, contains another attractive garden shrub, *Escallonia*, native to the Andes and south Brazil (See Chilean section in the Great Glass House).

# ALTINGIACEAE, *the sweet gum family*

Liquidambar styraciflua (from North America) with developing fruit (left)
L. acalycina from China in flower (below)

# GROSSULARIACEAE, *the gooseberry family*

*Ribes cereum (wax currant), lives throughout the western United States. Its pink flowers bloom in early spring and attract hummingbirds. Its inferior ovary develops into a berry-like fruit that turns bright red in the autumn. The dried floral tube still clings to the end of the fruit when it is ripe*

*Ribes rubrum (red currant) (below)*

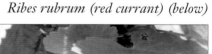

*Fruit of Ribes uva-crispa (the gooseberry, far left)*

*Ribes sanguineum is a North American native frequently used as a garden plant in the UK, left*

93

**Eudicots**

**Core eudicots**

**Saxifragales** Dumortier

    **Saxifragaceae** Jussieu           30 genera/625 species

        Genera include:

        *Astilbe* Buchanan-Hamilton ex D. Don (astilbe, false spirea)

        *Bergenia* Moench (bergenia)

        *Boykinia* Nuttal (boykinia)

        *Chrysosplenium* L. (golden saxifrage)

        *Darmera* Voss (umbrella plant)

        *Heuchera* L. (coral bells)

        *Rodgersia* A. Gray (rodgersia)

        *Saxifraga* L. (saxifrage)

        *Tellima* R. Brown (fringe-cup)

        *Tiarella* L. (foamflower)

This is a small family of herbaceous plants often with a basal rosette of leaves. It is much loved by arctic-alpine specialists. Saxifraga means 'rock-breaker' and these plants often grow in rocky mountain areas. Indeed one of the latter, *S. oppositifolia*, has its southerly limit in Britain in the Brecon Beacons. Other members of the family are widely grown as garden plants.

    **Crassulaceae** J. Saint-Hilaire         29 genera/1,380 species

        Genera include:

        *Aeonium* Webb & Berthelot (aeonium, Canary Island rose, pinwheel)

        *Crassula* L. (crassula, jade plant)

        *Dudleya* Britton & Rose (cliff lettuce)

        *Echeveria* de Candolle (hen and chickens)

        *Kalanchoe* Adanson (felt plant, maternity plant, panda plant)

        *Sedum* L. (sedum, stonecrop)

        *Sempervivum* L. (house leek, hen and chickens)

        *Umbilicus* de Candolle (pennywort)

The Crassulaceae is a cosmopolitan family of herbs and small shrubs occurring in mainly warm dry regions of the world. Its members are characterised by very fleshy, wax-covered leaves which act as reservoirs and allow plants to colonise very dry places such as walls (e.g. wall pennywort, navelwort: *Umbilicus rupestris*) and stony, dry areas (stone crops and house-leeks: *Sedum* spp.). Botanically they have some importance because, in addition to their fleshy tissues, they have a different kind of metabolism by which sunlight energy is trapped in the day to form acids that are combined with carbon dioxide in the night so that the plant can keep its stomata (ventilators) closed during hot dry days. Such plants are called CAM plants: Crassulacean acid metabolism. The sedums are important garden plants and the sap in their fleshy leaves was widely used to cool burns. It is also said that they were planted on thatched roofs as a protection against lightning and subsequent fire.

# SAXIFRAGACEAE, *the saxifrage family*

*There are two separate styles and stigmas in the flowers Bergenia cordifolia (bergenia) (above and below left)and Saxifraga (mossy saxifrages) (above right) hybrids. A ring of stamens surrounds the gynoecium*

*Heuchera parvifolia (alpine alumroot) (left and above), lives on cliffs and rock outcrops in the Rocky Mountains*

# CRASSULACEAE, *the stonecrop family*

*Sedum lanceolatum (spearleaf stonecrop) a native of the western United States, is able to grow on rocky outcrops*

*Kalanchoe daigremontiana (maternity plant) forms little plantlets on the margins of its leaves*

*Sempervivum tectorum, is sometimes called hen and chickens because the rosettes produce offshoots. Its generic name means 'always living,' and refers to its vegetative reproduction. Two rings of stamens surround the carpels. Once a rosette has bloomed, it dies, but its off-shoots live on*

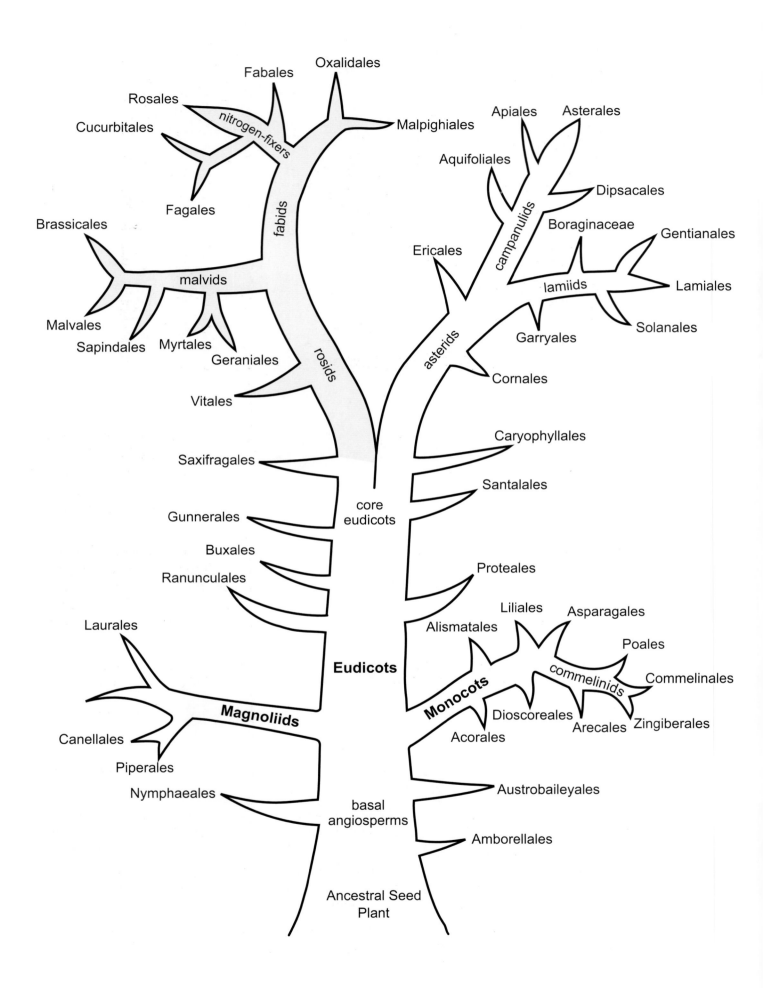

# INTRODUCING THE ROSIDS

The rosids make up about a third of flowering plants, but it is not easy to list structures that define them all. As a group, rosids are quite old, with fossils of at least 94 million years of age. They have apparently radiated quickly and developed a wide variety of forms. This makes it difficult to use plant structures to determine their relationships. The DNA tells a great deal of their story, and botanists have made important progress in reading gene sequences and finding the related groups. The picture is still emerging, and the work continues.

Rosids include many woody plants, but also many herbs. Many have numerous stamens, often in two or more whorls. Most have separate petals rather than fused corollas, with the cucumber family being a notable exception. A number of families, best exemplified by the rose family, have a hypanthium, also called a floral tube or floral cup. The hypanthium covers an inferior or half-inferior ovary and may extend up from it, surrounding the style. The evening primrose family, Onagraceae, has amazing examples of long floral tubes.

Compound leaves are common in rosids, as are stipules, which are usually small, paired structures at the base of the petiole (stem of the leaf). Stipules can be tendrils, spines, leaf-like or glands.

Plant forms include trees, shrubs, vines, and herbaceous plants. Succulents occur in the spurge family. A few members of the loosestrife family and mustard family are aquatics. One family in the Oxalidales has a single insectivorous species, the Australian pitcher plant, *Cephalotus*.

The rosids are divided into two main subgroups, fabids and malvids, as well as several orders of rosids that belong to neither subgroup, e.g. the grape order (Vitales).

The fabids were originally called the eurosids I. Fabid members in this guide are: the geranium family in the Geraniales; the evening primrose, myrtle and loosestrife families of the Myrtales; the cucumber and begonia families of Cucurbitales; the bean family of Fabales; the alder, oak, beech, southern beech, she oak, leatherwood and walnut families of Fagales; the diverse order Malpighiales, which includes the willow, violet, flax, spurge, and passionflower families; the Oxalidales; and Rosales, which includes the rose, elm, buckthorn, sea buckthorn, nettle, and mulberry families.

The malvids, originally called the eurosids II, is a smaller rosid branch. This tour visits the mustard family of Brassicales, the mallow family of Malvales, and the Sapindales, which includes the sumac, citrus, and soapberry plus maple families.

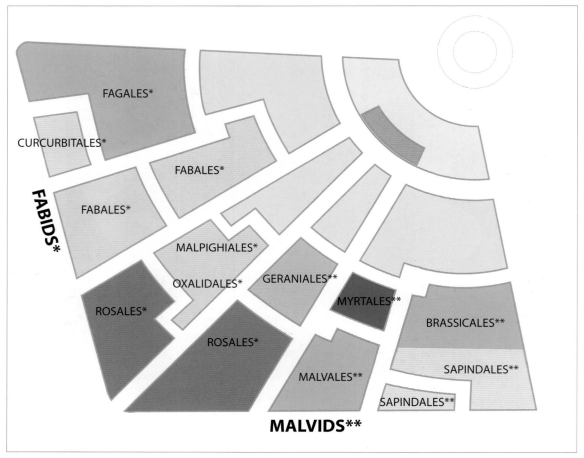

Quadrant 2. *Rosid orders*

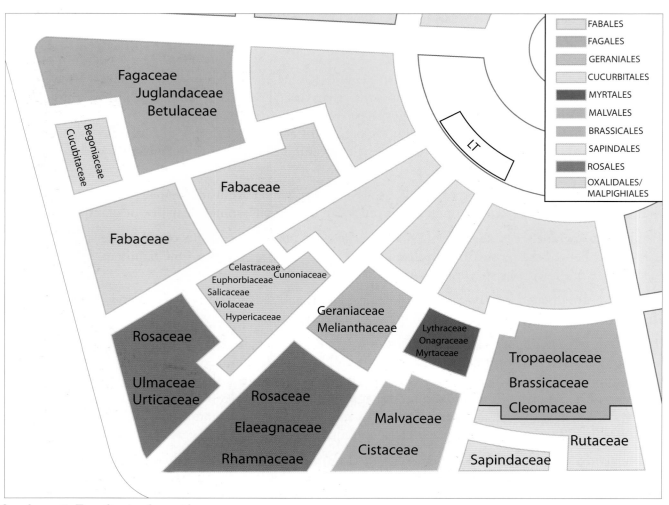

Quadrant 2. *Families in the rosids*

*Overview of eudicot borders in Quadrant 2, with Great Glasshouse in background and a herbaceous border in the foreground*

*Fabales bed in Quadrant 2, with Tropical House and monocot beds in background*

**Unplaced Rosids**

**Vitales** Reveal

     **Vitaceae** Jussieu                  13 genera/725 species

          Genera include:

          *Ampelopsis* Michaux (blueberry climber)

          *Cissus* L. (grape ivy, kangaroo vine)

          *Parthenocissus* Planchon (Boston ivy, Virginia creeper)

          *Tetrastigma* (Miquel) Planchon (chestnut vine)

          *Vitis* L. (grape)

This small family of predominantly climbers (lianes) occurs in tropical to warm temperate regions. The best known genus is *Vitis* which is grown for its fruits as grapes, or when dried as currants, raisins and sultanas. When fermented, it produces wine in areas with Mediterranean climates throughout the world. *Vitis vinifera* is the most widely used species, and the source of Pinot Noir, Chardonnay and Cabernet Sauvignon, but other species used include *V. labrusca*, *V. amurensis* and *V. rotundifolia*.

# VITACEAE, *the grape family*

The grapes are a family of vines. They climb using tendrils that grow opposite a leaf. The leaves are palmately veined or lobed, or palmately compound. The flowers are tiny and have inconspicuous sepals and petals. Two carpels make up the gynoecium. The fruit is a berry with one to four seeds

*Vitis labrusca (fox grape) in flower (top) and with developing fruits (above). This species is a native of the eastern United States*

*Ampelopsis brevipedunculata (porcelain berry) has tiny flowers with an inconspicuous perianth, but they attract large numbers of bees (left). The variegated cultivar, shown here in flower, is less invasive than the green-leaved species and is more desirable as a landscape plant*

*Parthenocissus quinquefolia (Virginia creeper) has climbing tendrils with adhesive disks at their tips. This differentiates it from Ampelopsis, which lacks the disks. Dependable autumn colour makes Virginia creeper valuable as an ornamental. The flowers are inconspicuous*

**Eudicots**
**Fabids**
**Fabales** Bromhead
    **Fabaceae** Lindley or **Leguminosae** Jussieu      720 genera/19,500 species

This cosmopolitan family includes herbs, shrubs, and trees and has four subgroups. They are known for their root nodules, which contain nitrogen-fixing bacteria. The flowers of the subgroups look very different, but they all have one carpel with a superior ovary. Most have pod-like fruits which are called legumes. The legume is best exemplified by the pea pod. It is, of course, the seed which makes this family, and particularly the papilionoids so important economically. Think of the garden pea, which exemplifies the two colyledons or embryonic leaves of the dicots very clearly. The colyledons are full of energy-rich storage tissues including both carbohydrate (starch and sugar) and protein, the latter in particular resulting in the pea family (including peas, beans, lentils, peanuts) being so nutritionally valuable. Members of the family frequently have swellings on the roots which house bacteria that trap nitrogen from the air into ammonium (another example of symbiosis). These natural fertilisers are passed on to the plant and stored in the seeds, making them excellent meals for vegetarians. The leaves, too, e.g. in clover and alfafa, are important fodder crops.

This second largest family in the eudicots is subdivided into three major groups and one small one, each with very distinctive flowers.

| | | | | | |
|---|---|---|---|---|---|
| (i) | papilionoids | Papilionoideae | (iii) | caesalpinioids | Caesalpinoideae |
| (ii) | mimosoids | Mimosoideae | (iv) | cercids | Cercideae |

### Subfamily Faboideae or Papilionoideae
Genera include:

| | |
|---|---|
| *Arachis* L. (peanut) | *Lens* Miller L. (lentil) |
| *Astragalus* L. (locoweed, milk vetch) | *Lupinus* L. (lupin) |
| *Cytisus* Desfontaines (Scotch broom) | *Medicago* L. (alfalfa, lucerne) |
| *Erythrina* L. (coral tree) | *Phaseolus* L. (bean) |
| *Genista* L. (broom, greenwood) | *Pisum* L. (pea) |
| *Glycine* Willdenow (soybean) | *Robinia* L. (locust tree, black locust) |
| *Glycyrrhiza* L. (licorice) | *Sophora* L. (pagoda tree, kowhai) |
| *Indigofera* L. (indigo) | *Trifolium* L. (clover) |
| *Lablab* Adanson (hyacinth bean) | *Ulex* L. (gorse) |
| *Laburnum* Fabricius (golden chain) | *Vicia* L. (vetch) |
| *Lathyrus* L. (everlasting, sweet pea) | *Wisteria* Nuttall (wisteria) |

The subfamily has a typical flower best exemplified by the sweet pea. Petals are five, the two basal ones forming a boat-shaped structure surrounding a tube of stamens and a single carpel (the pea pod). All British members of the Fabaceae are papilionoid and include clovers, vetches, gorse, broom, bird's foot trefoil, peas and beans. These are herbs or shrubs, but garden members include trees such as the locust tree (*Robinia pseudoacacia*: North America), the scholar tree (*Sophora*) and *Laburnum* (southern Europe). The latter demonstrates that some papilionioid seeds are toxic. Indeed *Laburnum* is probably the most frequent cause of poisoning in children.

Polygalaceae, a family close to the Fabaceae, has very similar flowers to the Papilionoideae because they possess the lowermost part of the corolla in the form of a keel with terminal tuft and two large lateral wings. It contains trees, shrubs and herbs, but is represented in the British flora by minute examples of the latter. The milkworts (*Polygala vulgaris* and *P. serpyllifolia*) are so called because they were once thought to increase milk yields in cows (or even nursing mothers!).

# FABACEAE OR LEGUMINOSAE; FABOIDEAE, *the pea subfamily*

*Medicago sativa (alfalfa) a forage crop plant*

*A Lupinus hybrid (garden lupin)*

*Wisteria sinensis*

*Trifolium pratense (red clover) has trifoliolate leaves*

*Lablab purpureus, hyacinth bean*

*Vicia cracca (tufted vetch)*

*Robinia neomexicana (New Mexico locust)*

*Erythrina fusca (kaffirboom or coral tree)*

**Eudicots**
**Fabids**
**Fabales** Bromhead
 **Fabaceae** Lindley or **Leguminosae** Jussieu
 **Subfamily Mimosoideae**
  Genera include:
  *Acacia* Miller (acacia, mimosa, wattle)
  *Albizia* Durazzini (silk-tree)
  *Calliandra* Bentham (powderpuff)
  *Mimosa* L. (mimosa, sensitive plant)
  *Prosopis* L. (mesquite)
  *Senegalia* Raphinesque - Schmaltz (acacia, gum arabic)

This subfamily comprises mainly trees and shrubs from tropical and subtropical regions with some members, e.g. *Albizia*, showing a typical Gondwanan distribution. In many cases, the distinctive parts of the flower are the brightly coloured stamens which, together with scent, attract insect visitors. Our most familiar *Acacia*, *A. dealbata* is the mimosa, one of the many Australian wattles (see Great Glass House). Their petals and tiny leaves are usually compound bipinnate. African acacias, now placed in the genus *Senegalia*, are spiny bushes or trees common in dry areas.

 **Subfamily Caesalpinioideae**
  Genera include:
  *Caesalpinia* L. (bird-of-paradise)  *Hoffmannseggia* Cavanilles (Indian rushpea,
  *Cassia* L. (cassia, golden or pink shower) hog potato)
  *Ceratonia* L. (carob, lotus bean)  *Parkinsonia* L. (palo verde, Jerusalem thorn)
  *Gleditsia* L. (honey locust)  *Senna* Miller (senna)
  *Gymnocladus* Lamarck (coffee tree)  *Tamarindus* L. (tamarind)

This subfamily contains shrubs or trees with some very colourful flowers, almost as exotic as orchids, and is widely planted in gardens in frost free climates, e.g. *Caesalpinia* (bird-of-paradise) and *Cassia*. Leaves are compound, but may have just two leaflets. The flowers have five similar petals. The fruits of *Cassia acutifolia* from the Middle East are called senna pods and have been widely used as a purgative.

### Another Group of Fabaceae

Cercideae was formerly included in the subfamily Caesalpinioideae, but genetic analysis showed that it is an independent branch at the base of the Fabaceae. *Cercis*, below left, and *Bauhinia* (orchid trees), below right, are members of this tribe. The Judas tree, *C. siliquastrum*, has flowers similar to the papilionoid forms. It is so called because traditionally it is considered to have been the tree from which Judas Iscariot hanged himself.

# FABACEAE OR LEGUMINOSAE: MIMOSOIDEAE, *the mimosa subfamily*

*Mimosa rupertiana (sensitive briar) has leaflets that fold up when they are touched*

Note that in all three genera the conspicuous parts of the flower are the stamens which are brightly coloured and may be very long. The petals are tiny. The leaves are usually bipinnately compound (but see Acacia melanoxylon).

*Albizia julibrissin (silk tree), above left. The leaves of this Acacia melanoxylon (blackwood), above right, appear to be simple, but instead, they are expanded, flattened petioles, which are called phyllodes. The leaf blade does not form*

# FABACEAE OR LEGUMINOSAE: CAESALPINIOIDEAE, the caesalpinia subfamily

*Caesalpinia pulcherrima (Barbados pride), above left, is an ornamental shrub grown in areas with mild winters.*

*Senna roemeriana (twoleaf senna), above centre, native to N. America is poisonous to livestock.*

*Male flowers of Gymnocladus dioica (Kentucky coffeetree), above right, a dioecious species with large, bipinnately compound leaves*

*Hoffmannseggia glauca (hog potato), right, is a small, weedy species with bipinnately compound leaves. It is a native of southwestern North America*

**Eudicots**
**Fabids**
**Rosales** Perleb
    **Rosaceae** Jussieu               85 genera/3,000 species

Rosaceae is a cosmopolitan, largely temperate, family recently divided into three subfamilies following molecular studies. The subfamilies are Rosoideae, Spiraeoideae and Dryadoideae. More detailed information on this new classification can be found in a paper by D. Potter and co-workers in this book's reference list.

### Subfamily Rosoideae
Genera include:

*Acaena* Mutis ex L. (piri-piri, bidibidi strawberry)
*Acomastylis* Greene (alpine avens)
*Agrimonia* L. (agrimony)
*Alchemilla* L. (ladies mantle)
*Fragaria* L. (strawberry) is now placed in *Potentilla*

*Geum* L. (avens, herb bennet)
*Potentilla* L. (cinquefoil, strawberry)
*Rosa* L. (rose)
*Rubus* L. (blackberry, raspberry, dew berry)
*Sanguisorba* L. (burnet)

This new subfamily corresponds broadly to the traditionally accepted subfamily except that *Kerria* and *Rhodotypos*, eastern Asian representatives that grow in our gardens, are now transferred to the Spiraeoideae. The Rosoideae contains considerable variability in flowers and fruit. *Rosa* itself is probably the most economically important garden flower, the latter produced by multiple hybridisations such that the origins of our garden varieties are obscure. It is also important in the perfume industry. There are a number of native British species including the very abundant *R. canina* (dog rose), *R. pimpinellifolia* (burnet rose of sand dunes) and *R. rubiginosa* (sweet briar or eglantine). All possess conspicuous fruits called hips. These are an important source of vitamin C and are grown to produce rosehip syrup. Hairs surrounding the seed have long been used by children as an itching powder. Quite different fruits are found in *Rubus* including *R. fruticosus* (blackberry), *R. idaeus* (raspberry), *R. loganobaccus* (loganberry) etc. In contrast to these clusters of single seeded fleshy units in *Rubus*, the fruit of strawberry is described as false, because the single seeded fruits (the gritty bits) are embedded on the surface of a very fleshy, brightly coloured receptacle that originally supported other floral parts. Other members have dry fruit often with feathery or hooked (*Geum*) appendages to the single seeded units (achenes). Other devices to disperse the fruits include bristles and hooks on fruits of *Agrimonia* and *Acaena* whose distribution on islands in the Southern Hemisphere is thought to relate to dispersal by sea birds that trap seeds in their feathers. Garden plants include cultivars of British wildflowers such as *Potentilla*, *Alchemilla* and *Sanguisorba*.

### Subfamily Dryadoideae
    Genera include:
    *Cercocarpus* Kunth
        (mountain mahogony)
    *Dryas* L. (mountain avens)
    *Purshia* de Candolle ex Poiret
        (cliff rose)

This small subfamily contains herbs, shrubs and small trees. Apart from *Dryas*, which has a circumpolar distribution, its members are confined to western North America. A uniting character that separates this subfamily from the two remaining ones is the presence of the nitrogen-fixing bacterium *Frankia* in its root nodules. *Dryas octopetala* (above) occurs locally in North Wales on ledges and crevices on mountains. Its fruits are clusters of achenes with long feathery extensions as are seen in some rosoids.

# ROSACEAE, *the rose family*: SUBFAMILY ROSOIDEAE

*Hybrid tea roses (above) serve to show the features of Rosa flowers. They typically have a cup-shaped receptacle. The five sepals, the numerous stamens and the petals attach to the rim of this floral cup. The ovaries of the one or more separate carpels are embedded down in the orange receptacle (below centre). The styles and stigmas stick out from the middle of the flower (above right). A rose hip is the thickened, floral cup with persistent green sepals. It contains mature achenes, the true fruits. However, there are many other kinds of fruits in this family as exemplified by the feathery fruits (below right) of Geum triflorum*

 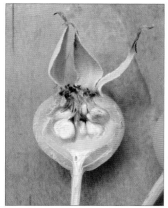 

*Blackberries (above) and strawberries (below) have many separate carpels in their flowers. In the blackberry, the ovaries become druplets, small drupe-like fruits that aggregate to form the berry. The dried style can be found on the druplets of immature blackberries*

*Potentilla fruticosa, shrubby cinquefoil (above), is native to western and northern United States and Europe. It is probably not closely related to other Potentilla members and will be renamed in the future*

**Rosaceae** Jussieu
### Subfamily Spiraeoideae

Genera include:

*Amelanchier* Medikus (service berry, snowy mespilus)

*Aronia* Medikus (chokeberry)

*Aruncus* L. (goat's beard)

*Chaenomeles* Lindley (japonica, quince)

*Cotoneaster* Medikus (cotoneaster)

*Crataegus* L. (hawthorn, may)

*Cydonia* Miller (quince)

*Exochorda* Lindley (pearl bush)

*Filipendula* Miller (dropwort, meadowsweet)

*Kerria* de Candolle (kerria)

*Malus* Miller (apple, crab-apple)

*Physocarpus* (Cambessèdes) Maximowicz (ninebark)

*Prunus* L. (plum, cherry, apricot, peach, almond)

*Pyracantha* M. Roemer (firethorn, pyracantha)

*Pyrus* L. (pear)

*Sorbaria* (Seringe) A. Braun (false spirea)

*Sorbus* L. (mountain ash, whitebeam)

*Spiraea* L. (bridewort, spirea)

*Mespilus* L. (medlar) is now included in *Crataegus*

*Photinia* is now placed in *Aronia*

This is the largest subfamily in the Rosaceae and comprises mostly trees and shrubs. Further subdivision into tribes has not been completely resolved, although broad groupings formerly placed in subfamilies Maloideae and Spiraeoideae remain intact. Thus a new super tribe (Pyrodeae) has been named to include those genera formerly placed in the Maloideae. It has flowers with many stamens and a cup-shaped ovary below the five petals that develops into a fleshy fruit called a pome. Thus the small outgrowths at the top of a *Malus* (apple) or *Pyrus* (pear) mark the remains of the sepals. Garden representatives include *Amelanchier*, *Aronia*, *Chaenomeles*, *Cydonia*, *Pyracantha* and *Sorbaria*. British natives include the may tree or hawthorn (*Crataegus*). A local Welsh name, Blodau marw mam (flowers-death-mother), is based on the local superstition that may flowers taken into the house cause maternal death. Elsewhere may is merely considered unlucky and the source of much folklore. Another native is *Sorbus* and includes the mountain ash or rowan (*Sorbus aucuparia*) and whitebeam, (*S. aria*). Indeed species of *Sorbus* comprise many of our rare Welsh plants. Thus *S. domestica* (service tree) although grown in gardens in the UK, was found about twenty years ago in the wild on cliffs in S. Glamorgan. Dr Quentin Kay thinks the plants have found refuge there for thousands of years. Limestone cliffs and gorges in the Brecon Beacons are home to a number of rarities including *S. minima*, *S. leptophylla* and the rarest of them all, *S. leyana*. The latter is being studied, with the aim of increasing its distribution in the wild, at the National Botanic Garden of Wales where you can also see a unique display of these Welsh rarities.

The flowers of *Prunus* are superficially similar to those of the apple and pear, but the fruit contains just one seed surrounded by a hard coat and fleshy, often delicious, tissues. The fruit is called a drupe. Among the numerous species of *Prunus* are the plum, cherry, peach, apricot and almond. Welsh natives include *P. spinosus* (blackthorn or sloe), that gives the flavour to sloe gin, and *P. avium* (wild cherry or gean). *Prunus* is also an important garden genus. Many of the more familiar species derive from eastern Asia, and it is speculated that apricots and peaches, for example, first reached Europe via the silk route. Other useful garden plants with plates, tassels or clusters of small flowers include *Spiraea* (brideworts), *Aruncus*, *Exochorda*, *Physocarpus* and *Kerria*. Many of the fruits in this group are follicles and some seeds are winged.

# ROSACEAE, *the rose family*: SUBFAMILY SPIRAEOIDEAE

*Flowers of Malus pumila (apple), left, have three to five carpels. The fleshy, edible part of the fruit forms from the enlarged floral cup. The sepals attach to the rim of the cup, and one can often find their remains on the end of the mature fruit. The ovary becomes the apple's core. The tough membrane around the seeds is the endocarp, the inner wall of the ovary sometimes called cook's toenails when found in apple pie*

*Malus pumila (apple)*

*Chaenomeles hybrid (quince)*

*Apricots (above), peaches, nectarines, and cherries have one carpel in their flowers. Their fruits, commonly called stone fruits, are drupes. The exocarp and mesocarp, which are the skin and pulp of the fruit, are the edible parts. The stony endocarp has the seed inside. Almonds are also a member of this group. Their outer layers are leathery. The edible part of almonds is the seed within the endocarp*

*Sorbus leyana (Ley's white beam)*

*Sorbaria sorbifolia (false spirea), above left, is one of several shrubs with a mass of small flowers. Others include Spiraea japonica (spirea), centre, and Filipendula vulgaris (dropwort or meadow sweet), above right*

**Eudicots**

**Fabids**

**Rosales** Perleb

    **Elaeagnaceae** Jussieu          3 genera/45 species

        Genera:

        *Elaeagnus* L. (Russian olive, silverberry)

        *Hippophae* L. (oleaster, sea buckthorn)

        *Shepherdia* Nuttall (buffalo berry)

This is a small family of shrubs whose leaves have a metallic tinge due to a covering of scales or hairs. *Hippophae rhamnoides* (sea buckthorn) with its silvery leaves and orange berries, is the only British native. It naturally colonises sandy shores of eastern England, but has become a menace on our Welsh sand dunes, where originally it was planted to stabilise them. It is unusual in that it harbours nitrogen - fixing bacteria in its roots which allow it to colonise nutrient-poor habitats. *Elaeagnus*, the familiar garden shrub, is insect pollinated, as evidenced by its very sweet smelling flowers. The third genus in the family is *Shepherdia*, a native of North America.

    **Rhamnaceae** Jussieu          57 genera/950 species

        Genera include:

        *Ceanothus* L. (California lilac, ceanothus)

        *Frangula* Miller (alder buckthorn)

        *Krugiodendron* Urban (leadwood)

        *Rhamnus* L. (buckthorn, cascara, sagrada)

        *Ziziphus* Miller (Chinese jujube)

This is a family of trees and shrubs. Many members have spines. Its flowers are small, but often occur in large masses. There are two British natives (buckthorns). *Rhamnus cathartica* has black berries producing a strong purgative (as its species name suggests), and is a source of the artist's pigment 'sap-green' (other species produce yellow dyes). Its slashed bark is bright orange. The other, *Rhamnus frangula*, has wood which was the best source of charcoal for gunpowder and was thus cultivated. Its slashed bark is lemon yellow. Garden favourites include *Ceanothus* (North American) whose roots contain nitrogen-fixing bacteria.

    **Ulmaceae** Mirbel          7 genera/c. 50 species

        Genera include:

        *Planera* J. F. Gmelin (planer tree)

        *Ulmus* L. (elm)

        *Zelkova* Spach (zelkova)

The Ulmaceae is a cosmopolitan family of trees with tiny, bisexual flowers that have no petals and are wind-pollinated. Its wood provides valuable timber. The winged, dry fruits of the elm, which are known botanically as samaras, mature and are shed as the new foliage begins to grow in the spring. The word samara literally means "elm seed" in Latin. Mature trees of the British native, *Ulmus procera* (English elm) have virtually disappeared from our landscape, because of attacks of Dutch elm disease. This is a fungal wilt which blocks the water conducting tubes of the plant. Its spores are carried by the Dutch elm beetle, *Ceratocystis ulmi*. Major infection occurred in the 1960s, but some of the plants recovered and produced suckers, only to be reinfected in the 1990s. There is some evidence from vegetational history recorded in pollen extracted from peat, that similar attacks occurred about 5000 years ago. A sharp decrease in elm pollen (the elm decline) may have resulted from disease, but it is also possible that early farmers were cutting down the trees and using branches for bedding or even fodder.

# ELAEAGNACEAE, *the sea-buckthorn family*

*Eleagnus, 'quicksilver'*

*Eleagnus spungens 'Maculata'*

# RHAMNACEAE, *the buckthorn family*

*The small flowers in the Rhamnaceae have four or five tiny, cup-like petals that are often clawed, and that attach to a disk at the flower's base. A stamen lies above each petal. The pistil is usually three-carpellate. Fruits are either a berry-like drupe or one that splits into three and flings out its seeds*

*A Ceanothus hybrid sometimes called California lilac, although they are not related to the true lilacs in the family Oleaceae*

*Rhamnus frangula (alder buckthorn). Its fruits are berry-like*

# ULMACEAE, *the elm family*

*Ulmus pumila (Siberian elm) blooms in freezing weather (below left). It is wind-pollinated and produces abundant, often allergy-triggering, pollen. The ovaries quickly enlarge, appearing as green disks (below centre). The mature fruits blow away before the leaves are large enough to block the wind. The leaf of American elm is typical of the family - simple, with a serrated margin, strong pinnate venation and an asymmetrical base (right)*

**Eudicots**

**Fabids**

**Rosales** Perleb

**Moraceae** Link                    38 genera/1,150 species

Genera include:

*Artocarpus* Forster & Forster f. (breadfruit)

*Broussonetia* L'Héritier ex Ventenat (paper mulberry)

*Ficus* L. (fig, strangler fig, weeping fig, rubber tree, bo tree, banyan tree)

*Maclura* Nuttall (Osage orange)

*Morus* L. (mulberry)

The Ficaceae is a cosmopolitan family of shrubs and trees found in tropical to warm temperate regions. It is distinguished from the closely related Urticaceae by the presence of latex, and contains some extremely unusual fruiting structures. That in the fig (*Ficus*) results from enlargement of the receptacle to form an almost closed flask with small flowers on the inside. Figs are pollinated by small wasps which lay their eggs in the ovaries of some of the inflorescences and then transfer pollen on escaping. The resulting small fruits are numerous achenes that remain within the flask-shaped structure (syconium). Thus the edible fig is described as a multiple fruit or syncarp. The genus *Ficus* itself has more than 700 species distributed in tropical and sub-tropical regions. Although *Ficus elastica*, the India rubber plant, is restrained to a pot in our living rooms, in the wild in India and Malaysia it forms enormous trees, whose branches are supported by a host of aerial roots. In *Morus* (mulberry), the fruit is fleshy and looks a bit like a raspberry. It was introduced into Britain as a food plant for silk-worms.

**Urticaceae** Jussieu                    55 genera/1,650 species

Genera include:

*Boehmeria* Jacquin (ramie, Chinese grass)

*Laportea* Gaudichaud-Beaupré (wood nettle)

*Parietaria* L. (pellitory of the wall)

*Pilea* Lindley (aluminium plant)

*Soleirolia* Gaudichaud-Beaupré (mind-your-own-business, mother-of-thousands)

*Urtica* L. (stinging nettle)

Urticaceae is mainly an herbaceous family, but with some shrubs or trees in the tropics where most taxa occur. Fibres (*Boehmeria* = ramie) and stinging hairs are often present. Britain has two genera, *Urtica* and *Parietaria*, both with typical tassels of small, inconspicuous, wind-pollinated flowers. *Urtica dioica* (stinging nettle) thrives only on ground rich in phosphates, and thus is found in the wake of human and animal activity. The plant is covered by hairs which pierce the skin and inject a mixture of histamines and acetylcholine, the source of intense itching. Young shoots, however, can be used as a substitute for spinach. Nettles are also used in soups and herbal teas, as well as in the treatment of uterine haemorrhage and nervous eczema. *Parietaria judaica* is traditionally a medicinal plant, and has been used to treat kidney and bladder stones, presumably because it colonised walls and screes.

# MORACEAE, *the fig and mulberry family*

*Ficus carica (common fig)*

*Maclura pomifera (Osage orange, bois d'arc)*

*Artocarpus altilis (breadfruit)*

*Inflorescences of Morus nigra (black mulberry) (above left) appear as soon as the buds unfurl. The flowers are unisexual. The whole female inflorescence will become a single mulberry. The developing fruits still have the remains of the two stigmas on each segment. The ripe fruit (above right) is an aggregate of drupes that are each surrounded by enlarged, fleshy tepals*

# URTICACEAE, *the nettle family*

*Urtica dioica, stinging nettle, has tiny whitish, male and female flowers. The male, above, has conspicious anthers folded towards the centre in bud. When mature, the filament straightens outwards and flings out the anther which releases the pollen*

*Pilea mollis (creeping Charlie) an ornamental pot plant*

**Eudicots**

**Fabids**

**Fagales** Engler

While members of the Cucurbitales are herbaceous, mainly tropical plants, the Fagales are trees, with simple alternate leaves, and male and female flowers.

**Nothofagaceae** Kuprian          1 genus/34 species

    Genus:

    *Nothofagus* Blume (southern beech)

The southern beech, *Nothofagus*, is considered an iconic Gondwanan genus. It has a long history from late Cretaceous time as fossils that are found in rocks from Southern Hemisphere continents including Antarctica. It now occurs in South America, New Zealand, New Caledonia, New Guinea and Australia. It was originally considered to be a genus within the Fagaceae but genetic work and careful examination of the reproductive structures has led to the genus being restricted to its own family, the Nothofagaceae. The group arose from original fagalean ancestors which may have occurred in the eastern Southern Hemisphere continents, as there is no evidence that the group has ever been in Africa. While deciduous behaviour in trees is common in the Northern Hemisphere, it is uncommon in the South, but in South America, *Nothofagus* contains both evergreen and deciduous forms. The latter tend to occupy harsher, drier, colder, high altitudes sites than the co-occurring evergreen species (e.g. *N. pumilio*) which are found in moist forests. *Nothofagus* is an extremely important timber tree in the Southern Hemisphere, second only to the eucalypts.

**Fagaceae** Dumortier          7 genera/970 species

    Genera include:

    *Castanea* Miller (chestnut)

    *Castanopsis* (D. Don) Spach (golden chestnut)

    *Fagus* L. (beech)

    *Lithocarpus* Blume (tanbark oak)

    *Quercus* L. (oak)

Fagaceae is a small family almost completely confined to the temperate Northern Hemisphere with most genera concentrated in North America. Male flowers in the Fagaceae are in catkins, with adaptations similar to those in Betulaceae. In the beech (*Fagus*), the male flowers are in globose heads. Female flowers are single (e.g. in *Quercus*, the oak) or in small clusters. The fruit is a single-seeded nut, borne in a small cup in the oak or within a spiny covering in the edible chestnut (*Castanea*) and beech (*Fagus*).

Oak and beech are the most familiar trees of the British landscape. In Wales, oakwoods form the climax communities in uplands and lowlands. Beech naturally occurs only in the east. Common uses were fuel and rough timber, but "maidens or standard" trees are still grown for their high quality timber. Their fruits are eaten by animals. The sweet chestnut, *Castanea sativa*, probably introduced by the Romans, is also eaten by people, but in the past, selected acorn varieties were also human food in the Mediterranean region.

# NOTHOFAGACEAE, *the southern beech family*

*Nothofagus menziesii foliage*　　　*N. solandri male flowers*　　　*N. solandri foliage*

# FAGACEAE, *the beech family*

*The female flowers of oaks (above left) are tiny and inconspicuous. They are three-carpellate, with an inferior ovary that is covered in bracts. There is no perianth. The male flowers are in catkins (above right), as they are in all the families of this order. The fruits of oaks are acorns. The cap is several rows of bracts that surround the developing fruit. The shapes of the simple, alternate leaves range from ovate with entire margins to the familiar lobed oak leaves. Quercus rubra (northern red oak) in bloom (above centre)*

*As the young acorns develop (above left), they are almost covered by the bracts of their cup at first. Later, the green acorn grows out of the bracts, still bearing the remains of the tiny styles and stigmas. The acorns take one or two years to mature, depending on the species of oak. Fruit of Fagus sylvatica (centre). Shoots of Fagus sylvatica (beech) emerge from their pointed bud scales in May (right)*

**Eudicots**

**Fabids**

**Fagales** Engler

    **Myricaceae** A. Richard ex Kunth       4 genera/50 species

        Genera include:

        *Morella* de Loureiro

        *Myrica* L. (bog myrtle, sweet gale)

Myricaceae is a small, but cosmopolitan, family of aromatic shrubs and small trees. However, it is absent from Australia and New Zealand. Shrubby members usually having nitrogen-fixing bacteria in their roots, and hence are able to colonise swampy, nutrient-poor habitats. The British native *Myrica gale*, the bog myrtle or sweet gale, grows as a small shrub on wet acid heathlands in North Wales. It gives off a strong perfume and its aromatic resin is used for scenting candles and for flavouring beer and food. Its volatile oils have insect repellent properties. In other parts of the world, the wax on the fruits of *Morella cerifera* is rich in palmitic acid and has been used in soap making. The bark of *Morella esculenta* contains poisons and dyes.

    **Juglandaceae** Perleb       7-10 genera/50 species

        Genera include:

        *Carya* Nuttall (pecan, hickory)

        *Engelhardtia* Leschenault de la Tour ex Blume (engelhardtia, cheo tia)

        *Juglans* L. (walnut)

        *Pterocarya* Kunth (wingnut)

Juglandaceae is a small, mainly warm temperate family of trees. It is usually characterised by large compound leaves and by a fruit with outer fleshy and inner hard coverings that enclose an embryo in which the two cotyledons are 2-lobed corrugated or leaflike structures. A typical example is the walnut (*Juglans*). *Carya illinoinensis* produces pecans. In contrast *Pterocarya fraxinifolia*, grown on parkland as an ornamental tree, has winged fruits. *Carya*, *Juglans* and *Engelhardtia* all produce wood sought-after for furniture.

# MYRICACEAE, *the bog myrtle family*

*Myrica gale foliage and buds (above)*

*Morella faya, evergreen foliage and fruits*

# JUGLANDACEAE, *the walnut family*

*Flowers of Juglandaceae are unisexual, with both sexes on one tree. The leaves are odd-pinnately compound. The male flowers form in long catkins. The female flowers grow into green drupes that have a leathery outer husk. Inside the husk, a stony endocarp, like a peach stone, encloses the seed. Botanically speaking, what we crack is not a nut, but rather this endocarp*

*Juglans microcarpa, little walnut, (above left) female flowers; (above centre) developing drupes; (above right) and mature drupes that have dried and cracked, revealing the brown, ridged endocarp that encloses the seed*

*Carya illinoinensis (pecan trees) have staminate catkins, left. The fruits (drupes) have a woody endocarp that holds the edible seed, above*

**Eudicots**

**Fabids**

**Fagales** Engler

### Casuarinaceae R. Brown                    4 genera/95 species

Genera include:

*Casuarina* L. (she-oak, iron wood)

The family consists of trees and shrubs, mainly from Australia, but also from New Guinea and New Caledonia. One species occurs in coastal areas of the Pacific and Indian Oceans. The form of the plants is typical of xerophytes (plants which are adapted to dry environments) where the photosynthetic surfaces are very reduced to restrict water loss. In casuarinas, the stomata are hidden in grooves in the green stems that give them the "switch" habit similar to the form of a number of plants from widely separated taxonomic groups such as the horse-tail (*Equisetum*) and the gymnosperm *Ephedra* (look for it in the Chilean section of the Great Glass House). There are male and female plants in most species. The male flowers are reduced to anthers that are produced from the joints of the segments near the ends of the branchlets. The female flowers with red stigmas are in a small dense spike on older wood. These eventually develop into a "cone" containing the winged seeds and are released en masse after the fires that occur regularly in the areas where they grow. The wood grain has some similarity to that of oak giving the common name, she-oak. In the widespread coastal *C. equisetifolia* the wood is very hard and hence the name, iron wood.

### Betulaceae Gray                    6 genera/140 species

Genera include:

*Alnus* Miller (alder)

*Betula* L. (birch)

*Carpinus* L. (hornbeam)

*Corylus* L. (hazelnut, filbert)

*Ostrya* Scopoli (hop hornbeam)

The Betulaceae, in common with the Fagaceae, is a small family now confined to the temperate Northern Hemisphere with most members concentrated in North America. It is characterised by male and female flowers (unisexual) borne on the same plant. The male catkin is an elongate structure – a stem bearing lots of small flowers. The hazel (*Corylus*) catkins, known as lambs tails, provide a good example of a male inflorescence. The most conspicuous parts of the flower are the pollen-producing stamens. Petals and sepals are reduced so that they do not obstruct the liberation of pollen into the wind. The lack of showy petals and nectar is a characteristic of wind-pollinated plants as is their production of abundant small, smooth, pollen grains. A further adaptation is the production of the catkins before the leaves open. In hazel, the female flower, which produces the nut, looks like a small bud with red hairs (stigmas) at the tip. Successful pollination will produce the hazel nut, surrounded by a cup-shaped structure. By contrast, in *Betula*, there are both male and female catkins. Numerous fruits (nutlets) are produced, each enclosed in a small bi-winged structure, which is also dispersed by the wind. The family also includes alder (*Alnus*), a climax tree in moist western Britain, in contrast to the birch (*Betula)* which was a pioneering plant after the last glaciation. Hornbeam (*Carpinus*) has wood too hard to be popular with carpenters, but has uses in smelting and charcoal production.

# CASUARINACEAE, *the she-oak family*

*Casuarina nana (she-oak) female cone and female flowers (above left) and green photosynthetic stems (above right)*

# BETULACEAE, *the birch and alder family*

*Alnus incana (grey alder) shown (left) in early spring with the remains of last year's fruits and this years immature inflorescences (white arrow, female; black arrow, male); far left, as the male flowers mature; centre, in early fruit development*

*Male (above left) and female (above right) catkins of Corylus avellana (hazel). The female flowers are visible as tiny, red threadlike stigmas. Each will develop into a nut enclosed in a cup of bracts*

*Betula nigra (black birch) has upright female influorescence unlike those in alder (above)*

119

**Eudicots**
**Fabids**
**Cucurbitales** Dumortier
    **Cucurbitaceae** Jussieu        122 genera/940 species
        Genera include:
        *Apodanthera* Arnott (melon-loco)
        *Bryonia* L. (bryony)
        *Citrullus* Scrader (watermelon)
        *Cucumis* L. (cucumber, gherkin, cantaloupe, muskmelon, honeydew melon)
        *Cucurbita* L. (summer and winter squash, marrow, pumpkin, ornamental gourd)
        *Ecballium* A. Richard (squirting cucumber)
        *Echinocystis* Torrey & A. Gray (wild cucumber, bur cucumber)
        *Lagenaria* Seringe (bottle gourd, calabash)
        *Luffa* Miller (loofah, vegetable sponge)

Cucurbitaceae is a mainly tropical family, dominated by climbing herbaceous forms in which climbing is achieved by spring-like tendrils that are modified leaves. The form and tissue composition of the 'fruit', developed from the inferior ovary, make this such an economically important family containing cucumber, gherkin and melon (*Cucumis*), pumpkin, marrows and courgettes (*Cucurbita*), gourds for ornaments and utensils (*Lagenaria*), watermelon (*Citrullus*) and *Luffa*. The only British native representative is the white bryony (*Bryonia dioica*: here the species name indicates there are male and female plants), whose bright red berries replace the more typical fruits and form autumn garlands in hedgerows. These berries are very poisonous, as is the whole plant, particularly the root.

## The Branch of the Nitrogen-Fixing Partnerships

It appears that sometime back in the reaches of angiosperm history, an ancestral rosid developed the ability to form a beneficial symbiotic relationship with nitrogen-fixing bacteria. Among its descendants are all the plants that are able to house nitrogen-fixing bacteria in root nodules. This clade holds the orders Fabales, Fagales, Rosales and Cucurbitales.

Members of these orders that have the nitrogen-fixing symbiosis were formerly classified in several unrelated families and orders. It is hard to see how such a complex process could have arisen several times. Root nodule formation requires many steps and many gene products from both the host and the bacterium. Phylogenic classification gives a more logical picture, since it is more probable that all these families shared a common ancestor. The most famous root nodule formation occurs between the Fabaceae, the bean or legume family, and bacteria of genus *Rhizobium* and related genera. This symbiosis allows the plants of Fabaceae to grow in poor soils. The plants not only thrive, they add nitrogen to the soil. Before the advent of the Haber process for chemical nitrogen fixation, legume crops and their nitrogen-fixing bacteria offered agriculture a vital means to increase soil fertility.

In other families of this clade, the filamentous bacteria of genus *Frankia* form nitrogen-fixing root nodules. In the Rosales, nitrogen fixers in the rose family, Rosaceae, include the alpine dryads of genus *Dryas*, mountain mahogany of genus *Cercocarpus*, fernbush of genus *Chamaebatiaria*, and cliffrose of genus *Purshia*. The buckthorn family, Rhamnaceae, has several nitrogen-fixing genera, including *Ceanothus*, which includes common shrubs of the California chaparral biome. Buffalo berry in genus *Shepherdia* and Russian olive in genus *Elaeagnus* are nitrogen-fixers of the family Elaeagnaceae.

In the Cucurbitales order, there are two families that have nitrogen-fixing members. Coriariaceae is a family of shrubs whose native habitats are scattered in several continents—Central and South America, the Mediterranean area, and parts of Asia and the South Pacific. Some members of its sole genus, *Coriaria*, are grown as ornamentals. Datiscaceae is a small family with a single genus of herbaceous perennials, *Datisca*. There are species native to California and Mexico, as well as the Middle East and northern India.

Biogeography certainly did not unite the nitrogen-fixing species, nor did structural studies. The story was revealed by their DNA sequences.

# CUCURBITACEAE, *the squash or cucumber family*

*The Cucurbitaceae are important food plants. They are bush-like herbs or vines with tendrils. The leaves are palmately veined and have coarse, rough hairs. The plants are monoecious. The female flowers have an inferior ovary. This is the immature fruit (courgette or cucumber) beneath the corolla. The three lobes of the stigma and the three sections of the fruits reflect the three-carpellate gynoecium. All the stamens are united into a single structure. The five petals are fused at their bases, which is unusual for a rosid*

*Many cultivars of Cucurbita pepo exist. These include courgettes and golden zucchini*

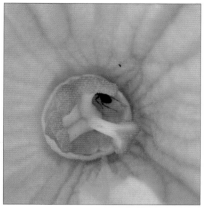

*The female flower has three stigma lobes*

*Male flowers have all the stamens fused together and a plain green stem*

*The corolla sits on top of the yellow inferior ovary in Cucurbita pepo (above left)*

*Above right is the female flower of a parthenocarpic or greenhouse cucumber, a horticultural cultivar of Cucumis sativus. It develops fruits without pollination, and therefore has seedless fruits. Female flowers are always formed, but male flowers are produced only during periods of stress or if plant hormones are applied*

*Berries of Bryonia dioica (white bryony)*

**Eudicots**

**Fabids**

**Cucurbitales** Dumortier

     **Begoniaceae** C. Agardh           2 genera/1,401 species

          Genera:

          *Begonia* L. (begonia, including fibrous, tuberous and Rex begonia)

          *Hillebrandia* Oliver (hillebrandia, Hawaiian begonia)

Begoniaceae is a small, widely distributed, tropical family. Its mainly succulent herbs are often found in damp, shady woods. Those members with tubers are usually found in drier, cooler areas in the Andes and South Africa. *Begonia* itself is important horticulturally as a house or bedding plant. The typically asymmetric shaped, somewhat succulent, leaf (elephant ear) of *B. rex* demonstrates an important feature of many plant cells. When cut surfaces of the leaves are kept moist and pressed onto soil, they develop small masses of cells that produce new plants. This shows that even the mature cells of the leaf retain the potential to develop into entire new plants. Imagine this happening in a human! Many species of *Begonia* have red undersides to their leaves. Where this occurs in plants, it is commonly an indication that they are forest floor dwellers. The pigment here and in other forest floor species acts as a mirror, reflecting light back through the overlying green tissues (giving a double pass) thus increasing photosynthetic efficiency.

# BEGONIACEAE, *the begonia family*

*Begonia sp. Male flowers (above left) have yellow anthers. A female flower (above right) shows its twisted yellow stigmas. The begonias have leaves with an asymmetrical base. The leaves are thick and nearly succulent, and they are often toothed or lobed. The plants are monoecious. The male flowers usually have two large and two small tepals. The female flowers usually have five tepals. Their ovary is inferior and has three wings (below left). The stigmas of the three-carpellate pistil are curled and are bright yellow, just like the anthers. This colouring tricks pollen-carrying insects into landing on the stigma in search of more pollen, and so promotes pollination. The female flower of this tuberous begonia (below right) has a green, winged ovary*

*Begonias cultivated as houseplants are usually hybrids and grown as summer annuals. Many begonias, such as the three shown below, are grown for their striking foliage. Begonia masoniana (iron cross), below right*

123

**Eudicots**
**Fabids**
**Oxalidales** Heinze

    **Oxalidaceae** R. Brown          5 genera/565 species
        Genera include:
        *Averrhoa* L. (star fruit)
        *Oxalis* L. (oxalis, wood sorrel, shamrock)

Oxalidaceae is mainly a tropical family of shrubs and herbs, but the only British native is the small herb, *Oxalis acetosella* (wood sorrel). Its species name describes the sour taste of the leaves caused by calcium oxalate, which has given its name to the genus. The leaves, sometimes used in salads, have three leaflets, which are folded back when in sleep position at night. A number of species are sold as shamrocks, because they have trifoliate leaves. Others are common garden weeds, readily propagated from their seeds, tubers or rhizomes.

*Oxalis* flowers are radially symmetrical, with five equal petals. There are ten stamens in two whorls, with the outer ones shorter than the inner ones. The gynoecium usually has five-carpels, with five separate styles. In many species, the styles vary in height from flower to flower. The fruit is a ribbed or angled capsule.

    **Cunoniaceae** R. Brown        27 genera/340 species
        Genera include:
        *Bauera* Banks (river rose)
        *Cunonia* L. (butterspoons)
        *Eucryphia* Cavanilles (leather wood)
        *Weinmannia* L. (kamahi, towai)

This is a mostly Southern Hemisphere family of evergreen climbers, shrubs and small trees growing in Australia, New Zealand, New Guinea and New Caledonia. *Cunonia* has an unusual distribution with one species in S. Africa (*C. capensis*) grown for its wood and attractive cylindrical flower heads and the remaining sixteen grow in New Caledonia. Most species occur in *Weinmannia*. Evergreen *Bauera* from eastern Australia has solitary bowl-shaped flowers. *Eucryphia* species are important timber plants in China and Australia. They produce distinctly flavoured honey in Tasmania.

    **Elaeocarpaceae** Jussieu      12 genera/600 species
        Genera include:
        *Aceratium* de Candolle (aceratium, carabeen)
        *Aristotelia* L'Héritier (wineberry)
        *Crinodendron* Molina (Chilean lantern tree)
        *Elaeocarpus* L. (blueberry ash, Indian bead tree)

This small family of evergreen shrubs and herbs occurs in tropical into warm temperate climates excluding Africa. *Crinodendron* is the best known in our gardens. Two species occur in Chile and Argentina. *C. hookerianum* has spectacular bell-shaped crimson flowers leading to its name, the Chilean lantern tree. *Aristotelia* (Peru, Australia, New Zealand) is grown for its wood, and in Britain as an ornamental.

# OXALIDACEAE, *the oxalis family*

*This close up (right) of Oxalis pes-caprae (Bermuda buttercup) (left) shows the characteristic two level arrangement of stamens in the genus with five taller inner ones and five shorter outer ones. Like many Oxalis species, it is a noxious weed that reproduces vegetatively with small bulb-like structures.*

*Ribbed capsules (fruits) of Oxalis stricta, (below right) a pest of greenhouses and lawns in North America.*

*Oxalis acetosella (wood sorrel) with trifoliate leaves below left*

# ELAEOCARPACEAE, *the elaeocarpus family*

# CUNONIACEAE, *the leatherwood family*

*Eucryphia sp. flowers and fruit*

*Crinodendron hookerianum (Chilean lantern tree)*

**Eudicots**

**Fabids**

**Malpighiales** Martius

    **Euphorbiaceae** Jussieu           229 genera/6,500 species

        Genera include:

        *Acalypha* L. (chenille plant, copper leaf, Jacob's coat)

        *Codiaeum* Rumf ex A. Jussieu (croton)

        *Croton* L. (croton)

        *Euphorbia* L. (spurges, poinsettia)

        *Hevea* Aublet (rubber)

        *Jatropha* L. (coral plant, physic nut)

        *Manihot* Miller (cassava, tapioca)

        *Mercurialis* L. (dog's mercury)

        *Ricinus* L. (castor oil plant)

Euphorbiaceae is a widespread, but mainly tropical, family. It ranges from trees, shrubs to herbs, with the latter typical of the two British representatives, *Mercurialis* and *Euphorbia*. Tropical euphorbias form shrubs, and in desert areas they look like cacti with fleshy stems and leaves reduced to spines. When leaves and stem are broken they exude a milky irritant sap which is sometimes used to treat warts. Their flowers are small, associated with tube-shaped structures called cyathia which contain nectar. Flowers are surrounded by saucer-shaped bracts that, when brightly coloured and enlarged, make the euphorbias such valuable horticultural plants. The most spectacular of all is *Euphorbia pulcherrima* (poinsettia). Two very different members of the family are manihot (*Manihot esculenta*) and the caster oil plant (*Ricinus communis*). The roots of manihot are an important food-plant of the tropics: its tuberous roots are filled with starch and it is the source of Brazilian arrow root. Caster oil comes from the seeds of *R. communis*, but they are also the source of a deadly poison, ricin. The seeds of *Jatropha* are currently exploited as a biofuel. The principal source of natural rubber is the tropical tree, *Hevea brasiliensis*, which, although native in South America, is largely grown in south-east Asia.

# EUPHORBIACEAE, *the spurge family*

*The floral bracts of Euphorbia pulcherrima (poinsettia) are often mistaken for petals. The real flowers are cup-like inflorescences called cyathia. The cups have yellow nectar glands on the rim. The stigmas of this variety are red and the anthers are yellow*

*Euphorbia marginata (snow-on-the-mountain)*

*Euphorbia sp.*

*Ricinus communis (castor bean) has bright red stigmas and cream-coloured stamens*

*Euphorbia tirucalli (pencilbush)*

*Euphorbia obesa (baseball plant)*

*Euphorbia milii (crown of thorns)*

127

**Eudicots**

**Fabids**

**Malpighiales** Martius

    **Passifloraceae** Roussel        25 genera/725 species

        Genera include:

        *Passiflora* L. (passionflower)

The flowers of *Passiflora* are amongst the most exotic and complex in the plant kingdom. They are borne on vines that climb by means of tendrils. Species are found mainly in Central and South America, but occur worldwide. They were first collected and illustrated by missionaries, who saw religious symbolism in the floral parts. Thus the ten sepals and petals represent the ten apostles, the ring of threadlike and twisted outgrowths (corona) of the petals is the crown of thorns. The central column is the cross supporting the three stigmas that represent three nails and so on.

The complexity of the flower is, of course, related to pollination mechanisms, and changes in architecture, colour and flowering time relate to the habits of their equally exotic pollinators, be they humming birds, bats or butterflies. Indeed the caterpillars of the heliconiine butterflies are unaffected by the cocktail of poisonous alkaloids found in *Passiflora* leaves that are lethal to other herbivores.

The fruit is edible. The commonest commercial variety of *Passiflora edulis* originally came from Brazil, but is now cultivated in vast quantities in the tropics.

# PASSIFLORACEAE, THE PASSIONFLOWER FAMILY

*Passifloraceae is a family of vines with very distinctive flowers. They usually have one or more rows of fringe-like corona above the petals. The stamens and pistils are attached to a raised stalk in the middle of the flower. The filaments of the five stamens attach to the middle of the broad anthers. At the end of the stalk, three styles and stigmas project from the ovary. The fruit is a berry. The leaves have a variety of forms, but many are three-lobed*

*Passiflora vitifolia, right, (perfumed or crimson passionflower) has green anthers and pink styles that end in fat white stigmas*

*Passionflowers usually have five sepals and five petals. The sepals are coloured like the petals and may be fused at their bases*

*Passiflora incarnata, (purple passionflower or maypops) is native in the USA from Texas to the east coast and north to southern Pennsylvania, (left)*

*Fruits of passionflowers have a tough outer covering that surrounds their many flattened seeds. The seeds have a delicious, jelly-like covering, which is the only edible part of the fruit. Immature fruit of P. incarnata (below left)*

*Passiflora membranacea, below, is native to southern Mexico and Central America. It illustrates that passionflowers come in a variety of forms. It has large purple-red bracts at the base of the flower. The petals and sepals are cream-coloured. The leaves are oval, without lobes*

**Eudicots**
**Fabids**
**Malpighiales** Martius
    **Salicaceae** Mirbel            54 genera/1,200 species
         Genera include:
         *Azara* Ruiz & Pavón (azara, vanilla tree)
         *Idesia* Maximowicz (wonder tree)
         *Populus* L. (aspen, cottonwood, poplar)
         *Salix* L. (willow)

The Salicaceae originally contained the two arborescent genera *Salix* (willow) and *Populus* (poplar), but molecular studies have indicated a close relationship with about half of another family, the Flacourtiaceae, in the Malpighiales. *Salix* and *Populus* are now placed in the tribe Saliceae. They are mainly trees in the temperate region of the Northern Hemisphere, with dwarf forms extending into arctic and alpine areas, where willows are pollinated by insects. Some species have a global distribution, with the exception of Australasia. Female and male flowers are both catkins. They are borne on separate plants and produce bright colour and nectar at a time when not many plants are flowering. Willows have long been used in basket-weaving and making cricket bats, but their more recent uses include water filtration and as a biofuel. However their lasting value to mankind is as the original source of a medicinal drug. Infusions of willow bark have long been used as a remedy for colds and rheumatism, but in the nineteenth century the active chemical, salicylic acid, was isolated from willow and from meadow sweet. Later a similar chemical, acetylsalicylic acid, was synthesised and was named aspirin, probably the most widely used drug in the world. It was unfortunately (for willow!) named after the meadow sweet, then called *Spiraea ulmaria* [Look at *Filipendula ulmaria* in the Rosaceae]. *Populus* flowers are wind pollinated. Wind is also the vector for seed dispersal in poplar and willow. Former members of the Flacourtiaceae in the Salicaceae are widely distributed, but predominantly comprise a tropical group of woody plants including quite tall trees. Specimens are grown here as ornamentals. Other species produce fleshy acid fruits, which are eaten after prolonged soaking or boiling (they contain cyanides!) or pressed for oil. South American *Azara* has simple evergreen leaves with showy fragrant flowers composed of stamens (but not petals!) and purple/white berries. *Idesia*, a single species from China, Japan and Korea, is grown for its foliage and red berries.

    **Violaceae** Batsch            24 genera/700 species
         Genera include:
         *Hybanthus* Jacquin (green violet)
         *Viola* L. (violet, pansy)

Violaceae is a cosmopolitan family containing woody as well as herbaceous plants. The most familiar genus, *Viola*, contains about half the 800 species in the family and occurs mainly in temperate and mountainous areas of the Northern Hemisphere. Its flowers are bilaterally symmetrical and have five petals. The lower petal typically has a nectar spur. Nectar guides, lines on petals that show pollinating insects to the nectar inside, are often present. There are five short, stout stamens fitted tightly around the pistil. Violets produce flowers that are insect-pollinated in the spring, but later in summer they may produce inconspicuous self-pollinating flowers that are described as cleistogamous, meaning literally "closed mating." Some violets have ant-dispersed seeds. These seeds have an edible, external oil body that rewards the transporting insect. The garden variety, the pansy, is probably a hybrid between the arable weed *Viola tricolor* (lions ear, Johnny-jump-up, heart's ease) and another wild species *V. arvensis* (the field pansy). Both are found naturally in Britain. Larger and more brightly coloured forms are continually selected and crossed, thus exploiting the very wide range of colours, violet, yellow, blue, reddish purple, white etc. found in wild populations.

# SALICACEAE, *the willow family*

*Male willow catkins with stamens fully extended*

Willows, have a single bud scale covering their flower buds. Willows are difficult to identify to species. Many hybridise in nature

Female Salix sp. catkins, just blooming (left) and with maturing fruits (above) and fuzzy seeds

Young male catkins of North American Populus deltoides (cottonwood) are reddish until the anthers mature

# VIOLACEAE, *the violet and pansy family*

Violet fruits reflect the three-carpellate gynoecium. They split at maturity, and the margins of the ovary wall curl in and squeeze the seeds until they shoot away. Green and mature fruits of the Viola canadensis (Canadian white violet), right, show the three-fold structure

*Viola riviniana, left*

The nectar spur of V. corsica (Corsican violet) protrudes behind its sepals

Violet family members are favourite horticultural subjects. Viola tricolor (above left) is one of the species that were crossed to produce garden pansies (above right)

**Eudicots**

**Fabids**

**Malpighiales** Martius

**Linaceae** de Candolle ex Perleb 10 genera/280 species

Genera include:

*Linum* L. (linseed, flax)

*Reinwardtia* Dumortier (yellow flax)

*Hesperolinon*, *Mesynium* and *Adenolium*

are now placed in *Linum*

Linaceae is a cosmopolitan family containing herbs, shrubs and trees. Molecular analyses might well reduce its membership. Best known are the herbaceous flaxes. The oil from *Linum usitatissimum* seeds (linseed) is used in the manufacture of paints and linoleum as well as providing a high omega-3 oil used in food. The rest of the plant, but mainly the flower stalks, produces the fibres that have been used for 10,000 years to make linen. The species is now being grown as a crop plant in Britain.

**Hypericaceae** Jussieu 8 genera/480 species

Genera include:

*Hypericum* L. (St. John's wort, rose of Sharon)

The Hypericaceae mostly consists of trees and shrubs that grow in temperate regions as well as tropical mountains. It was once included in the family Clusiaceae (Guttiferae). Hypericaceae is included here because it contains the tribe Hypericae and hence some of our garden plants. *Hypericum* itself is characterised by opposite leaves dotted with glands. In the British native *H. perforatum* (perforated St. John's wort), prominent glands are associated with transparent areas. This is a herb applied on poultices for wounds and burns. Indeed other members of the genus are also important medicinal plants used in the treatment of depression. The construction of the flower is best seen in rose of Sharon, *H. calycinum*, now naturalised in the UK, where the central flask shaped ovary topped by a single style is surrounded by countless stamens, and five free petals. Tutsan, *H. androsaemum*, has much smaller, but typical, flowers, and its fruit is a single black berry. It is probably a native that has reinvaded our gardens. Its common name comes from the French toute-saine (all heal), but it has been used principally as a diuretic.

# LINACEAE, *the flax family*

*Flowers of Linaceae have five petals, which fall off soon after the flower blooms. They also have five sepals. These remain to cover the developing fruit. There are five stamens and usually a divided style*

*Linum grandiflorum (scarlet flax)*

*Linum usitatissimum (cultivated flax)*

*Dried and split capsules of Linum lewisii (prairie flax)*

# HYPERICACEAE, *the St John's wort family*

*Hypericum maculatum (imperforate St John's wort)*

*Hypericum calycinum (rose of Sharon)*

*Hypericum androsaemum (tutsan), right*

*Fruit of Hypericum kouytchensa, left*

**Eudicots**

**Malvids**

**Geraniales** Dumortier

    **Geraniaceae** Jussieu                5 genera/650 species

        Genera include:

*Erodium* L'Héritier ex Aiton (storksbill, heronsbill)

*Geranium* L. (wild geranium, hardy geranium, cranesbill, herb Robert)

*Pelargonium* L'Héritier ex Aiton (geranium)

Geraniaceae is a cosmopolitan family of herbs and small shrubs most prolific in temperate regions but not found in wet tropics. It is an easily recognised family because flowers have five, free, conspicuous petals and its seedpods extend into a long beak: hence the common names, cranesbill and storksbill. Plants have simple to often palmate divided leaves with hairs filled with aromatic oils. Our much loved houseplants - the cultivated 'geraniums' - actually belong to *Pelargonium*, which has a greatest density of species in South Africa. Dispersal of seeds is preceded by separation of the five parts of the long beak so that the seed-containing compartments are either curled back as in *Geranium* or twisted into corkscrews as in *Erodium*. These "corkscrews" help push the seed into the soil. The economic value of the family is in horticulture and some of the wild species in the UK now have cultivars in gardens. Of local note is *Geranium sanguineum* (bloody crane's bill) which is usually associated with the limestones of the north of England but also occurs on limestone cliffs in Gower and the Great Orme. The commonest native representative is herb robert (*G. robertianum*), with its very distinctive mousy smell.

# GERANIACEAE, *the geranium or crane's bill family*

*Erodium cicutarium (common storksbill) is a small weedy plant named for its fruits. Its generic name comes from the Greek erodios, meaning "heron." The fruit is a capsule that splits into five sections. Each seed has a corkscrew awn that helps push it into the soil*

*Geranium pratense (meadow cranesbill)*

*Geranium caespitosum var. fremontii (Fremonts geranium) is native to the southern Rocky Mountains. It is a hardy perennial. The seeds develop under the cover of the persistent calyx (white arrow). Its fruits are capsules that split and coil up when they are mature, flinging out their seeds. Compare this method with the corkscrews of Erodium*

*Garden and houseplant geraniums belong to genus Pelargonium, as do scented geraniums, ivy geraniums and regal geraniums. This genus originated in South Africa and plants are not hardy outside in the UK*

**Eudicots**

**Malvids**

**Myrtales** Reichenbach

    **Lythraceae** J. Saint-Hilaire               31 genera/600 species

        Genera include:

        *Cuphea* P. Browne (cuphea, cigar plant)

        *Decodon* J. Gmelin (swamp loosestrife)

        *Lagerstroemia* L. (crepe myrtle)

        *Lawsonia* L. (henna)

        *Lythrum* L. (purple loosestrife)

        *Punica* L. (pomegranate)

Lythraceae is a mainly tropical family of herbs, shrubs and trees with a few temperate representatives. Its flowers have a calyx tube that persists after flowering and expands as it covers the developing fruit. The flower petals are crumpled in the bud and remain wrinkled after they open. The stamens attach inside the calyx tube and have filaments of different lengths. The gynoecium has two or more carpels, but one style. The fruits of this family are usually capsules. *Lythrum salicaria*, the purple-loosestrife, is the commonest British native. It grows in wetlands and along rivers. Loosestrife comes from the Greek and relates to the then perceived tranquilising properties of the plant. *Lythrum* is interesting botanically because of the architecture of the flowers called tristyly that encourages cross pollination. Three style lengths are matched by three stamen lengths. The flowers with the longest styles have short and medium length stamens. The medium length styles are accompanied by long and short stamens, and the short style flowers have medium and long stamens. To add to this complexity the longest styles have stigmas with the largest papillae and the longest stamens, the largest pollen. All these adaptations result in the absence of self pollination, and ensure cross pollination in flowers where stigmas and stamens are at the same level. A similar, but simpler, mechanism called distyly is found in primroses.

*Lawsonia inermis* (henna) is the source of a hair dye and also produces the dye, Titian red, for wool. The fleshy seeds of *Punica granatum*, the pomegranate, are now popular in cookery and in health drinks. Extracts from its bark have been used as a remedy for dysentry and diarrhoea and as an infusion said to paralyse tapeworms which are then expelled using a food purgative.

# LYTHRACEAE, *the loosestrife family*

*Punica granatum (pomegranate) is native to western Asia and has been cultivated in the Mediterranean region since prehistoric times. The fruit of pomegranates is a large berry whose seeds have a fleshy outer covering. This juicy seed covering is the edible part. The flower's calyx tube becomes the fruit's thick, leathery rind. The carpel walls enclose the seeds in several chambers*

*The genus Cuphea has tubular flowers. The fused sepals form the tube. Cuphea llavea (bat-faced cuphea) has only two petals, which are scarlet. They attach at the end of the calyx tube*

*Lythrum salicaria (purple loosestrife)*

*Lagerstroemia indica (crepe myrtle) has strongly clawed petals, which means that the petals taper to a narrow base. Its calyx tube has pointed lobes. After the flower blooms, the points fold inward and cover the developing ovary. As the ovary grows, it protrudes out of the persistent calyx*

**Eudicots**

**Malvids**

**Myrtales** Reichenbach

    **Onagraceae** Jussieu                   22 genera/656 species

        Genera include:

        *Camissonia* Link (suncup, evening primrose)

        *Chamerion* (Rafinesque-Schmaltz) Rafinesque-Schmaltz (rose bay willowherb, fireweed)

        *Circaea* L. (enchanter's nightshade)

        *Clarkia* Pursh (clarkia)

        *Epilobium* L. (willowherb)

        *Fuchsia* L. (fuchsia)

        *Ludwigia* L. (seedbox)

        *Oenothera* L. (evening primrose)

        *Gaura* is now included in *Oenothera*

        *Zauschneria* is now included in *Epilobium*

The Onagraceae, a family dominated by herbs, has a global distribution. Its members colonise a wide range of habitats and extend from the Arctic to the tropics. Like the poppy family, the flowers are characterised by parts in fours but, unlike the Papaveraceae, the ovary is inferior. Flowers of Onagraceae have four sepals, four petals, four to eight stamens and a four-carpellate gynoecium. The pollen is bound together by sticky threads. Strings of pollen can be seen on the anthers of evening primroses without using a magnifying lens. The stigma has four lobes that may be short or long. The ovary is inferior. A floral tube connects the ovary to the base of the perianth. In some species, this tube is much longer than the corolla itself. The fruit is usually a capsule that splits into four sections, each derived from a carpel.

*Oenothera*, the evening primrose, is very well known to botanists because of ring-shaped configurations of its chromosomes during cell division (meiosis). It has also become popular in complementary medicine. Evening primrose oil contains gamma-linolenic acid, whose therapeutic properties are believed to alleviate problems relating to fatty acid metabolism. Although a number of species are found in the British countryside, all have been introduced – and some are escapes from cultivation for their oil. The commonest wild species are the willow herbs (*Epilobium* and *Chamerion*). The most spectacular is the rosebay willow herb, an opportunist and successful coloniser of all waste spaces and of areas following burning. The seeds of the plant with plumes of hairs are very easily transported by wind in drifts, sometimes described as a summer snowstorm. Its spread throughout Britain can be attributed to the development of the railways, and in urban areas, the bomb-sites of World War II. For gardeners, the most versatile member of the Onagraceae is *Fuchsia*. It was first introduced, as *F. magellanica*, from South America (Chile and Argentina) as an ornamental. The genus also occurs naturally in New Zealand.

# ONAGRACEAE, *the evening primrose family*

*Oenothera speciosa (showy evening primrose)*

*Epilobium canum (California fuchsia)*

*A hybrid Fuchsia, with pink sepals and purple petals*

*Chamerion angustifolium (rose bay willowherb) in bloom (far left) and with mature, splitting capsules (left). The small seeds are wind-dispersed. The plants colonise disturbed soils such as burned areas and hence are also known as fireweed*

*Oenothera biennis (evening primrose) inflorescence (above left) with buds at the top and developing ovaries below. The mature capsules (above middle) split into four parts*

*Oenothera lindheimeri (gaura)*

**Eudicots**

**Malvids**

**Myrtales** Reichenbach

    **Myrtaceae** Jussieu           131 genera/5,500 species

        Genera include:

        *Acca* O. Berg (pineapple guava)

        *Callistemon* R. Brown (bottlebrush)

        *Chamelaucium* Desfontaines (waxflower)

        *Eucalyptus* L'Héritier (eucalyptus, gum tree)

        *Eugenia* L. (Australian bush cherry, Surinam cherry)

        *Leptospermum* J. Forster & G. Forster (tea tree)

        *Luma* A. Gray (myrtle)

        *Metrosideros* Banks ex Gaertner (New Zealand Christmas tree)

        *Myrtus* L. (myrtle)

        *Pimenta* Lindley (allspice)

        *Psidium* L. (guava)

        *Syzygium* Gaertner (clove tree, mace)

The Myrtaceae is a Gondwanan family of woody plants. Its family distribution is predominantly in the Southern Hemisphere particularly in Australia, South America and to a lesser extent in southern Africa. However the family also occurs in Indonesia, the Pacific islands and into Southeast Asia. There is only one species in Europe, *Myrtus communis*, found in the Mediterranean region. Members range from small prostrate shrubs to trees that have been recorded as the tallest flowering plants, almost as tall as the redwoods from California. The tallest trees are in the group *Eucalyptus* that grow in cool wet environments in southern Australia. The characteristics of the flower are an inferior ovary and usually a brush blossom form in which the male parts, the anthers, are visually the most prominent part of the flower. Another distinctive feature is the presence of oil glands in the leaves and other primary tissues. The family is broadly divided into two groups on the basis of fruit characteristics. Most Australian representatives have capsular fruits, which are dry when mature and often are retained for a number of years, thus forming a woody seed bank on the plant. This is advantageous in fire-prone environments where many of the species grow so they have a seed store for regeneration after fires. The seeds are protected from the heat of the fire in the capsules and then released en masse into the low competition environment which helps enhance seedling establishment. The other fruit type is a fleshy berry (e.g. *Eugenia*) either eaten or used in jellies. The family is more famous for the dried flower buds of *Syzygium aromaticum* which is the source of cloves. The essential oil is used as a flavouring (eg. in toothpastes and apple tarts) but a constituent, eugenol, has antibacterial and analgesic properties applied in dentistry. Distilled and rectified oil from *Eucalyptus* is used as an antiseptic, expectorant and inhalant for catarrh.

Economically many of the trees provide very high quality wood for structural building and furniture, and pulp for paper making. Guavas and *Acca* are popular fruit trees and the berries of *Myrtus communis* are the basis of a liqueur made in Sardinia. The flowers of eucalypts provide an abundant source of nectar for honey production in Australia. Oil with good lubricating properties and in some cases medicinal value is produced from the leaves. Many species are used in horticulture as the flowers of groups such as *Callistemon* (bottlebrush) and *Leptospermum* (tea tree) are often very showy and attractive.

# MYRTACEAE, *the myrtle family*

Eucalyptus flowers (above right) have a thick fringe of stamens. The sepals and petals form a cap that covers the stamens in bud and falls off when the flower blooms. Despite the numerous stamens, there is one style and one stigma. The fruits (above) are woody and have an X-shaped opening from which the seeds exit

Stamens of Callistemon (bottle-brush flowers) have prominent red filaments (far right). Its developing fruits retain the style and stigma at first, as well as the floral tube (right). Later, this tube or hypanthium becomes a woody covering around the fruit

Edible flowers of Acca sellowiana (pineapple guava) previously called Feijoa sellowiana. The plants and the fruits of this South American native are commonly called feijoas

A pink-flowered cultivar of Leptospermum scoparium (tea tree) shows the broad floral disk with the red stamens attached at its rim

**Eudicots**

**Malvids**

**Sapindales** Dumortier

**Anacardiaceae** R. Brown          69 genera/850 species

Genera include:

*Anacardium* L. (cashew)

*Cotinus* Miller (smoke bush)

*Mangifera* L. (mango)

*Metopium* P. Browne (Florida poisonwood)

*Pistacia* L. (pistachio nut)

*Rhus* L. (poison ivy, sumac)

*Schinus* L. (peppertree)

*Toxicodendron* is often included in *Rhus*

The Anacardiaceae is a mainly tropical family but it extends into Europe and temperate Asia and America. It contains such diverse economically important plants as *Mangifera indica* (mango), *Pistacia* (a producer of oil and edible nuts, *P. vera*), *Anacardium occidentale* (cashew nuts) and *P. lentiscus*, whose cut stems exude a resin which yields a turpentine. The most familiar representatives in British gardens belong to the genus *Rhus*. *R. coriara* (sumac) is from southern Europe, while *R. typhina* (stags horn sumac) is North American and freely spreads by suckers. *Cotinus coggygria* (once *R. cotinus*) is called the smoke bush because it has large smoke-like clusters of flower stalks. A number of plants contain substances (urshiols) that cause skin irritation, which explains why some people get skin rashes while they peel mangoes. Others do not. However most people respond to the various species of *Rhus* that comprise the poison ivies.

**Rutaceae** Jussieu          158 genera/1,900 species

Genera include:

*Boronia* J. E. Smith (boronia)

*Choisya* Kunth (Mexican orange)

*Citrus* L. (orange, lemon, lime, grapefruit, tangerine, kumquat)

*Cneorum* L. (cneorum)

*Correa* Andrews (Australian fuchsia)

*Dictamnus* L. (burning bush, gas plant)

*Ruta* L. (rue)

*Skimmia* Thunberg (skimmia)

In flower structure, this family, widespread in warm temperate and warm parts of the world, has some similarities with the flower of the Geraniaceae (parts in 5s), but has a disc-like structure below the ovary. Its members possess, often scented, oil glands. Most are woody shrubs. It is quite a large family divided into tribes. *Boronia* (with phenomenal perfume) and *Correa* are confined to Australia. Another tribe contains the useful garden plants, *Skimmia japonica* and *Choisya ternata* (south-west North America). *Ruta* itself is essentially a Mediterranean shrub. *Ruta graveolens* is a frequently cultivated, strongly smelling herb, first introduced by the Romans. The most familiar tribe includes the *Citrus* genus that contains oranges, lemons, limes and grapefruits whose fleshy fruits have oily peel. Most are natives of China, and their botanical relationships and names are confused by centuries of cultivation and breeding.

# ANACARDIACEAE, *the sumac family*

*Rhus typhina (stags horn sumac)*

The flowers of Anacardiaceae are small and unisexual. The plants are usually dioecious

Cashew nuts are the seeds of Anacardium occidentale. They develop in a kidney-shaped fruit at the end of an enlarged pedicel. When the fruit is mature, the pedicel becomes fleshy and red. Botanically it is known as a pseudofruit. Cashew apples have a very high vitamin C content. The mature cashew nut is actually the seed inside the tan shell. Cashew nuts are always sold without their shells because the oil in the shell can produce blisters on people's skin. The shells are heated to extract the oil, known as cashew nut shell liquid (CNSL), which has a number of industrial uses

# RUTACEAE, *the citrus family*

*Dictamnus albus, burning bush or gas plant, was named because in still, warm air, the fumes it gives off can be lit with a match. The fruits of gas plant are covered in red oil glands (above right)*

*A Citrus x limon (lemon) flower (above left), and young fruits (above right). Citrus flowers have their stamens arranged in a ring, and there is a disk at the ovary base. The stigma is knob-like with a dimple in the middle*

*Ruta graveolens (rue, or herb-of-grace) has flowers with parts in multiples of four or five. There are eight to 10 stamens. The ovaries are deeply lobed and have glands dotting their outer surface*

**Eudicots**
**Malvids**
**Sapindales** Dumortier
    **Sapindaceae** Jussieu                 131 genera/1,450 species
        **Subfamily Sapindoideae** Burnett
           Genera include:
           *Exothea* Macfadyen (inkwood)
           *Koelreuteria* Laxmann (goldenrain tree)
           *Litchi* Sonnerat (lychee)
           *Sapindus* L. (soapberry)
           *Xanthoceras* Bunge (yellow horn)

The Sapindaceae are trees and shrubs with numerous small flowers. They possess saponins, soap-like chemicals which yield a lather when added to water (e.g. *Sapindus saponaria*, the soapberry tree) but are toxic on injestion, causing lysis of red blood cells. The now subfamily Sapindoideae is tropical to sub-tropical. A Chinese member (*Litchi chinensis*: the lichee) has a fleshy layer surrounding the seed. *Koelreuteria* and *Xanthoceras* will be planted in the Double Walled Garden. These are small shrubs with lovely pinnate leaves and panicles of flowers with colourful, bladder-like fruits.

        **Subfamily Hippocastanoideae** Burnett
           Genera include:
           *Acer* L. (acer, maple)
           *Aesculus* L. (horse chestnut, buckeye)
           *Billia* Peyritsch (Billea)
           *Dipteronia* Oliver is now included in *Acer*

This small subfamily contains just four genera, two of which are familiar trees, *Acer* and *Aesculus*. The acers usually have simple leaves with various dissected lobes, the character that contributes to their wide use as garden ornamentals. *Acer campestre*, the field maple, is a common hedgerow tree in Wales. Its wood is hard and fine-grained and thus much valued in production of bowls and musical instruments, including the favoured wood for harps. Frames have been discovered in Saxon burial mounds, including the Sutton Hoo ship, where a maple harp frame was found wrapped in a seal skin. The sycamore (*A. pseudoplatanus*), although a common countryside tree, was probably introduced into Britain in the fifteenth or sixteenth century and some would now term it an invasive weed. However the time of its introduction is controversial: it may have been earlier because similarly shaped leaves are found on church wood carvings towards the end of the thirteenth century. Its pale, almost colourless, wood is much used for kitchen tables, rolling pins and wooden spoons. Its fine grain make it easy to clean. In Wales it has been used for love spoons and clogs. In North America and Italy, the rising sap of *A. saccharum* in the spring is concentrated to form maple syrup.

*Aesculus hippocastanum* grows wild in the mountains of the Balkans and was introduced to Britain in the late sixteenth century. Even today most specimens have been planted. The horse chestnut was so called because it was given to horses for food and medicine in its native Turkey, rather than in reference to the horseshoe-shaped scars left on leaf fall. As well as providing endless satisfaction to children as 'conkers', the rich brown seeds, are a source of aescin, a chemical proved effective in curing sprains and bruises particularly in horses! Indeed horse chestnut is now grown as a crop to produce the chemical. The white powdery content of the nuts has been used as a kind of flour, but only after soaking them in hot water to leach out the mild poison. The froth produced when cars drive over fallen conkers on wet days, demonstrates the presence of saponin, which is used as an additive to shampoos and shower gels and is a character used in detecting relationship with the Sapindoideae.

## Soapberry Family Revisions

The traditional classification placed horse chestnuts, soapberry trees, and maples in their own families, but recent studies show that these are all closely related. Maples and horse chestnuts now make up a subfamily, Hippocastanoideae, of the Sapindaceae. A second main group is the soapberry subfamily, Sapindoideae, which is mainly tropical. Members of the soapberry subfamily have alternate, pinnately compound leaves. Maples and horse chestnuts, members of the Hippocastanoideae, have opposite leaves. A Chinese shrub, *Xanthoceras*, makes up another branch of the soapberry family. The last subfamily, Dodonaeoideae, is composed of shrubs that grow in tropical or warm temperate climates and are mostly Australian natives.

# SAPINDACEAE, *the soapberry, maple and horse chestnut family*
# SAPINDOIDEAE, *the soapberry subfamily*

*Koelreuteria paniculata (goldenrain tree) has bisexual flowers and male flowers in one inflorescence (left and above). The ovaries develop into three-sided capsules. These papery, inflated capsules break into three segments, each attached to one or two seeds (right). The light, thin capsule wall aids in wind dispersal of the seed*

# HIPPOCASTANOIDEAE, *the maple and horse chestnut subfamily*

*Acer negundo (box elder) have their male flowers (left) and female flowers (right) on separate trees. The female flowers have two long, white stigmas*

*Aesculus glabra (Ohio buckeye)has palmately compound leaves. The tall, pyramidal inflorescences arise on the ends of the new growth. The stamens are curved and stick out past the petals. Some of the flowers have only stamens. Others are bisexual. The fruits have a prickly outer layer. Mature fruits contain a single large seed*

*Flowers of Aesculus hippocastanum (horse chestnut) have poisonous nectar (right)*

*Acer platanoides (Norway maple) in fruit (left)*

145

## Malvaceae and Its Subfamilies

In traditional classifications, the mallow family, Malvaceae, was closely associated with three other familie – Bombacaceae, Sterculiaceae, and Tiliaceae. When botanists studied the DNA from these families, they found them so closely related that all four families were combined into an enlarged Malvaceae. In the Angiosperm Phylogeny Group classification, there are nine subfamilies in the enlarged mallow family. Two of the subfamilies, Malvoideae and Tilioideae, have temperate members. They are included in this tour. All the subfamilies have tropical members. There is still a great deal of study to be done to sort out all the genera in Malvaceae, and it is quite possible that further rearrangement of the subgroups will occur when more information is available about its members.

**Eudicots**
**Malvids**
**Malvales** Dumortier
    **Malvaceae** Jussieu               113 genera/5,000 species
       **Subfamily Malvoideae** Burnett
          Genera include:
          *Abutilon* Miller (Chinese lantern)
          *Alcea* L. (hollyhock)
          *Althaea* L. (marsh mallow)
          *Alyogyne* Alefeld (blue hibiscus)
          *Callirhoe* Nuttal (buffalo rose, poppy mallow)
          *Gossypium* L. (cotton)
          *Hibiscus* L. (hibiscus, okra, rose mallow)
          *Lavatera* L. (tree mallow)
          *Malva* L. (mallow)
          *Sidalcea* A. Gray (miniature hollyhock)
          *Abelmoschus* is now included in *Hibiscus*

The arrangement of stamens makes this cosmopolitan subfamily instantly recognisable. They are numerous and form a conspicuous tube, best demonstrated in the tropical *Hibiscus*, the genus usually associated with Hawaiian garlands, but a cultivar of the Chinese hibiscus, *H. rosa-sinensis*. *Hibiscus esculentus* produces ladies fingers (okra). The mallows are common wildflowers in Britain (*Malva* and *Althaea*). The roots of *A. officinalis* were originally used to make the famous sweets (marsh mallows), because they contain a jelly-like material together with sugar and starch. Its mucillages also have medicinal properties that include treatments for ulcers, boils, catarrh and cystitis! *Alcea rosea*, the garden hollyhock, was probably introduced from western Europe by the crusaders. The most important economic plants are species of *Gossypium*, whose hairy seeds are the source of cotton.

       **Subfamily Tilioideae** Arnott
          Genera include:
          *Tilia* L. (lime tree, linden tree, basswood tree)

This widespread subfamily contains trees and shrubs and occasionally herbs. However it is best known for its timber trees, including *Tilia*, the lime or linden. It was the last arborescent genus to become naturally established in England and Wales after the last ice age. Its strongly perfumed flowers indicate that although its flowers are inconspicuous, they are insect pollinated. Quite different insect visitors, aphids, puncture its sap. The resulting honeydew secretions produce the sticky coating on cars parked beneath this common street tree.

# MALVACEAE, *the mallow family:* MALVOIDEAE, *the mallow subfamily*

*Cultivars of Hibiscus rosa-sinensis (Chinese hibiscus) (left), are available in many colours. This ornamental shrub is used in semitropical and mild winter climates*

*Abutilon cultivar (right)*

Fused parts characterise the flowers of the mallow subfamily. The stamens have the bases of their filaments fused into a tube that wraps around the pistil. The bases of the five petals are also fused with the filaments. These cover the ovary. The end of the style and the stigmas are the only part of the gynoecium that is visible. The style usually has five branches. The stigmas may be knobs or hair-like. The plants typically have slimy, mucilaginous sap

*Alcea rosea (hollyhock), left, has been bred in many colours, including red, pink, white, and yellow. The stamens mature first, followed by the filamentous gynoecia (below middle, pink structures). The fruits (right) are schizocarps*

# MALVACEAE, *the mallow family:* TILIOIDEAE, *the lime subfamily*

*Tilia trees have clusters of blossoms with a large, light green bract above each inflorescence. In the autumn, the bracts turn brown. When the fruits mature, the bract and fruits blow away as a unit. The filaments of the stamens are not fused, as they are in the mallow subfamily. Tilia americana (American basswood or linden), below*

Eudicots

Malvids

Malvales

**Thymelaeaceae** Jussieu                  45 genera/850 species

   Genera include:

   *Daphne* L. (daphne, mezereon, spurge laurel)

   *Daphnopsis* C. Martius

   *Dirca* L. (leatherwood)

   *Edgeworthia* Meissner (paper bush)

This widespread family of shrubs, which grows in dry, often fire-prone areas, is concentrated in South Africa and Australia and in a broad belt extending from the Mediterranean into Asia. A genus showing the latter distribution is *Daphne*, whose flowers have a cup-shaped receptacle extending into a tubular corolla with four free tips. The nectar at the base of the tube and the phenomenal fragrances attract long-tongued insects such as butterflies, moths and certain bees as pollinators. A very rare British native is *D. mezereum* (mezereon) with highly scented, purple flowers encircling short lengths of leafless stems. Moth pollinated *D. laureola* has green, but more musty, scented flowers. All parts of *Daphne* are highly poisonous but have been used in homeopathic and herbal medicines. *Dirca palustris*, the leatherwood, comes from North America. Its supple shoots are used in basket-making and its bark, for rope. The papery bark of *Edgeworthia* (China and Himalaya) is used to make expensive paper e.g. in bank notes. *Edgeworthia chrysantha* (the paper bush) has clusters of sweetly smelling, yellow flowers similar to those of *Daphne* in general appearance.

**Cistaceae** Jussieu                  9 genera/170 species

   Genera include:

   *Cistus* L. (rock rose)

   x *Halimiocistus* Spach

   *Halimium* (Dunal) Spach

   *Helianthemum* Miller (rock rose)

   *Hudsonia* L. (beach heather)

This is a small family of herbs and shrubs, whose flowers are characterised by numerous stamens, and normally five petals and sepals. In Britain it is represented by the rock roses, confined to limestones and dry calcareous soils (see front cover). In our gardens, the genus *Cistus* has much larger showy flowers, a reminder of Mediterranean habitats. Many of its species have uses in perfuming soaps, deodorants etc. *Cistus incanus* subsp. *creticus* may be the source of myrrh. The x in front of *Halimiocistus* indicates a hybrid, while the generic name includes the two parent genera, *Halimium* and *Cistus*.

# THYMELAEACEAE, *the Daphne family*

*Daphne mezereum*
*(mezereon)*

*Daphne laureola (spurge laurel)*

*Daphne odora*

# CISTACEAE, *the rock-rose family*

*Cistus x laxus var. hirsutus*

*C. symphytifolius var. symphitifolius*

*Cistus x obtusifolia*

*Helianthemum*
*nummularium (rock rose).*
*Note the characteristic*
*somewhat crumpled*
*appearance of the petals*

**Eudicots**

**Malvids**

**Brassicales** Bromhead

**Tropaeolaceae** Jussieuex de Candolle        1 genus/95 species
Genus:

*Tropaeolum* L. (nasturtium, canary creeper)

This small family contains just one genus, *Tropaeolum*, which occurs naturally in cool mountainous areas from Mexico southwards into Chile. Best known in our gardens is the nasturtium (*T. majus*) from Peru. It has typical peltate (umbrella-shaped) leaves that contain peppery mustard oils and showy flowers with nectar-containing spurs. The latter are present in much smaller but equally attractive flowers of climbers e.g. *T. speciosum* and *T. peregrinum*.

**Limnanthaceae** R. Brown        2 genera/10 species
Genera include:

*Floerkea* Willdenow (false mermaid)

*Limnanthes* R. Brown (poached egg flower)

This small family of succulent annuals is found in moist habitats of temperate North America. *Limnanthes*, comes particularly from California, and its most cultivated species, *L. douglasii* (poached egg flower) is so called because its sweetly smelling buttercup-like flowers have bright yellow centres and white edges.

**Resedaceae** Gray        9 genera/80 species
Genera include:

*Reseda* L. (dyer's weed, mignonette)

This small family of herbaceous plants had its origins in the Mediterranean, then extended eastwards into India, south into Africa and westwards even into the Americas. British natives, *Reseda lutea* and *R. luteola*, are at their western limits. *Reseda* has inconspicuous flowers aggregated into long spikes characterised by an asymmetric arrangement of stamens. *R. luteola*, frequently found on waste ground has been cultivated at least since Neolithic times for its excellent bright yellow dye, used by Romans to colour silk for wedding clothes. *R. lutea* (the wild mignonette) has a musky smell that is completely overshadowed by that of *R. odorata*, garden mignonette, which is cultivated for its essential oils used in perfume manufacture.

# TROPAEOLACEAE, *the nasturtium family*

*Tropaeolum tricolor, a climber in the Chile section of the Great Glasshouse (above)*

*The showy flower of T. majus (above right) with nectar containing spur (hidden here)*

*T. peregrinum (canary creeper) with divided leaves growing near Cochabamba, Bolivia (right)*

## RESEDACEAE, *the mignonette family*

*Reseda luteola. Note the asymmetrical arrangement of the stamens and the three carpels*

## LIMNANTHACEAE

*Limnanthes douglasii var. sulphurea*

151

**Eudicots**
**Malvids**
**Brassicales** Broomhead
    **Brassicaceae** Burnett or **Cruciferae** Jussieu          321 genera/3,400 species

         Genera include:

*Alyssum* L. (perennial alyssum)

*Arabis* L. (arabis, rockcress)

*Armoracia* P. Gaertner, Meyer & Scherbius (horseradish)

*Aubrieta* Adanson (aubretia)

*Brassica* L. (broccoli, Brussels sprout, cabbage, canola, cauliflower, kale, kohlrabi, mustard greens, pak-choi, turnip and many herbaceous weeds)

*Capsella* Medikus (shepherd's purse)

*Cardamine* L. (cuckoo flower, lady's smock, milk maids)

*Crambe* L. (sea kale, giant kale)

*Draba* L. (whitlow grass)

*Erysimum* L. (wallflower)

*Heliophila* Burman f. ex L.

*Hesperis* L. (rocket, dame's rocket)

*Iberis* L. (candytuft)

*Isatis* L. (woad)

*Lepidium* L. (garden cress, pepperwort)

*Lunaria* L. (honesty, money plant)

*Matthiola* R. Brown (stock)

*Pachyphragma* (de Candolle) Reichenbach (pennycress)

*Raphanus* L. (radish)

*Sisymbrium* L. (hedge mustard, rocket)

*Thlaspi* L. (pennycress)

The Brassicaceae is another example of a family which has recently changed its name. Once known as the Cruciferae, it now embraces the name of the important genus *Brassica*, because the laws of botanical nomenclature recommend that the family name should be based on a generic name (genus) within it. Families with these 'out of favour' names are ones which were very early recognised and usually have economic importance. They include the grasses (Graminae → Poaceae), umbellifers (Umbelliferae → Apiaceae), the dead nettles (Labiatae → Lamiaceae) and the peas (Leguminosae → Fabaceae). Note too that the new names have the correct family suffix – aceae.

The Brassicaceae is a cosmopolitan, especially temperate family. Most of its members are herbs, but rare examples have almost a palm-like habit. They produce mustard oils (glycosides) with a strong peppery taste. Related plants often share the ability to synthesise a particular class of molecules. The plant tissues contain a precursor molecule and enzymes that can convert it to the active form, produced when the tissues are damaged. Such a system gives the plant a defence against herbivores, as the mustard oils are released when the plant is eaten. This keeps most insects and many mammals away from most brassicas. The cabbage white butterflies and a few other insects have evolved the ability to tolerate mustard oils and exploit mustard family plants.

The family contains important crop plants, some of which have fleshy tap roots e.g. turnips, swedes, radishes and sugar beet, while in others the leaves, e.g. cabbage, sprouts (giant buds), or flower heads (cauliflower, sprouting broccoli) are eaten. It is quite remarkable that all these above-ground vegetables have been bred by humans from mutations of the wild cabbage, *Brassica oleracea*. Some seeds are used to produce vegetable oils, e.g. oil seed rape, or are used in the kitchen in prepared mustard. Glycosides produce the characteristic flavour of leaves of water-cress and rocket and the roots of the horseradish. Less important now is woad (*Isatis tinctoria*), whose leaves produce a dark blue dye. Thought to have been introduced into Britain by the Celts, it was used to daub the bodies of Ancient Britons.

# BRASSICACEAE OR CRUCIFERAE, *the mustard family*

*The typical mustard flower has four petals and six stamens. Four of the stamens are longer than the other two, as seen in Crambe cordifolia, (giant kale) (above). The flowers are two-carpellate. The tall, slender inflorescence keeps growing as long as conditions allow. The cross shape formed by the petals gave this family its original name, Cruciferae*

*This is a large family, with many weedy species that often grow on disturbed soil on roadsides and vacant lots. Thlaspi arvense (pennycress) (above middle), and Descurainia sophia (flixweed) (above right), are examples. The inflorescence has buds and young flowers at the top, with older flowers and developing fruit below. The fruit is called a silicle if it is short and wide or a silique if it is long and thin. These fruits have two outer covers over a central partition or septum. The seeds form on both sides of the septum*

*Broccoli, one of the many Brassica oleracea cultivars, has yellow flowers (above left), although the shoots are usually picked and eaten while the flowers are in bud. The whole plant with tight clusters of buds is shown (above right)*

*This Erysimum x marshallii (Siberian wallflower), above, has elongating gynoecia and young siliques below these*

*If Raphanus sativus, radish plants, are left in the ground after the root has grown, they put up a tall shoot and bloom. Their flowers have clawed, white petals*

*Aubrieta deltoidea (below) is a favourite rock garden plant. Like most garden members of this family, it is an early spring bloomer*

**Eudicots**

**Core eudicots**

**Santalales** Dumortier

    **Santalaceae** R. Brown                        44 genera/875 species

        Genera include:

        *Phoradendron* Nuttall (bigleaf, desert and Christmas mistletoe)

        *Santalum* L. (sandalwood)

        *Viscum* L. (mistletoe)

        Note: The former mistletoe family, Viscaceae, is included here in the Santalaceae, but its placement is still controversial.

Santalaceae is a family of hemiparasites, plants that can make their own food, but which also tap into other plants for water and minerals. It includes several mistletoes and the sandalwood trees, *Santalum*.

The mistletoes grow on the branches of a host tree. They have special roots, called haustoria, that penetrate the host and link to its vascular system. The flowers are small and inconspicuous. The fruits have a sticky outer covering. Some mistletoes shoot their seeds onto the bark of nearby trees. Birds' beaks, feet and faeces carry others to new hosts.

The British representative, *Viscum album*, is steeped in folklore, although now more frivolously associated with the Christmas kissing tradition. Mistletoe is particularly associated with apple orchards and is grown as a cash crop in the Welsh Borderland. In Medieval times it was thought to have magical properties and more recently was central to druidical rituals. It does have medicinal properties and was traditionally used to treat high blood pressure, arteriosclerosis, hypertension, headache and hysteria. More recently it has been investigated as a source of a cytotoxic agent against lung and colon cancers and as an immune stimulant.

# SANTALACEAE, *the mistletoe and sandalwood family*

*Phoradendron macrophyllum, bigleaf mistletoe, has green leaves and stems. This one is parasitising a cottonwood tree in the United States. Its fruits are white berries that are poisonous to humans, but not to birds*

*Phoradendron californicum, desert mistletoe, grows on mesquite and other legume trees. Its fruits are pale red berries. This mistletoe has a partnership with Phainopepla, a bird that depends on its berries as a major food source and disperses the seeds*

*General overview (above left) and berry and flowers (above right) of Viscum album, a native in Britain*

# INTRODUCING CARYOPHYLLALES

The order Caryophyllales holds approximately 6% of the eudicots and about 30 families. Although this branch is far smaller than the rosids or asterids, it contains a wide variety of plant forms and adaptations. Included are succulents and the cacti, both champions at life in arid climates. Several groups, including ice plants, are able to grow in salty soils, another environment that challenges the plant's ability to retain water.

Several families of insectivorous plants are part of Caryophyllales. These include the Venus fly trap family, Droseraceae, and the Asian pitcher plant family, Nepenthaceae.

Many families in this order have a unique group of pink pigments called betalains. These pigments provide the intense red of beets and the vivid pink of cactus flowers. Some families, including Caryophyllaceae, have anthocyanins, the same pink pigments as most of the other flowering plants.

One thing all Caryophyllales share is simple, entire leaves. The flowers are much more variable than the leaves. The flowers are often complex and deceptive in structure. The calyx may be coloured and take over the function of petals. Even when the flowers have petals and sepals, it seems these structures do not develop in the same way as they do in other flowering plants.

**Eudicots**
**Core eudicots**
**Caryophyllales** Perleb
    **Tamaricaceae** Link                 5 genera/79 species
         Genera include:
         *Tamarix* L. (tamarix, salt cedar)

This very small family of steppe, desert and sea-shore plants is able to tolerate saltpans and drought. The minute leaves and green stems that characterise the switch habit, also seen in the Casuarinaceae, are adaptations to reduce evaporation from exposed surfaces. This makes *Tamarix gallica*, where small pink flowers are aggregated into sprays, an excellent plant for 'difficult' coastal gardens. It was introduced into Britain from the Mediterranean at least 500 years ago. The manna of the Bedouin comes from *T. mannifera* and is produced as exudates on stems infested by scale insects.

    **Plumbaginaceae** Jussieu            29 genera/730 species
         Genera include:
         *Acantholimon* Boissier (prickly thrift)
         *Armeria* Willdenow (sea pink, thrift)
         *Ceratostigma* Bunge (plumbago)
         *Limonium* Miller (statice, sea lavender)
         *Plumbago* L. (Cape plumbago, leadwort)

The Plumbaginaceae is a cosmopolitan family many of whose members live in water-stressed environments at altitude, on salt-steppes or salt marshes. Once thought to be close relatives of the Primulaceae, flowers in the Plumbaginaceae have five petals, five stamens and a five carpellate gynoecium with only one seed per capsule. In Britain members include the pink-flowered thrift, *Armeria maritima* and common sea lavender, *Limonium vulgare*. The latter, like statice its cultivated relative, has flowers that can be dried because the calyx is thin and papery. It is also highly coloured. The name Plumbaginaceae has its roots in the Latin for lead (*plumbum*), because it was once thought that its members could cure lead poisoning. Certainly like many salt-marsh plants, thrift can tolerate much higher concentrations of metals than many other plants, and does colonise lead and other mine spoil heaps.

# TAMARICACEAE, *the Tamarix family*

*Tamarix sp. growing on steppe at Ghost City near Karamay, Xinjiang, China*

# PLUMBAGINACEAE, *the thrift family*

*Armeria maritima (sea pink or common thrift), whole plant and close-up view of an inflorescence (left and far left)*

*Ceratostigma plumbaginoides (dwarf plumbago), bottom left*

*Limonium perezii is one of several salt-tolerant species that are commonly called sea lavender. Shown here is a close-up view of the flowers with their purple calyces and white corollas*

**Eudicots**

**Core eudicots**

**Caryophyllale**s Perleb

    **Polygonaceae** Jussieu                46 genera/1,200 species

        Genera include:

        *Bistorta* (L.) Adanson (bistort)

        *Eriogonum* Michaux (sulphur flower, eriogonum)

        *Fagopyrum* Miller (buckwheat)

        *Fallopia* Adanson (Japanese knotweed, black bindweed, Russian vine)

        *Persicaria* (L.) Miller (knotweed)

        *Polygonum* L. (knotweed, bistort)

        *Rheum* L. (rhubarb)

        *Rumex* L. (sorrel, dock)

        NOTE: *Bistorta*, *Fallopia*, and *Persicaria* may be included in *Polygonum*

This predominantly temperate family has many widely distributed genera. They are mainly herbs. A typical feature in the family is the ochrea, a membraneous extension clasping the stem at the leaf base. Rhubarb (*Rheum rhaponticum*) exemplifies this. Flowers in the family are small and individually inconspicuous. They are aggregated into loose feathery or more compact inflorescences. They are wind pollinated and produce one-seeded dry units (achenes). In the UK many are common weeds e.g. sorrels, knotweeds and docks. The broad-leaved dock, *R. obtusifolius*, is best known for soothing nettle stings. *Rumex* species contain anthraquinones and are mild purgatives. The edible part of the rhubarb is the leaf stalk (petiole). Calcium oxalate occurs throughout the plant, but is concentrated in the leaves making them very poisonous. Japanese knotweed (*Fallopia japonica*) is the most pervasive alien weed in the UK today, but was once admired in Victorian gardens and planted in Swansea to stabilise coal-tips. Russian vine (*F. baldschuanica*) has equally vigorous vegetative growth. Fortunately for our native flora, a recently discovered hybrid between the two fallopias does not combine their vigour – but promises to be a useful garden plant in the future.

# POLYGONACEAE, *the knotweed or dock family*

*Persicaria amplexicaulis is grown as an ornamental*

*Fallopia japonica (Japanese knotweed) is an invasive pest. It has hollow upright stems useful as pea-shooters. In Carmarthenshire, its leaves and young stems were cooked and eaten*

*Eriogonum umbellatum (sulphur flower or sulphur buckwheat), right, is native to the western United States*

*The ochrea in Polygonum sp, left*

*Rheum rhaponticum (rhubarb) flowers (above) and fruits (far left). Note the ensheathing leaf base around a green leaf bud at the base of the edible petioles (left)*

159

Eudicots

**Core eudicots**

**Caryophyllales** Perleb

    **Caryophyllaceae** Jussieu        85 genera/2,630 species

        Genera include:

        *Agrostemma* L. (corn cockle)

        *Arenaria* L. (sandwort)

        *Cerastium* L. (chickweed, snow-in-summer)

        *Dianthus* L. (pink, sweet William, carnation)

        *Gypsophila* L. (baby's breath, gypsophila)

        *Minuartia* L. (sandwort)

        *Sagina* L. (pearlwort)

        *Saponaria* L. (soapwort)

        *Silene* L. (campion)

        *Stellaria* L. (chickweed, stickwort)

        *Lychnis* L. (campion, catchfly, Maltese cross) is now placed in *Silene*

The Caryophyllaceae is a family of herbaceous plants, which is widely distributed in mainly temperate regions of the world with rare examples at altitude in the tropics. It provides some of our most treasured wild-flowers, including stitchworts, campions, ragged robin and corn cockle. Floral parts are usually in fives and there are often ten stamens. Its simple entire leaves are produced in pairs at the swollen regions (nodes) of the stem. The latter will be familiar to gardeners and flower arrangers because they are very well illustrated in *Dianthus*, the pinks. The genus, which is thought to have originated in the Mediterranean, was probably part of the Norman invasion of Britain. Seeds of the wild carnation or clove pink, *D. caryophyllus*, were transported with wood and stone building material (hence still found in castles). Descendants eventually became central to the breeding programme that produced our border pinks today. Indeed some of the first recorded (and subsequently overlooked) experiments on hybridisation, performed by Thomas Fairchild in 1717, involved placing the pollen of the wild carnation on the stigmas of sweet William (*D. barbatus*), that resulted in the production of 'Fairchild's mule'. However, there are also native species in the British flora, e.g. *D. armeria*, the Deptford pink, and possibly *D. gratianopolitanus*, the Cheddar pink, a rarity growing on limestone cliffs in the Cheddar Gorge.

*Silene dioica*, red campion, has either male or female flowers borne on separate plants as the species name suggests. The stamens are usually a whitish colour, but occasionally a purplish black. This colour is produced by fungal spores, which are then transfered by the plant's insect pollinator to another host.

# CARYOPHYLLACEAE, *the pink family*

*Dianthus chinensis (China pink), above left, and Silene chalcedonica (Maltese cross), above right*

*Cerastium tomentosum (snow-in-summer)*              *Silene dioica (red campion)*

*Members of the pink family usually have enlarged nodes with opposite leaves. The petals of this family typically have notches or "pinking". The petals are clawed, which means that their bases narrow markedly. The gynoccia range from two to five carpels with the ovary fused, but the stigmas and styles are free. The fruit is a capsule*

*The five petals, Silene latifolia subsp. alba (white campion) are so deeply notched that they look like twice that number. A tubular calyx encloses the base of the petals. This species is dioecious. In the female flower, the young green ovary, as revealed by peeling back the perianth, is topped by its five separate styles and stigmas. As the fruit matures, the green ovary enlarges inside the striped, persistent calyx, which was peeled back for the photo. The mature capsule has a ring of teeth that fold back from the top, exposing the loose seeds in the cup-shaped, dry ovary*

Eudicots
**Core eudicots**
**Caryophyllales** Perleb
**Amaranthaceae** Jussieu                 175 genera/2,000 species

**Note:** This family includes the former Chenopodiaceae, the goosefoot family, which is no longer recognised.

Genera include:

*Alternanthera* Forsskaol (Jacob's coat)     *Gomphrena* L. (globe amaranth)
*Amaranthus* L. (tassel flower, foxtail)     *Ptilotus* R. Brown (pussy tale)
*Atriplex* L. (salt bush)     *Salicornia* L. (glasswort, saltwort, samphire)
*Beta* L. (beets, chard)     *Salsola* L. (Russian thistle, tumbleweed)
*Celosia* L. (cockscomb)     *Spinacia* L. (spinach)
*Chenopodium* L. (goosefoot, fat-hen)

This tropical to temperate family mainly of herbaceous plants, includes some invasive weeds. The individual flowers are very small, but sometimes aggregated into attractive, often gaudy inflorescences. These, together with variegated leaves, give the family horticultural importance. *Amaranthus caudatus* (variously called love-lies-bleeding, tassel flower or foxtail) has vivid crimson pendulous tassels, while *Celosia* (cockscomb) may have plumes or fan-shaped convoluted crests. *Gomphrena* has aggregations of colourful bracts with tiny protruding flowers, while *Ptilotus* has cylindrical spikes of very small flowers with long protruding white hairs. *Alternathera* species (e.g. Jacob's coat) are useful foliage plants. Plants originally attributed to the Chenopodiaceae are widespread herbs, but with some shrubs and small trees. They are colonisers of low-lying salt plains, pampas, prairies, steppes etc. where water is often in short supply and salt accumulates. Thus the plants are often highly adapted halophytes. They may be fleshy, with small leaves and coverings of hair. Their wind-pollinated flowers are inconspicuous with no distinction between sepals and petals; fruits are one seeded. The leaves of *Chenopodium album* (fat-hen) were used by prehistoric communities in the UK as a vegetable, its place today taken by *Spinacia oleracea* (spinach). Species of *Atriplex* and *Chenopodium* are important fodder plants in dry areas across the world. Fleshy stems resembling spineless cacti or succulents characterise *Salicornia europaea* (common glasswort or samphire) which is now regarded as a gourmet vegetable. However, the most important economic species is *Beta vulgaris*. Its tendency for roots to swell and accumulate sugar during a two year life cycle has been exploited by breeders to produce below ground sugar beet, beetroot, mangal-wurzel, mangold and above ground spinach beet/swiss chard. A cross section through a beetroot reveals numerous concentric circles, produced by a rather unusual form of additional (secondary) growth.

**Aizoaceae** Martinov                 127 genera/1,860 species

Genera include:

*Carpobrotus* N. E. Brown (Hottentot fig)     *Lampranthus* N. E. Brown (ice plant)
*Delosperma* N. E. Brown (ice plant)     *Lithops* N. E. Brown (living stones)
*Fenestraria* N. E. Brown (baby toes)     *Malephora* N. E. Brown (ice plant)
*Glottiphyllum* Haworth (tongue leaf plant)     *Mesembryanthemum* L. (Livingstone daisy)

*Aptenia* N. E. Brown (heartleaf ice plant) is now placed in *Mesembryanthemum*

Aizoaceae as defined here includes the Mesembryanthaceae. Members of the latter with very showy brightly coloured daisy-like flowers are particularly concentrated in South Africa, but they also occur in coastal areas in Australia and the Mediterranean. The remaining members of the expanded families, whose limits have been determined by DNA studies, mainly grow in New and Old World tropics and often near coasts. Their economic value lies in horticulture. They are interesting botanically because their succulent leaves store water and sugar for survival through periods of drought and they undertake crassulacean acid metabolism (CAM) (see Crassulaceae). Some show an adaptation, in the form of an internal filtering layer of calcium oxalate crystals, to withstand strong sunshine. *Lithops*, the living stone plant, is so called because its two leaves mimic the surrounding pebbly soil surface and such camouflage distracts grazers.

# AMARANTHACEAE, *the amaranth and goosefoot family*

EUDICOTS

*Salicornia europaea (samphire)*

*Celosia sp. (cockscomb)*

*Beta vulgaris cicla (chard) cultivar*

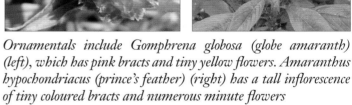

*Spinacia oleracea (spinach) is dioecious, which means it has male (left) and female (right) flowers on separate plants*

*Ornamentals include Gomphrena globosa (globe amaranth) (left), which has pink bracts and tiny yellow flowers. Amaranthus hypochondriacus (prince's feather) (right) has a tall inflorescence of tiny coloured bracts and numerous minute flowers*

CORE EUDICOTS

# AIZOACEAE, *the ice plant family*

*Mesembryanthemum cordifolium (heartleaf ice plant) has succulent leaves, but thinner ones than most of this family have*

*Delosperma cooperi is among the hardiest of ice plants, meaning that they can survive lower temperatures than most. Many ice plants cannot survive freezing!*

*Lithops species are called living stones for good reason. Growers of succulents cultivate many types of these plants. Only the tops of the two succulent leaves protrude above ground*

CARYOPHYLLALES

**Eudicots**

**Core eudicots**

**Caryophyllales** Perleb

    **Nyctaginaceae** Jussieu               27 genera/350 species

        Genera include:

        *Abronia* Jussieu (sand verbena)

        *Acleisanthes* A. Gray (angel trumpets)

        *Allionia* L. (trailing four o'clock)

        *Bougainvillea* Commerson ex Jussieu (bougainvillea)

        *Mirabilis* L. (four o'clock plant, marvel of Peru)

        *Nyctaginia* Choisy (devil's bouquet)

This tropical to warm temperate family of herbs, trees and shrubs is concentrated in the New World. Leaves of some members are eaten, but the major economic value of this plant rests with ornamentals such as *Bougainvillea* hybrids and species of *Mirabilis*. *Mirabilis jalapa* is the source of a resin and has also been used as a purgative.

    **Portulacaceae** Jussieu            20 genera/325 species

        Genera include:

        *Claytonia* L. (spring beauty, winter purslane)

        *Lewisia* Pursh (lewisia)

        *Portulaca* L. (portulaca, purslane)

Members of the Portulaceae are succulents whose leaves are modified to withstand high light intensities and dry environments, e.g. *Claytonia megarhiza*, is typical of harsher high altitude environments. It is a cosmopolitan family with a concentration of taxa in western North America. Indeed the two species of *Claytonia* that have escaped into the wild in the U.K. come from there. *Claytonia perfoliata* (spring beauty) occurs widely on sandy soils. In contrast *C. sibirica* (spring purslane) grows in damp shady places particularly in the north and west. *Claytonia perfoliata* has small white flowers that occur above a saucer-like structure formed by fusion of two opposite leaves. The latter are edible and can be eaten boiled or raw. Some botanists would place *Claytonia* and *Lewisia* in the Montiaceae family.

# NYCTAGINACEAE, *the four o'clock family*

The genus Mirabilis includes M. jalapa (four o'clock or marvel-of-Peru) which is a native of tropical South America. Its flowers open in the late afternoon and remain open at night

M. multiflora (wild four o'clock) grows throughout the southwestern United States

This Bougainvillea hybrid has small white flowers. The larger pink structures are floral bracts

The flowers of Nyctaginaceae are deceptive. What appears to be a fused corolla is actually coloured, fused sepals. There are no petals. Usually there are bracts at the base of the flower. The bracts may be green or brightly coloured. The bracts of Bougainvillea help attract pollinators and later assist in seed dispersal

# PORTULACEAE, *the purslane family*

Portulaca grandiflora (moss rose) has been bred to have extra tepals, and when this occurs, it is called a double flower. The original form had a single row of tepals. Flowers can be white, pink, orange, or red

Lewisia rediviva (bitterroot) grows in the Rocky Mountains region of the USA

Claytonia megarhiza (alpine spring beauty) grows in harsh, high altitude environments

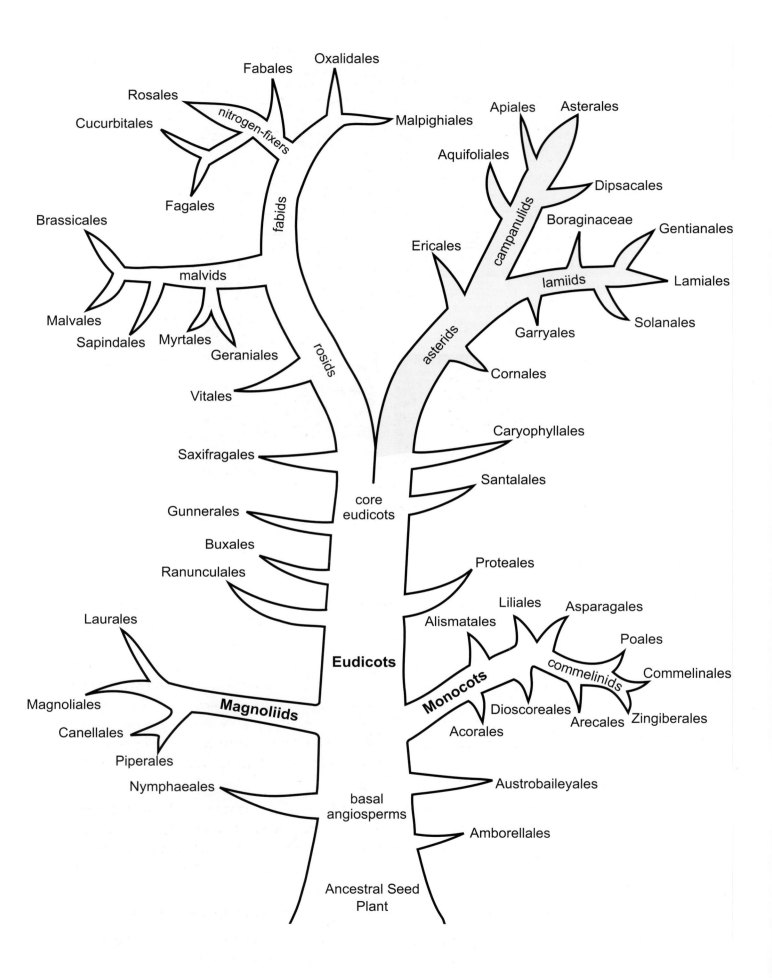

Fabales
Oxalidales
Rosales
nitrogen-fixers
Cucurbitales
Malpighiales
Fagales
Apiales
Asterales
Aquifoliales
Dipsacales
Brassicales
campanulids
Boraginaceae
Gentianales
Ericales
malvids
fabids
lamiids
Lamiales
Malvales
asterids
Sapindales
Myrtales
Solanales
Geraniales
Garryales
rosids
Vitales
Cornales
Caryophyllales
Saxifragales
Santalales
Gunnerales
core
eudicots
Buxales
Proteales
Ranunculales
Liliales
Asparagales
Alismatales
Poales
Laurales
commelinids
Commelinales
**Eudicots**
Magnoliales
Dioscoreales
Zingiberales
**Magnoliids**
**Monocots**
Arecales
Canellales
Acorales
Piperales
Nymphaeales
Austrobaileyales
basal
angiosperms
Amborellales
Ancestral Seed
Plant

# INTRODUCTION TO THE ASTERIDS

The asterids are a major branch of the core eudicots, with a third of the angiosperm species. There are four major subgroups - the Cornales order, the Ericales order, lamiids and campanulids.

Cornales includes the hydrangea family, the dogwood family, and the stickleaf family. Ericales is a large order that includes the heath, phlox, primrose, and camellia families. The lamiids include Gentianales with the dogbane, gentian and madder families. Lamiales, another large order of lamiids, holds the acanthus, mint, olive, and plantain families, and Solanales holds the nightshade and morning glory families. The borage family, Boraginaceae, is not assigned to an order, but is also a part of lamiids. The campanulids, include the Aquifoliales with the holly family, Apiales with the carrot family, Asterales with the sunflower and bellflower families, and Dipsacales with the honeysuckle and teasel family.

As a group, asterid flowering plants are easier to describe than the other main branch, the rosids. The photo above, a petunia flower with the corolla split and folded back, illustrates some features that euasterids have in common. The petals are fused, which led to an older name for this group, the Sympetalae. The number of stamens equals the number of petals, and the stamens are usually joined to the fused petals. The gynoecium is usually two-carpellate.

Cornales and Ericales include plants that do not have fused petals and some that have numerous stamens.

The asterids include trees, shrubs, vines, herbaceous plants and aquatics. Some members of the dogbane family, Apocynaceae, are succulents. Insectivorous plants occur in the Ericales.

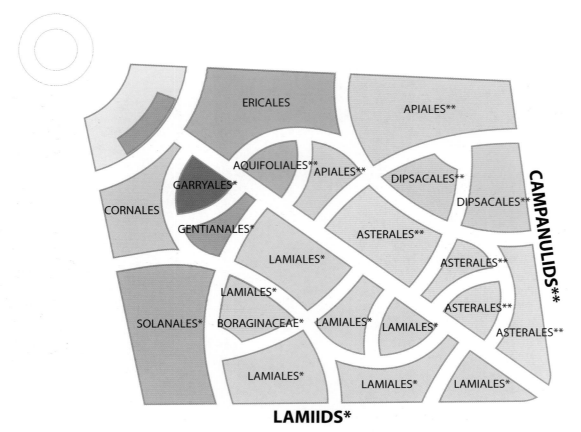

*Quadrant 3, Orders of asterids*

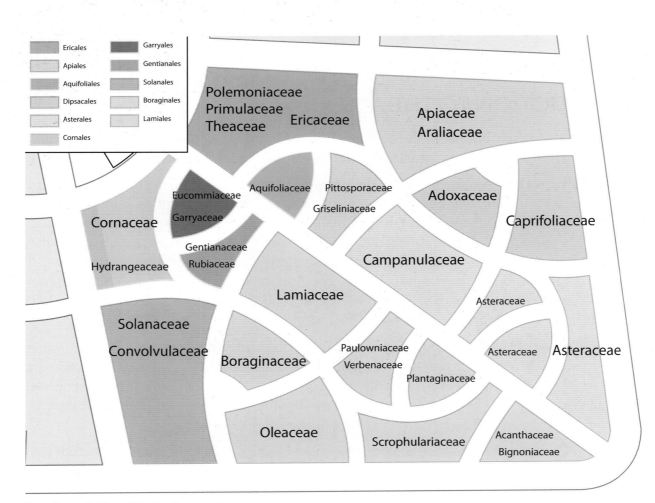

*Quadrant 3, Families in the asterids*

*Quadrant 3, Overview of the asterids*

*Quadrant 3, Cornales, a basal order in the asterids*

*Apiales, an example of a campanulid order in Quadrant 3*

*Solenales, an example of a lamiid order in Quadrant 3*

**Eudicots**

**Asterids**

**Cornales** Dumortier

    **Cornaceae** von Berchtold & J. Presl    2 genera/80 species

        Genera:

        *Alangium* Lamarck

        *Cornus* L. (Cornelian cherry, dogwood)

The Cornaceae once included a number of genera such as *Aucuba* and *Griselinia* which are now transferred to other families, such that only two genera remain. Of these the dogwoods (*Cornus*) are the most familiar. The flowers have four stamens and four petals, but these should not be confused with the four large bracts that make native species and cultivars such attractive garden plants. The flowers in fact are small, and clustered at the centre of the bracts and open nearly simultaneously. The simple leaves of Cornaceae have entire margins and are usually opposite. The fruits that develop from inferior ovaries are small drupes and are white, red, blue or blue-black in various species. *Cornus* species are planted as ornamental shrubs and produce superb autumn colour.

    **Hydrangeaceae**    18 genera/300 species

        Genera include:

        *Decumaria* L. (climbing hydrangea)

        *Deutzia* Thunberg (deutzia)

        *Hydrangea* L. (hydrangea)

        *Jamesia* Torrey & A. Gray (wax flower)

        *Philadelphus* L. (mock orange, syringa)

This is a north temperate family of shrubs, climbers and herbs, but best known to us from the garden shrubs, *Hydrangea*, *Deutzia* and *Philadelphus*. In the *Hydrangea* inflorescence, the showy 'petals' are in fact sepals and the flowers are sterile: the fertile ones are small and inconspicuous. The colour of the inflorescences in red and blue flowered forms, e.g. *H. macrophylla*, depends on the amount of aluminium in the soil, with increased availability leading to a change from red to blue. Aluminium availability is low on limy soils with high pH, and flowers are then red, but aluminium uptake can be enhanced by addition of iron to the soil. At pH less than 5.5, flowers will be blue. Some species produce alkaloids toxic to man and cattle, but which can be used as drugs (hydrangin). Flowers of the strongly perfumed mock orange, *Philadelphus*, were used to scent water by ancient Greeks and pre-Columbian Mexicans.

    **Loasaceae**    14 genera/265 species

        Genera include:

        *Eucnide* Zuccarini (rock nettle, stingbush)

        *Kissenia* R. Brown ex Endlicher

        *Loasa* Adanson

        *Mentzelia* L. (blazing star, stick-leaf)

        *Petalonyx* A. Gray (sandpaper plant)

Loasaceae is predominantly a family of temperate herbs, climbers, shrubs and small trees found in Mexico and extending into South America. It has only one genus, *Kissenia*, in the Old World. As its common name, the blazingstar family, suggests it has large showy flowers with numerous stamens. Its leaves have barbed hairs that often contain silica; some have stinging hairs. *Loasa* is a genus of over a hundred species with yellow, white and red flowers with five bract-shaped petals and conspicuous nectaries.

# CORNACEAE, *the dogwood family*

*Two cultivars of Cornus kousa (Kousa dogwood) have bracts with slightly different colours and shapes. The ball of flowers at the centre of the bracts develops into a cluster of fruits (above left and middle)*

*Cornus mas (Cornelian cherry) with clusters of small flowers lacking bracts*

# HYDRANGEACEAE, *the hydrangea family*

*Philadelphus sp. (mock orange) is named for the sweet, orange-like fragrance of its flowers (left). There are many cultivars of Hydrangea macrophylla (garden hydrangeas). The lacecap cultivars have tiny fertile flowers (centre and right) in the centre and large, showy sterile flowers around the outside. The mophead cultivars have only the larger, sterile flowers*

# LOASACEAE, *the blazing star or stickleaf family*

*Mentzelia nuda (bractless blazing star) flowers open in the late afternoon and stay open all night, an adaptation for hot, arid climates, above left. The flower (middle) and fruits (right) of Mentzelia reverchonii (yellow stick-leaf). The fruit is a roughly cylindrical capsule with persistant sepals around the top rim. These plants are also well adapted to arid or semi-arid areas*

**Eudicots**

**Asterids**

**Ericales** Dumortier

    **Balsaminaceae** A. Richard                2 genera/1,000 species

        Genera include:

        *Impatiens* L. (busy lizzie, touch-me-not, balsam, impatiens)

This is essentially a tropical family of slightly fleshy herbs with a few temperate species in the genus *Impatiens*. The latter is best known in Britain from annual bedding plants and the extremely invasive weed, Himalayan balsam, which is outcompeting native plants along our rivers.

The annuals have fleshy, translucent stems. Their leaves often have toothed margins. The flowers have three sepals, one of which forms a spur, a long, curved, hollow tube that holds nectar. The flowers are bilaterally symmetrical, with a corolla of five petals. In some species, a pair of joined petals on either side makes the flower appear to have fewer than five petals. The anthers are fused and form a cap over the stigma. The fruit is a capsule. In some species, commonly known as touch-me-nots, this capsule literally pops when it is touched, quickly splitting into curled segments and flinging its seeds away.

    **Polemoniaceae** Jussieu                23 genera/375 species

        Genera include:

        *Cobaea* Cavanilles (cup-and-saucer vine)

        *Collomia* Nuttal (collomia, tiny trumpet)

        *Gilia* Ruiz & Pavón (gilia, blue bowls, thimble flower)

        *Phlox* L. (phlox)

        *Polemonium* L. (polemonium, Jacob's ladder)

This small family comprises principally herbs, but with some small trees and climbers (*Cobaea*). It is mainly confined to the New World. Flowers have petals that are fused to form a variety of corolla shapes. These range from bell-shaped in *Cobaea*, to funnel-shaped in *Polemonium*, to narrow tubes with plate-like platforms (*Phlox*) to needle-like tubes (*Gilia*). Such variation is, of course, linked to a wealth of pollinators including bees, flies, beetles, humming birds, Lepidoptera and bats (*Cobaea*). The stamens of some species are different lengths or are attached to the corolla at different heights which encourages cross-pollination (see also Primulaceae). A British native is *Polemonium caeruleum* (Jacob's ladder) largely confined to scree and ledges in the Derbyshire and Yorkshire Dales.

# BALSAMINACEAE, *the impatiens family*

*Impatiens walleriana (busy lizzie or bedding impatiens) is grown as a summer annual. It is well adapted for shady, understorey environments*

*The sepal that forms the nectar spur is much larger than the other two. Only one of the small sepals is visible*

*Impatiens glandulifera (Himalayan balsam or policeman's helmet) is an invasive riverside alien in the UK*

# POLEMONIACEAE, *the phlox family*

*Phlox paniculata (summer phlox): a garden species, above left. Phlox subulata (moss pink), above right*

*Phlox condensata (alpine phlox), left*

*Polemonium caeruleum (Jacob's ladder), right*

**Eudicots**

**Asterids**

**Ericales** Dumortier

    **Primulaceae** Batsch ex Borkhausen          60 genera/2,575 species

        Genera include:

        *Anagallis* L. (pimpernel)

        *Androsace* L. (rock jasmine)

        *Ardisia* Swartz (marlberry)

        *Cyclamen* L. (cyclamen)

        *Dodecatheon* L. (shooting star)

        *Hottonia* L. (featherfoil, water violet)

        *Lysimachia* L. (yellow loosestrife, creeping Jenny)

        *Myrsine* L. (Cape beech)

        *Primula* L. (primrose, cowslip, oxslip, polyanthus)

        *Soldanella* L. (shooting star)

        *Trientalis* L. (chickweed wintergreen)

Primulaceae is a cosmopolitan family with a temperate to tropical distribution with evergreen trees, shrubs, climbers and herbs. The latter include many arctic-alpines. Woody representatives, often showing the pachycaulous habit, were formerly included, together with *Cyclamen*, in the Myrsinaceae. Primulaceae flowers show radial symmetry with fused floral parts in fives that typifies the Ericales. *Primula* is the most familiar representative together with *Soldanella* and *Dodecatheon*. *Primula* has a very interesting arrangement of floral parts that promotes cross pollination and hence cross fertilisation. Note that at the centres of all flowers in a single plant there can either be a small sphere (the stigma on which pollen is trapped – the pin-eyed type of flower), or a cluster of stamens (the thrum-eyed type). If you split open the two types, the pin form has stamens at exactly the same level in the petal tube as is the stigma in the thrum type. Thus when the pollinator visits the flower, pollen will brush off at exactly the right position on its body to be deposited on the stigma of the second type. You could argue that self pollination would occur if pollen in the thrum type drops down on to the stigma, but evolution has thought of that. The pollen grains are too big to become lodged in the depressions on the stigma – and in the pin type they are so small that there would be insufficient food reserves to permit growth of the pollen tube along the long style to the ovary. So pollen fits too! This type of pollination (called distyly) is seen in isolated plants in 25 families e.g. *Pulmonaria* and *Forsythia* – an excellent example of convergent evolution. In some flowers e.g. *Lythrum*, *Oxalis* and *Pontederia* (a monocot), there are three positions!

The leaves and calyx of *Primula obconica*, drumsticks, bear glandular hairs containing a benzoquinone derivative which can cause severe dermatitis after sensitisation.

The genus *Cyclamen* has some horticultural importance. It occurs naturally in the Mediterranean region eastwards to Iran. *Cyclamen* grows from a corm, and disperses its seeds by the uncoiling of a spring-like flowering stalk that coils up after flowering. Its seeds are sometimes ant-dispersed. The corms of *C. purpurascens* (sowbread) contain triterpanol saponins (cyclamin) that can cause convulsions and paralysis on injection of even small amounts.

# PRIMULACEAE, *the primrose family*

*Dodecatheon pulchellum (shooting star) is native to the western United States*

*Thrum (above left) and pin-eyed (above right) types of Primula vulgaris (primrose). Note the stamens attached half way down the floral tube in the pin-eyed type*

*Primula vialii, sometimes called the orchid primrose, is a native of China. Its red calyxes provide a bright contrast to the pale purple flowers. The tall, slender inflorescence is unusual in the primrose family (above left). The drumstick primrose P. denticulata is also called the Himalayan primrose (above centre). Primula veris (cowslip) has a long history of cultivation in Europe, where it originated (above right)*

*Cyclamen hederifolium flowers (left) and coiled stalks bearing fruit (right)*

*C. coum*

*Lysimachia vulgaris (yellow loosestrife)*

**Eudicots**
**Asterids**
**Ericales** Dumortier

    **Theaceae** De Mirbel ex Ker-Gawler         7 genera/240 species
        Genera include:
        *Camellia* L. (camellia, tea)
        *Franklinia* Bartram ex Marshall (Franklin tree)
        *Gordonia* Ellis (loblolly bay)
        *Schima* Reinwardt ex Blume (schima)
        *Stewartia* L. (stewartia)

This is a tropical to warm temperate family of usually evergreen shrubs. The most familiar representative in UK gardens is *Camellia japonica*, a native of Japan, and a lover of acidic soils. *Camellia japonica* was given its generic name by Linnaeus in honour of a Jesuit priest called Father Kamel. It is first recorded in Britain in 1739, and was joined in the earliest part of the twentieth century by *C. salvensis* from China. This was grown from seed collected by the great plant hunter, George Forest. Pollen from white flowers of *C. japonica* was crossed with that from pink flowers of *C. salvensis* at Caerhays Castle in Cornwall, and produced the hybrid *C.* x *williamsii* which flowers profusely in late winter, and conveniently, unlike its paternal parent, sheds dying blooms. Less spectacular are the flowers of *C. sinensis*, whose dried leaves have been used to make the tea drunk in the UK since 1768, when they first were imported from China. Originally probably from China, *Camellia sinensis* has been widely cultivated in India, and a second species, *Camellia assamica*, is native to upper Assam, an Indian state. The various forms of tea are the product of different methods in the manufacturing process, although sometimes other plants plus additives are used too. Thus for example, Earl Grey contains oil of bergamot (a type of *Citrus*) in addition to *Camellia*.

    **Diapensiaceae** Lindley         5 genera/13 species
        Genera include:
        *Diapensia* L. (diapensia, pincushion plant)
        *Galax* Sims (galax, beetleweed, wand flower)
        *Shortia* Torrey & A. Gray (oconee bells, fringe bells)

The Diapensiaceae is a small family of low growing evergreen shrubs or perennial herbs, with leaves arranged in dense or loose rosettes. It is found in the Northern Hemisphere and comprises chiefly alpine and Arctic plants. *Diapensia lapponica* is the only European species. Originally confined to Scandinavia, the species was discovered in Scotland in 1951, thus adding another family to the British flora. *Shortia* with beautiful trumpet-shaped flowers has an unusual (disjunct) distribution with one species in the mountains of North Carolina and two in eastern Asia. *Galax urceolata* (wand flower) has spikes of insignificant white flowers and comes from open woodlands of southeastern USA.

    **Actinidiaceae** Gilg & Werdermann         3 genera/355 species
        Genera include:
        *Actinidia* Lindley (kiwi fruit, Chinese gooseberry)

Actinidiaceae is a very small tropical to subtropical family. *Actinidia* is a genus of climbers, often with colourful foliage, that comes from eastern Asia. *A. deliciosa* (=*A. chinensis*) produces hairy brown fruits, once called the Chinese gooseberry, but now the kiwi fruit, because it was developed as an economic product and extensively marketed by New Zealanders.

# THEACEAE, *the tea family*

*Camellia japonica flower and fruit (above left and right)*

*Camellia 'Cornish snow'*                    *Camellia 'R L Wheeler'*

# DIAPENSIACEAE,
## the diapensia family

# ACTINIDIACEAE,
## the kiwi fruit family

*Diapensia lapponica*                    *Actinidia sp. flowers*

**Eudicots**
**Asterids**
**Ericales** Dumortier
    **Ericaceae** Jussieu              117 genera/3,850 species

        Genera include:

*Andromeda* L. (bog rosemary)

*Arbutus* L. (madrone, strawberry tree)

*Arctostaphylos* Adanson (bearberry)

*Calluna* Salisbury (heather, ling)

*Cassiope* D. Don (white mountain heather, moss heather)

*Daboecia* D. Don (St Daboc's heath)

*Dracophyllum* Labillardière (dracophyllum)

*Empetrum* L. (crowberry)

*Enkianthus* Loreiro (Chinese bell flower)

*Epacris* Cavanilles (Australian fuchsia, epacris)

*Erica* L. (heath, heather)

*Gaultheria* Kalm ex L. (wintergreen, snowberry, tea berry)

*Kalmia* L. (mountain laurel, alpine laurel, sheep laurel, calico bush)

*Kalmiopsis* Rehder (kalmiopsis)

*Leucopogon* R. Brown (Australian currant)

*Leucothoe* D. Don (pearl flower)

*Pentachondra* R. Brown (beard-heath)

*Pieris* D. Don (lily-of-the-valley bush, pieris)

*Pyrola* L. (wintergreen)

*Rhododendron* L. (rhododendron, azalea)

*Richea* R. Brown (pandani)

*Trochocarpa* R. Brown (pink berry, cheese berry)

*Vaccinium* L. (bilberry, blueberry, cranberry, huckleberry, lingonberry, whortleberry)

Ericaceae is a large cosmopolitan family characteristic of moist, acidic, forest soils, yet it contains many members that live in other habitats. Members are common components of tundra biota, and may live on dry, sunny slopes on montane zones. The acid bog dwellers have special fungi (mycorrhizae) surrounding their roots that enable them to survive in such harsh environments. Many members of the Ericaceae are lime intolerant. Its woody members range from small plants with creeping stems e.g. bilberry (*Vaccinium*) to trees, *Rhododendron* and *Arbutus* (strawberry tree). There is a variety of flower shapes in the family including uniquely urn-shaped ones. Other forms are tubular, funnel-like, open bowls, little bells with tiny rounded lobes, and even comprise separate petals in a few. Stamens are usually ten, with pollen shed through a terminal small pore – like a salt cellar. The leaves of many species are smooth, thick, leathery and evergreen. Some, such as in heather and heath, have narrow and needle-like. While many members are horticulturally important as garden plants, the American species, *Vaccinium macrocarpon*, the cranberry has culinary uses. The bilberry, *V. myrtillus*, is a British native with edible fruits that were once widely collected in the Welsh Borderland and Gwent, where they are called wimberries. The pollen and nectar of our native heaths (*Erica*) are important sources of nutrients for honey bees in upland areas.

The epacrids are a subgroup within the Ericaceae that occurs mainly in Australia, but extends into South America. It differs from the remaining Ericaceae in that its members possess a single whorl of five stamens which shed pollen via a split rather than pore in the anther. In Australia, it dominates heathland much as ericaceous members do in the UK and South Africa. *Richea* is an amazing Australian genus with forms ranging from small herbs to small trees with rosettes of spear-shaped leaves.

# ERICACEAE, *the heath and heather family*

EUDICOTS

*Erica carnea (winter heath)*

*Arctostaphylos uva-ursi (bearberry) flowers and fruits (above centre and right)*

ASTERIDS

*Kalmia latifolia (mountain laurel)*

*Rhododendron hybrid (rhododendron)*

ERICALES

*Vaccinium myrtillus (bilberry)*

*Developing fruits of Arbutus unedo (strawberry tree)*

*Epacris paludosa*

181

**Eudicots**

**Lamiids**

(not placed in an order)

      **Boraginaceae** Jussieu              142 genera/2,450 species

          Genera include:

          *Anchusa* L. (alkanet, anchusa)

          *Borago* L. (borage)

          *Cryptantha* Lehmann ex G. Don (cryptantha, hidden flower)

          *Cynoglossum* L. (hound's tongue)

          *Echium* L. (viper's bugloss)

          *Heliotropium* L. (heliotrope)

          *Lithospermum* L. (gromwell)

          *Mertensia* Roth (mertensia bluebells, oyster plant)

          *Myosotis* L. (forget-me-not)

          *Phacelia* Jussieu (phacelia, wild heliotrope, scorpion weed)

          *Pulmonaria* L. (lungwort)

          *Symphytum* L. (comfrey)

**Note:** This family includes the former Hydrophyllaceae, the waterleaf family, which is no longer recognised as a separate family.

Boraginaceae is of uncertain taxonomic position as regards an order within the lamiids, but its members form a natural group in which the young flowerheads are usually curled up like a violin head. This is called a scorpioid inflorescence. The fruits of Boranginaceae are clusters of single-seeded units called nutlets that are usually arranged in fours. In *Symphytum*, *Borago*, *Anchusa*, *Pulmonaria* and *Myosotis*, a part of the flower remains attached to the nutlet. It is called an elaiosome and attracts ants. These then disperse the seeds. This is called myrmecochory. In many genera, including *Myosotis* (forget-me-not), *Symphytum* (comfrey) and *Echium* (bugloss), flower colour changes from red or purple in bud to blue on opening or after pollination. All these British representatives are herbaceous, but when perennial, as in many of the tropical sub-families, they can be woody. Many of our native plants have been used in herbal medicine e.g. comfrey (*Symphytum*) in poultices for sprains, ulcers and bruises. Comfrey also contains a compound called allantoin, used in treatment of connective tissues. When extracted from hound's tongue (*Cynoglossum officinale*) it has been used in the treatment for dog bites. Borage (*Borago officinalis*) comes from southern Europe and is grown in herb gardens to flavour drinks, notably Pimms. Traditionally it has been used to treat fevers and coughs and to reduce stress or depression. The white spotted leaves of *Pulmonaria officinalis* were thought to resemble lungs (hence the name) and therefore thought efficaceous for chest problems. It is still used as an infusion to treat inflammation of bronchial 'tubes'.

# BORAGINACEAE, *the borage family*

*Pulmonaria sp.*

*Flowers of Cynoglossum officinale (hound's tongue) and its fruits (right), which are four nutlets with hooked bristles*

*Anchusa sp. (above left)*

*Heliotropium sp. (above right)*

*This Phacelia species (left) of the waterleaf subfamily shows the typical coiled inflorescence, which is described botanically as scorpioid or helicoid*

*Borago officinalis (borage) is the herb for which the family is named (below left). It has coarse, bristly hairs that are easily seen. These are common in the family*

*Myosotis sylvatica (forget-me-not) flowers have a characteristic ring of yellow at their throat that turns to white in older flowers*

**Eudicots**

**Lamiids**

**Garryales**

    **Garryaceae** Lindley              2 genus/18-19 species

        Genera:

        *Aucuba* Thunberg (spotted laurel)

        *Garrya* Douglas ex Lindley (garrya, silktassel)

The family now includes the Aucubaceae, which together with *Garrya*, was once included in the Cornaceae. It shows a disjunct distribution in the New World and Asia. All species of *Garrya* are evergreen shrubs or small trees and grow in dry areas of south-west USA, Mexico and the Caribbean. *Garrya* has male and female catkins. In the UK, male plants are usually grown in gardens for their long green catkins that flower very early in the year. *Aucuba* contains three species found in the Himalayas and eastern Asia. Evergreen shrubs are grown in gardens for their large simple glossy leaves (*A. japonica*) that are sometimes variegated (spotted laurel), and for their brightly coloured berries. [Note like cherry laurel (*Prunus laurocerasus*) these have nothing to do with the true laurel]. *Acuba japonica* is dioecious, i.e. it has male and female plants. It is also mildly poisonous.

# GARRYACEAE, *the Garrya family*

*Garrya elliptica, male catkins in bud (above) and with dehisced stamens (below) extending beyond cup-shaped bracts*

*Aucuba japonica (spotted laurel) in fruit, in January (above)*

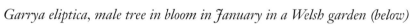

*Garrya eliptica, male tree in bloom in January in a Welsh garden (below)*

**Eudicots**
**Lamiids**
**Gentianales** Lindley

    **Rubiaceae** Jussieu               563 genera/10,900 species
        Genera include:
        *Bouvardia* Salisbury (bouvardia, firecracker bush)
        *Cephalanthus* L. (buttonbush)
        *Cinchona* L. (quinine)
        *Coffea* L. (coffee)
        *Galium* L. (bedstraw, goosegrass, cleavers, woodruff)
        *Gardenia* Ellis (gardenia)
        *Pentas* Bentham (pentas)
        *Psychotria* L. (ipecac)
        *Rubia* L. (madder)

Rubiaceae is a very large and mainly tropical family, with members extending into temperate regions. The great majority in the tropics are trees or shrubs. This is in marked contrast to the herbaceous forms in the British flora, in which leaves appear arranged in marked whorls. Perhaps the most familiar is the goosegrass or cleavers (*Galium aparine*), which clambers over other plants using its covering of hooked hairs. These are also apparent on the fruits which cause amusement to children. Other natives include lady's bedstraw (*G. verum*), once used to stuff mattresses because of its pleasant smell, and the even more sweetly smelling woodruff (*G. odoratum*), a British substitute for lavender. Other members of the family within the tropics are of major economic importance. Products include coffee (*Coffea*), drugs such as quinine (*Cinchona*), and ipecacuanha (ipecac: *Psychotria ipecacuanha*), as well as timber trees and the cultivated favourites *Gardenia* and *Pentas*.

    **Gentianaceae** Jussieu           85 genera/1,600 species
        Genera include:
        *Centaurium* Hill (centaury)
        *Eustoma* Salisbury (lisianthus, prairie gentian)
        *Exacum* L. (Persian violet)
        *Frasera* Walter (green gentian)
        *Gentiana* L. (gentian)
        *Gentianella* Moench (felwort)
        *Gentianopsis* Ma (fringed gentian)
        *Swertia* L. (star gentian)

This is a family of mainly herbs with a temperate world-wide distribution. The regular flower of *Gentiana* is typical of the family with its tubular shaped corolla of fused petals, which are twisted in bud. The brilliant colours of the alpine gentians are associated with insect pollination as is the nectar secreted into the base of the corolla. Corolla tube length can be related to the tongues of visitors. Thus the bright blue flower of *G. pneumonanthe* with a long tube is visited by the bumble bee, but *G. verna* with even longer and narrower tube is pollinated by Lepidoptera. *Gentiana verna*, the spring gentian, again with intensely blue flowers, is confined to Teesdale in the UK, but extends across central Europe into the mountains of Asia. Indeed most of the gentians are very rare in Britain, but purple flowered autumn gentian, *Gentianella amarella*, can sometimes be found in profusion on nutrient-rich dune slacks along the north and south coasts of Wales. Another more common member of the family, also found on cliffs and dunes, is the pink common centaury, *Centaurium erythraea*. It is named after the Greek centaur Chiron, who is said to have healed himself by using centaury after being wounded with a poisoned arrow. It certainly has been used in herbal medicine for controlling fever. *Centaurium scilloides* is one of the rarest plants in Wales occurring only on seacliffs near Newport, Pembrokeshire, and is currently being studied by conservationists at the Garden and the National Museum of Wales.

# RUBIACEAE, *the madder family*

*G. aparine (cleavers or goose grass) is covered with hooked hairs, including on its fruits (above)*

*Galium boreale (northern bedstraw), left*

*G. odoratum (sweet woodruff) is a European native. It is a useful garden perennial for shady areas*

# GENTIANACEAE, *the gentian family*

*The flowers of the gentian family have four to five petals that are fused, either just at the base or into a cup or bell shape. The stamens are attached to the petals, often near the base. The stems often have four ridges, called wings, that run their length. The gynoecium is two-carpellate, and has a superior ovary. There is one style, with one stigma that may have two lobes*

*Eustoma grandiflorum (prairie gentian or tulip gentian) (above left) is native to the grasslands of the midwestern United States. Horticultural varieties have been bred, including double-flowered ones with extra petals (above centre). Centaurium erythraea (centaury), above right*

*Gentianella amarella (autumn felwort) (above and right). Gentiana verna (spring gentian) a British native (far right)*

**Eudicots**

**Lamiids**

**Gentianales** Lindley

**Loganiaceae** R. Brown ex Martius        14 genera/400 species

The most notorious taxon is this small mostly tropical family of shrubs and climbers is *Strychnos toxifera*, the source of curare, that South American Indians used on arrow heads. It is also used more judiciously as a muscle relaxant in chest surgery. The poison, containing the alkaloids, strychnine and brucine, comes from seed coats. Other alkaloids are used in medicines and tonics.

**Apocynaceae** Jussieu        380 genera/4,700 species

Genera include:

*Amsonia* Walter (blue-star)

*Apocynum* L. (dogbane)

*Asclepias* L. (milkweed)

*Catharanthus* G. Don (Madagascar periwinkle)

*Ceropegia* L. (rosary vine, string of hearts)

*Hoya* R. Brown (waxflower, waxplant)

*Marsdenia* (*Stephanotis*) R. Brown (Madagascar jasmine)

*Matelea* Aublet (milkvine)

*Nerium* L. (oleander)

*Plumeria* L. (frangipangi, plumeria)

*Stapelia* L. (carrion flower, starfish flower)

*Strophanthus* de Candolle (climbing oleander, corkscrew flower)

*Vinca* L. (periwinkle)

Apocynaceae is now expanded to include the Asclepiaceae (milkweeds) based on molecular studies. It is a widespread tropical to subtropical family of trees, shrubs, herbs and particularly lianes. Some herbs, e.g. *Vinca* (periwinkle) extend into temperate areas. Their flowers show a wide-range of somewhat bizarre forms often related to the modification of the stamens. Indeed in many species, pollen is aggregated into small packages, called pollinia, accompanied by complex mechanisms for transferring them onto insect pollinators. Pollinia are also seen in the orchids.

The corolla itself is fused and tubular, flaring into five lobes. There are fringes at the throat of some species, as in oleander flowers. Milkweed flowers have hoods that are prominent structures above the corolla. The stigma can have a flattened top and be five-sided or two-lobed. The pistil usually has two separate ovaries that share a single stigma. Fruit types include drupes, berries and follicles. Follicles are often paired and contain seeds which have a tuft of hairs that aids in wind dispersal.

In *Stapelia*, the flowers commonly smell of carrion, are hairy and pollinated by flies that also lay their eggs on what they are tricked into believing is rotting meat. In the related *Ceropegia*, the five petals of the flower are united at their tips and the base of the flower forms a tube giving the flowers as a whole the appearance of lanterns. Most species of *Ceropegia* are climbers.

Many of the members produce latex and glycosides that make them important medicinal plants, although the drug, strophanthin (from *Strophanthus*), used to treat heart disease, was also the active ingredient on poison arrows. The Madagascan rosy periwinkle, *Catharanthus roseus*, is the source of the drugs, vinblastine and vincristine, central to the treatment of infant leukaemias and Hodgkin's disease. Apocynaceae contains important flowering ornamentals (e.g. frangipani, oleander) in tropical areas.

# APOCYNACEAE, *the dogbane and milkweed family*

*Nerium oleander (oleander) (above left) is used as an ornamental, but carries a potent poison in all its parts. The stamens of Vinca minor (common periwinkle) (above centre) form a cover over the stigma head. Note the low crown at the throat of the corolla. Hoya carnosa (waxflower) (above right) looks as if its fleshy flowers are made of plastic. It is grown as a houseplant*

*Fruits of Apocynum androsaemifolium (spreading dogbane), left, develop from the two separate ovaries of the flower. The shared stigma still joins the ends of these fruits*

*Plumeria rubra (frangipangi), right*

*Milkweeds are named for their milky sap. Their pollen forms in little packets called pollinia that stick to pollinating insects. The petals often fold back; the five hoods form a star shape above them. The central knob holds the stamens and pistil.*

*Asclepias speciosa (showy milkweed) has fragrant flowers with dark pink petals and light hoods. Its large, oval leaves have smooth margins*

*Asclepias asperula (antelope horns) has greenish white petals with white and reddish purple hoods. Each inflorescence commonly produces two, upturned fruits, hence the plant's common name*

**Eudicots**

**Lamiids**

**Solanales** Dumortier

    **Convolvulaceae** Jussieu             52 genera/1,650 species

        Genera include:

        *Convolvulus* L. (bindweed, bush morning glory)

        *Cuscuta* L. (dodder)

        *Dichondra* Forster & Forster f. (dichondra)

        *Ipomoea* L. (morning glory, sweet potato)

        *Jacquemontia* Choisy (clustervine)

        *Merremia* Dennstaedt ex Endlicher (Hawaiian wood rose)

        *Calystegia* R. Brown (hedge bindweed, false bindweed) is now included in *Convolvulus*

This small family, usually confined to warmer parts of the world has many climbers (twining clockwise, i.e. to the right). Latex canals often occur in its stems. The fused petals frequently form a funnel after untwisting from a bud. Its members include a leafless parasite, *Cuscuta*, with minute flowers on yellow to orange to pink thread-like stems, and the far more showy climbers, *Convolvulus* and *Ipomoea*. *Ipomoea purpurea* (morning glory) and other members of the genus are sources of hallucinogenic drugs, although recently it has been shown that the active ingredient is actually present in a fungus within the plant! The tubers of *I. batatas* are the yam or sweet potato. Of the British members, the field bindweed, a tiresome weed, belongs to *Convolvulus*, as does the hedge bindweed with very large, pure white trumpets and arrow-shaped leaves.

# CONVOLVULACEAE, *the bindweed or morning glory family*

*Hybrids of* Ipomoea indica *(morning glories), above left, are members of the same genus as sweet potatoes. Their fruits (*I. purpurea *illustrated right) are capsules that are covered by the persistent calyx while they develop. The sepals are typically separate or fused only at their bases. When the fruits are mature, the calyx dries and contracts, and the capsule splits and drops its seeds*

*Ipomoea batatas, fancy-leaved cultivars of sweet potato, are used as ornamentals*

*Convolvulus soldanella (sea bindweed) grows on sandy sea-shores*

*Convolvulus sepium (hedge bindweed). Rampant growth, deep rhizomes and long-lived seeds make any bindweed very difficult to eradicate*

*Ipomoea leptophylla (bush morning glory) is native to the western plains of the United States. It forms a huge storage root that helps it survive in its arid habitat and gives it its other name, manroot*

*Convolvulus tricolor (dwarf morning glory) is an annual ornamental plant whose flowers stay open all day*

**Eudicots**

**Lamiids**

**Solanales** Dumortier

    **Solanaceae** Jussieu          91 genera/2,450 species

        Genera include:

        *Atropa* L. (belladonna, deadly nightshade)

        *Brugmansia* Persoon (angel's trumpet)

        *Brunfelsia* L. (yesterday-today-and-tomorrow)

        *Capsicum* L. (chili pepper, bell pepper, paprika, pimento)

        *Cestrum* L. (night jasmine)

        *Datura* L. (datura, thorn-apple)

        *Hyoscyamus* L. (henbane)

        *Lycium* L. (desert thorn, Duke of Argyll's tea tree, wolfberry)

        *Mandragora* L. (mandrake)

        *Nicotiana* L. (tobacco, nicotiana)

        *Nierembergia* Ruiz & Pavón (cup flower)

        *Nolana* L.f. (little bells)

        *Petunia* Jussieu (petunia)

        *Physalis* L. (Cape gooseberry, Chinese lantern)

        *Quincula* Rafinesque (Chinese lantern, purple ground cherry)

        *Salpiglossis* Ruiz & Pavón (salpiglossis, painted tongue)

        *Schizanthus* Ruiz & Pavón (schizanthus, butterfly flower)

        *Solanum* L. (aubergine, eggplant, potato, tomato, nightshade, bittersweet)

        *Lycopersicon*, the garden tomato, is now included in *Solanum*

The Solanaceae is a widespread family of trees, climbers and shrubs with a concentration of genera in South America. Two of its subfamilies, the Solanoideae and Cestroideae, are of considerable economic importance as foods, ornamentals and drugs. The Solanoideae contains potatoes, tomatoes, capsicums and the genus *Datura*, grown as an ornamental plant but more importantly the source of a number of hallucinogenic drugs. These were well known to indigenous tribes in the Americas. Indeed all solanaceous plants, even edible ones such as potato and tomato, have parts that are poisonous. All contain active alkaloids such as hyoscyamine and its derivatives atropine and scopolamine. 'Green' potatoes possess solanadine, a highly toxic compound not destroyed by boiling. The forked foot of *Mandragora* (mandrake) has been interpreted as either male or female genitalia and used in rituals as an aphrodisiac with hypnotic and hallucinogenic side effects. More locally, deadly nightshade, *Atropa belladonna*, is one of the most toxic plants in the British flora, but its poison hyoscyamine is also used in medicine as a gastro-intestinal sedative and in dilating pupils of eyes. The name 'belladonna' derives from the use of atropine by Spanish ladies to make their eyes more beautiful. Henbane (*Hyoscyamus niger*) is also native and, as its name indicates, is poisonous. It was the poison favoured by Dr Crippen! Its very beautiful flowers have a repugnant smell reminiscent of old tea cloths. Flowers of the genus *Solanum* have very distinctive protruding stamens in clusters of five. The Cestroideae contains *Nicotiana* that produces nicotine, arguably the most lethal drug in the world, as well as familiar garden plants such as *Petunia* and *Salpiglossis*.

# SOLANACEAE, *the nightshade or potato family*

*Nicotiana (left), Petunia (centre) and Datura (right) species are important ornamentals. However, the majority of edible fruits develop from the more familiar solanoid flower as seen in the British native Solanum dulcamara*

*Solanum lycopersicum (tomato), above, bears fruits that are wonderfully edible, but the leaves and the stems are poisonous*

*A wide variety of peppers have been bred from the species Capsicum annuum including both sweet and hot peppers (chili - bottom right). Flower, inset*

*Solanum dulcamara, (bittersweet or woody nightshade) whose fruits are mildly poisonous (top and above)*

*Solanum melongena (above). The persistant calyx caps the stem end of the fruit*

*The fruits of Physalis ixocarpa (tomatillos) a relative of Chinese lanterns, develop within the calyx, which enlarges along with the growing fruits*

**Eudicots**

**Lamiids**

**Lamiales** Bromhead

    **Oleaceae** Hoffmansegg & Link       24 genera/800 species

        Genera include:

        *Chionanthus* L. (fringe tree)

        *Forestiera* Poiret (swamp privet)

        *Forsythia* Vahl (forsythia)

        *Fraxinus* L. (ash)

        *Jasminum* L. (jasmine)

        *Ligustrum* L. (privet)

        *Olea* L. (olive)

        *Osmanthus* Loureiro (osmanthus)

        *Syringa* L. (lilac)

This small family of woody plants provides some of our familiar garden shrubs and climbers including lilac (*Syringa*), jasmine, privet (*Ligustrum*) and *Forsythia*. The fused petals and small sepals are in fours (rarely fives), but the stamens and ovary parts are in twos. Of economic importance is *Olea europaea* (olive), which actually originated in western Asia. Oil is produced from its small plum-like fruit. A very different fruit is produced by an arborescent member, the ash (*Fraxinus excelsior*), a British native. Its compound leaves develop from black buds. Its seeds are dispersed by wind in winged fruits - ash keys (samaras). Ash wood is preferred when elasticity is required in addition to strength. It is therefore used for oars, walking and hockey sticks. It is not a particularly good timber tree, but has some value because of its fast growth.

# OLEACEAE, *the olive family*

This family is named for its oldest cultivated member, the olive. *Olea europaea* has been grown for its oily fruits since prehistoric times. Its two stamens are yellow when the flower first blooms. Later, they turn brown as they mature and release their pollen.

*Ligustrum lucidum (waxleaf privet)*

Spring-flowering bushes of the olive family include: *Forsythia hybrid (forsythia)*, above left, and *Syringa vulgaris (common lilac)*, above right

*Fraxinus sp.*, ash trees, are dioecious. Male trees (right) are planted more frequently in city landscapes, because the female trees produce abundant samaras. The branch in the bottom left photograph has both the current spring's female flowers, which are green and inconspicuous, and the previous year's fruits, the brown samaras. Bottom right shows male flowers

An excellent example of how molecular – DNA techniques have radically changed membership of families is found in new concepts of the foxglove family, the Scrophulariaceae. Traditionally the 'scrophs' have included a very wide range of flower forms, ranging through the foxglove, *Digitalis*, the snapdragon, *Antirrhinum*, and the speedwells, *Veronica*, (the latter including the hebes), and also of life strategies. Thus it included the yellow rattle, *Rhinanthus*, a semi-parasite which extracts nourishment from the roots of its neighbours on grasslands. Using information from sequences from a number of genes, the family has now been broken up and one of the most confident outcomes has been the removal of *Rhinanthus* to a family dominated by parasites, the Orobanchaceae (broomrapes). A British representative is the toothwort (*Lathraea squamaria*) which lacks chlorophyll and survives by extracting nutrients from the roots of trees including hazel, willow, and elm. Its spikes of dusty, pale pink flowers on white stems appear through fallen leaves in spring. The Scrophulariaceae remains as a small family containing *Scrophularia* (the figwort), *Verbascum* (the mullein) and *Nemesia*, with the addition of *Buddleja*, previously either placed in its own family or the Loganiaceae. *Buddleja davidii* (the butterfly bush) is a familiar shrub that was introduced to Britain in the 1890s and has rapidly spread across the UK along railway lines and waste spaces. It is now beginning to invade woodland – perhaps its beauty and its use as a food (nectar) source for butterflies makes it a more acceptable invasive weed! It was first recorded in China, near the Tibetan border, by Pierre David, the same French missionary who introduced the handkerchief tree (*Davidia*) to Europe. Missing from this list of the newly defined Scrophulariaceae are *Antirrhinum*, *Chelone*, *Digitalis* and *Veronica*. Initially this grouping was given the name Veronicaceae, and surprisingly within it, again based on a number of gene sequences, was added the smaller family Plantaginaceae, the plantains, as well as some aquatics, represented by *Callitriche* and *Hippuris*, the mare's tail. Indeed *Veronica* itself was shown to be very closely related to *Plantago*, which differs in that its flowers are small and insignificant because wind pollinated. According to the vicissitudes and rules of botanical nomenclature, the code insists that the new name for the family is the Plantaginaceae and not Veronicaceae.

**Eudicots**
**Lamiids**
**Lamiales** Bromhead

      **Plantaginaceae** Jussieu                101 genera/1,900 species
        Genera include:
        *Antirrhinum* L. (snapdragon)
        *Callitriche* L. (water star-wort)
        *Chelone* L. (shell flowers, turtle head)
        *Digitalis* L. (foxglove)
        *Linaria* P. Miller (toadflax)
        *Penstemon* Schmidel (penstemon, beard tongue)
        *Plantago* L. (plantain)
        *Veronica* L. (brooklime, speedwell, veronica)
        *Hebe* Commerson ex Jussieu (hebe) is now included in *Veronica*

Regardless of its family status now within the Plantaginaceae, the foxglove remains as one of the most well-loved wild flowers in Britain. The derivation of its name (the fox part) is controversial, but there can be no doubt that the Welsh version, Ffion, is becoming increasingly popular as a girl's name. The plants themselves are highly toxic, and have been widely used in folk medicine – often with fatal results. However it is best known as the natural source of the heart stimulants, including digitoxin and digoxin, which are extracted from its leaves. The snapdragon, *Antirrhinum*, in addition to its horticultural role, is very important in botanical research, because its flower mutants have provided much information on the genetic pathways involved in the evolution of all flowers – a sort of fruit-fly of the plant world. *Hebe*, one of our most versatile garden shrubs, is another example of a plant with a Gondwanan distribution in South America, Australia, but mainly New Zealand. It is now placed in the genus *Veronica*

# PLANTAGINACEAE, *the plantain and snapdragon family*

*Penstemon hallii*

*Antirrhinum majus
(snapdragon)*

*Linaria dalmatica
(dalmatian toadflax)*

*Digitalis purpurea (foxglove)*

*Members of this family were formerly included in Scrophulariaceae. Most have showy flowers with tubular corollas. The bump on the lower lip of snapdragon flowers restricts the pollinators that can enter to large, strong bees. Nectar guides, like those in foxgloves, are commonly present. The plantains have inconspicuous flowers with protruding stamens. Veronicas have only two stamens, but most of this family have four to five stamens. The penstemons are named for their five stamens, one of which usually has a tuft of hairs instead of an anther.*

*Veronica sp. formerly Hebe (above left). Veronica hybrid (above right). Veronicas have four petals, but the upper one is actually two fused together. The lower petal is narrower and more pointed than the others. The stamens are reduced to two. The Veronica sp. (above right) is a garden hybrid of speedwell*

*Plantains appear to have little in common with the other Plantaginaceae. Their leaves often have parallel veins, (far left) as shown by Plantago lanceolata (ribwort plantain). This is because the leaves are phyllodes, expanded leaf stems without blades. These common weeds are wind-pollinated and have a reduced perianth. Wooly plantain, Plantago patagonica (left), has a small, white, four-part corolla*

EUDICOTS

LAMIIDS

LAMIALES

197

**Eudicots**

**Lamiids**

**Lamiales** Bromhead

    **Scrophulariaceae** Jussieu                54 genera/1,800 species

        Genera include:

        *Buddleja* Houston ex L. (butterfly bush)

        *Diascia* Link & Otto (diascia)

        *Leucophyllum* Bonpland (silver leaf, Texas Ranger)

        *Nemesia* Ventenat (nemesia)

        *Scrophularia* L. (figwort)

        *Verbascum* L. (mullein)

The revised family Scrophulariaceae is only a fraction of its former self. Many of the traditional members have moved to families Plantaginaceae and Orobanchaceae. The remaining scrophs have open corollas that are fused at the base. They may have four or five stamens.

    **Paulowniaceae** Nakai              2 genera/7 species

        Genera include:

        *Paulownia* Siebold & Zuccarini (foxglove tree, empress tree)

Once considered a part of the Scrophulariaceae, *Paulownia*, native to east Asia and notably China, is now placed in its own family close to the Orobanchaceae. It is an attractive tree genus with spectacular inflorescences of foxglove-like flowers.

# SCROPHULARIACEAE, *the figwort family*

*Scrophularia
auriculata
(water figwort)*

*Mulleins are widespread weeds, as well as cultivated flowers. Verbascum thapsus (common mullein) is a biennial with very hairy leaves. It originated in Asia, and has spread via Europe across North America. The flowers have five stamens with yellow, hairy filaments*

*Garden annuals of the Scrophulariaceae. Cultivated nemesias include hybrds of Nemesia strumosa (above centre) and N. caerulea (above right). The Diascia hybrids (twinspurs) (above left), are named for the two nectar spurs. Both genera are natives of South Africa*

# PAULOWNIACEAE,
## the empress tree family

*Buddleja davidii (butterfly bush) has long, tapering inflorescences that are packed with small flowers. It is especially attractive to butterflies*

*Buddleja marrubiifolia (wooly butterfly bush) is a Texas native that is grown as an ornamental in arid climates*

*Paulownia tomentosa*

**Eudicots**
**Lamiids**
**Lamiales** Bromhead

    **Lamiaceae** Martinov or **Labiatae** Jussieu      238 genera/6,500 species

      Genera include:
      *Ajuga* L. (ajuga, bugle)
      *Callicarpa* L. (beautyberry)
      *Clerodendrum* L. (bleeding heart vine, glorybower)
      *Glechoma* L. (ground ivy)
      *Hyssopus* L. (hyssop)
      *Lamium* L. (lamium, dead nettle, yellow archangel)
      *Lavandula* L. (lavender)
      *Marrubium* L. (horehound mint)
      *Melissa* L. (lemon balm)
      *Mentha* L. (mint, peppermint, spearmint)
      *Moluccella* L. (bells of Ireland, shell flower)
      *Monarda* L. (horsemint, bergamot, bee balm, monarda)
      *Nepeta* L. (catnip, catmint)
      *Ocimum* L. (basil)
      *Origanum* L. (oregano, marjoram)
      *Perovskia* Karelin (Russian sage)
      *Phlomis* L. (Jerusalem sage)
      *Physostegia* Bentham (obedient plant)
      *Prunella* L. (self-heal, prunella)
      *Rosmarinus* L. (rosemary)
      *Salvia* L. (sage)
      *Scutellaria* L. (skullcap mint)
      *Stachys* L. (betony, lamb's ears)
      *Tectona* L. f. (teak tree)
      *Teucrium* L. (germander)
      *Thymus* L. (thyme)
      *Solenostemon* and *Coleus* are now placed in *Plectranthus* L'Heritier

The majority of members of the Lamiaceae are annual or perennial herbs of temperate Mediterranean climates, but, as so often occurs in widespread families, tropical representatives form large trees. Its flowers have a marked bilateral symmetry (zygomorphic) with the tubular fused corolla forming two lips, a character often associated with specialised insect pollination. The symmetry is also seen in its four stamens attached to five fused petals. At maturity when the petals have been shed four single-seeded units (nutlets) can be seen in the tube formed from the five fused sepals. Stems in herbaceous forms are square in section.

Ethereal oils are among the most notable characteristics of the family and are the reason for its use in herbal seasonings since the beginning of recorded history. The volatile oils form in glands on the surface of the leaves and are released on crushing. Thus many lamiates are found in the herb garden. These include *Origanum* (oregano), *Thymus* (thyme), *Mentha* (mint, spearmint), *Rosmarinus* (rosemary), *Lavandula* (lavender), *Salvia* (sage), *Ocimum* (basil). They are also familiar native plants e.g. yellow archangel (*Lamium galeobdolon*) and red dead-nettle (*L. purpureum*). The dead-nettles are so called because their leaves resemble those of the stinging nettle, but do not sting! Very common are *Ajuga reptans* (bugle), *Glechoma hederacea* (ground ivy) and *Prunella vulgaris* (self-heal), the latter so called because leaves were applied to wounds. *Origanum vulgare* (marjoram), thymes and mints also grow wild, but the most important type of mint is the hybrid, *M. piperita*, commercially grown for peppermints. Horticulturally important varieties include *Plectranthus* (once *Coleus*), *Monarda*, *Salvia*, *Molucella laevis* (bells of Ireland) and *Phlomis*. Recent research has shown that many former members of the Verbenaceae, particularly the tropical tree, *Tectona*, belong to the Lamiaceae. *Tectona grandis* grows to more than 30m high and produces the valuable timber, teak.

# LAMIACEAE OR LABIATAE, *the mint family*

*Physostegia virginiana (obedient plant)*

*Salvia darcyi (red mountain sage)*

*Stachys byzantina (lamb's ear)*

*Dried calyxes of Phlomis cashmeriana (Kashmir sage)*

*Moluccella laevis (bells-of-Ireland or shellflower) has enlarged green calyxes that dwarf its small white flowers (above far left). A calyx of fused sepals is characteristic of the mint family, but this species has especially large calyxes. Rosmarinus officinalis (Rosemary) (above left) is a shrub with narrow, inrolled, almost needle-like leaves. This variety of Ocimum basilicum (sweet basil) has relatively smooth, rippled leaves (above right). Basil was domesticated in India. Many culinary varieties have been bred. Thymus praecox (wild thyme), above far right*

*Lamium maculatum (spotted dead nettle), above left. Salvia officinalis (culinary sage) has variegated and normal leaf varieties (above centre). Plectranthus scutellarioides (coleus) is grown for its colourful leaves, which are relatively thin and have sparse hairs (above right)*

**Eudicots**
**Lamiids**
**Lamiales** Bromhead

**Acanthaceae** Jussieu                    212 genera/3,175 species
    Genera include:

*Acanthus* L. (acanthus, bear's breech)    *Justicia* L. (shrimp plant)
*Aphelandra* R. Brown (zebra plant)    *Ruellia* L. (ruellia, wild petunia)
*Avicennia* L. (black mangrove)    *Strobilanthes* Blume
*Hypoestes* Solander ex R. Brown    *Thunbergia* Retzius (black-eyed Susan vine)
    (polka-dot plant)

Acanthaceae is mainly a tropical to sub-tropical family, often found in damp and marshy places, but with representatives extending into temperate and drier areas. Hence some species of *Strobilanthes* and *Acanthus* can be grown in our gardens as impressive architectural plants. Leaves of *Acanthus* are favoured too by stone masons (e.g. on Corinthian columns) and furniture makers. *Thunburgia alata*, in contrast is a tropical climber, with brightly coloured, usually orange, flowers that possess very dark centres. These give it the name, black-eyed Susan vine.

The acanthus family has bracts, either beneath single flowers or in spike-like arrangements with the flowers peering out from between them. The bracts may be either green or brightly coloured. The flowers have corollas of four to five fused petals. Many, like *Justica*, have two-lipped corollas. There are usually four stamens, but some species, like *Ruellia*, have only two. The gynoecium is two-carpellate with a superior ovary. The fruits of the acanthus family are capsules that explosively release their seeds and fling them away.

**Bignoniaceae** Jussieu                    82 genera/810 species
    Genera include:

*Bignonia* L. (crossvine)    *Jacaranda* Jussieu (jacaranda tree)
*Campsis* Loureiro (trumpet vine or creeper)    *Kigelia* de Candolle (sausage tree)
*Catalpa* Scopoli (catalpa, Indian bean)    *Spathodea* Palisot de Beauvois (flame tree)
*Crescentia* L. (calabash)    *Tecoma* Jussieu (Cape honeysuckle)
*Incarvillea* Jussieu (hardy gloxinia)

Bignoniaceae is a tropical to subtropical family of trees and shrubs, with some lianas (especially in tropical America). Trees are grown all over the world as ornamentals because of their showy flowers. They include *Jacaranda*, *Catalpa*, *Crescentia* (calabash) and *Spathodea* (flame tree). Their seeds are normally winged or have fringes of hairs and occur in pods. The fruit-pods of *Kigelia* are particularly impressive, because they resemble large dangling marrows or sausages. *Catalpa bignonioides*, the Indian bean tree, has big, but more conventional pods, although it contains flattened seeds rather than beans. It is native to eastern North America, but very closely related species occur in Japan, China and Cuba.

**Verbenaceae** J. Saint-Hilaire                    35 genera/1,500 species
    Genera include:

*Aloysia* Palau i Verdera (lemon verbena)    *Lippia* L. (lemon verbena, fogfruit)
*Duranta* L. (golden dewdrop)    *Petrea* Jussieu (queen's wreath)
*Glandularia* J.F. Gmelin (mock vervain)    *Phyla* de Loureiro (frogfruit, wedgeleaf)
*Lantana* L. (lantana, shrub verbena)    *Verbena* L. (vervain, verbena)

This cosmopolitan (with exception of Australia) family shows a wide range in habit including small trees, shrubs, climbers and herbs. The latter characterises the only British representative, the somewhat nondescript vervain (*Verbena offinalis*), much valued by Anglo-Saxons as a charm and cure. Indeed many genera are known for their essential oils and medicines. Herbs and shrubs are useful garden ornamentals. In contrast, *Lantana camara*, although possessing colourful plate-like inflorescences, is one of the most noxious weeds of the tropics having spread from tropical America to Africa and many Pacific islands.

# ACANTHACEAE, *the acanthus family*

Acanthus mollis
(bear's breech)

Thunbergia alata (black-eyed
Susan vine)

Justica brandegeeana (red shrimp plant) has
bracts in shades of red. Its flowers are white
with red markings visible inside the corolla

# BIGNONIACEAE, *the trumpet vine family*

Campsis radicans (trumpet vine) a
native of eastern North America, has
red-orange flowers, above left. Yellow
varieties have been bred for horticultural
use. The fruits are long pods with a ridge
on either side

Catalpa speciosa (northern catalpa) has large white flowers with throat
markings (above centre). The fruits are very long (above right)

# VERBENACEAE, *the verbena or vervain family*

Verbena hybrids are available in many hues for use as
bedding plants

Lantana camara, hybrid variety of bush lantana

**Eudicots**

**Campanulids**

**Aquifoliales** Senft

   **Aquifoliaceae** von Berchtold & J. Presl       1 genus/400 species

      Genus:

       *Ilex* L. (holly, yerba maté)


This small cosmopolitan family of shrubs and trees is restricted to the genus *Ilex*, the holly. Most hollies have spiny leaf margins, but leaves with smooth margins also occur. Hollies are often evergreen, with shiny, leathery leaves. The flowers usually have four to six petals that are fused at the base. There is little or no style; the stigma is attached directly to the ovary. Hollies are usually dioecious, although there are a few cultivars with bisexual flowers. In the female flowers, there are staminodes, nonfunctional stamen-like structures. Likewise, the male flowers often have a remnant of a gynoecium. The fruit is a drupe with several stones. *Ilex aquifolium* like many other members of the species has inconspicuous flowers, often unisexual, in parts of fours. It is the only British species, but its range extends from the Atlantic coast through southern Europe into Iran. *Ilex paraguariensis* from South America is the major plant whose dried twigs and leaves are used to make maté, a tea drunk all over South America. It contains similar constituents to Chinese or Indian tea. These include xanthin, caffeine and theophylline. It acts as a stimulant and diuretic and is used in the relief of rheumatic pains and headaches.

# AQUIFOLIACEAE, *the holly family*

*The female flowers of holly clearly show the superior ovary in this Ilex aquifolium cultivar (above left). It has staminodes between the petals. The staminate flower of blue holly, Ilex x meserveae (above right), has four functional stamens that are attached to the petals*

*Cultivars of Ilex opaca (American holly), above left), and I. x meserveae (blue holly) (above right)*

*The fruits of hollies are drupes that ripen to red or black and that usually contain four to six stones. Each stone holds a single seed. The number of stones shows the number of carpels in the pistil. There is a dark disk (above right) on the end of the fruit, which is the remnant of the prominent stigma. Holly seeds often take a few years to germinate.*

**Eudicots**

**Campanulids**

**Asterales** Lindley

      **Campanulaceae** Jussieu                 84 genera/2,380 species

        Genera include:

        *Campanula* L. (campanula, Canterbury bells, bluebell [in Scotland], bellflower, harebell)

        *Codonopsis* Wallich (bonnet bellflower)

        *Jasione* L. (sheep's bit)

        *Lobelia* L. (lobelia, cardinal flower)

        *Nemacladus* Nuttall (threadstem)

        *Platycodon* A. de Candolle (balloon flower)

        *Trachelium* L. (throatwort)

        *Wahlenbergia* Schrader ex Roth (ivy-leaved bellflower, royal bluebell)

Campanulaceae is a cosmopolitan family predominantly of herbs, but with some shrubs and palm-like trees. Flowers have inferior, sometimes half inferior, ovaries. Free anthers form a tube and the style makes a brush that sweeps the pollen to the top. Anthers shed pollen in bud, and are a simple form of the united anthers of the Compositae. The family has four subfamilies, two of which hold the white and blue bellflowers where petals are united to form a bell and the lobelias shown here. A number of British native campanulas, all blue, exemplify justification of the use of Latin names, because in Scotland, *Campanula rotundifolia* is the bluebell, while in southern Britain it is known as the harebell, although also called a bellflower. The ivy-leaved variety found on upland moorland belongs to *Wahlenbergia hederacea*. Not all members have spikes of isolated flowers, the sheep's bit (*Jasione montana*) has close clusters of inconspicuous mauve flowers rather like those of certain members of the Caprifoliaceae. *Lobelia* flowers (the genus was once placed in its own family) have a wider range of colour, including red, magenta, and orange. They are bilaterally symmetrical. They typically twist upside down in the course of their development. Lobelia anthers are usually fused together and form a tube around the style. The flowers are never very closely aggregated. *Lobelia erinus*, a native of the Cape, is an important garden annual, while other members have elongate often lightly coloured inflorescences, e.g. *L. angulata*. These cultivars are herbaceous, but palm-like specimens in Africa form nests for gorillas, who eat the pith of the trunks. The Chilean *L. tupa* growing in the Great Glasshouse is a medicinal plant used as a narcotic in treating toothache, but is probably also hallucinogenic. The Indian tobacco, *Lobelia inflata* contains an alkaloid used in the treatment of asthma and chronic bronchitis. It is also used in anti-smoking products.

## The remarkable pollination mechanism of the Asterales

Many of the Asterales disperse their pollen through a process called sweeps-broom pollination. The anthers either stick together in a tube, as seen in the Compositae, or cling closely together around the immature style in some Campanulaceae (see *Platycodon* on facing page). The anthers release their pollen inward, where it is pushed out or picked up by the style as it grows upward through the anthers. Styles of this order may have special projections or other structures that gather the pollen and present it to pollinators. The branches of the style are initially closed. They open and reveal the stigmas only after the style has reached its full height, and pollinators have had an opportunity to gather the pollen.

# CAMPANULACEAE, *the bellflower family*

*The garden variety of Campanula glomerata (clustered bellflower) (above left) shows the three-branched style of this genus. This harebell flower, bud, and young fruit, C. rotundifolia (above centre), show the small inferior ovary. The corolla of C. takesimana (Korean bellflower) is white with purple spots inside (above right).*

*Trachelium rumelianum (Bulgarian throatwort) is an alpine plant with clusters of small flowers.*

*Lobelia erinus (above centre) is an annual that is used as a bedding and container plant. Lobelia siphilitica (great blue lobelia), above right, is native to the eastern United States.*

*The anthers adhere to the young, style (above left), the pollen-covered style elongates (above centre) and the style branches open (above right) in Platycodon grandiflorus (balloon flower).*

**Eudicots**

**Campanulids**

**Asterales** Lindley

> **Compositae** Giseke (**Asteraceae** Martinov)    1,590 genera/23,600 species
>
> (Genera are listed on the following pages under the individual tribes)

The original name of this family, Compositae, refers to the collection of numerous small flowers (florets) that form the familiar flower head. In the florets there is a central tube formed by joined stamens, which open to shed pollen inwards. This is pushed to the surface by the bifid style just like a sweep's brush, and spread by insects who are attracted by the brightly coloured flowering heads. The ovary is inferior and contains one ovule. The fruits are one seeded (achenes) and when mature may be topped by a parachute of hairs. These are well illustrated in the dandelion clock. The family has over 23,000 species (c. 1 in 10 of all flowering plants). Members occur all over the world. For such a large family, its economic importance is quite small. Lettuce (*Lactuca sativa*), chicory (*Cichorium intybus*) and artichokes (*Cynara cardunculus*) are eaten as vegetables, chamomile (*Chamaemelum nobile*) in herbal tea, while the sunflower (*Helianthus annuus*) produces seeds and oil. Horticulturally, it contains important garden plants and cut flowers (e.g. *Chrysanthemum* (*Dendranthema*), *Gerbera*, *Dahlia* etc.). The tropical and high altitude members are the most bizarre – even including small trees. The basal members of the family, viz Barnadesieae, *Stifftia* and *Mutisia* clades occur in South America. Look for *Barnadesia arborea* (below), with a pink inflorescence not at all like a daisy, in the Chilean section of the Great Glass House and the more familiar daisy-like *Gerbera* outside. This is a family where subdivision is still contentious, but modern molecular analyses are beginning to provide a solution. Traditional tribes are clearly not natural groups. They have a mix of ancestries. Our understanding of relationships within the sunflower family is still developing, but we will look to the future, even if that picture is still subject to change. The source for the following Compositae tribes is the findings of Vicki Funk and co-workers (Funk et al., 2005, listed in this book's references).

To give you an idea of the diversity of Compositae, there are currently at least 10 subfamilies plus additional groups proposed for it. The high number of North American taxa illustrated here reflects the geographical distributions of many of the tribes.

This tour visits the following groups:

Barnadesioideae subfamily

> Barnadesieae, tribe

Carduoideae, thistle subfamily

> Cardueae, the thistle tribe

Cichorioideae, Chicory subfamily

> Cichorieae, the lettuce tribe

Asteroideae, aster subfamily

> Anthemideae, the anthemis tribe
>
> Astereae, the aster tribe
>
> Coreopsideae, the coreopsis tribe
>
> Eupatorieae, the gayfeather tribe,
>
> Gnaphalieae, the everlasting tribe
>
> Helenieae, the sneezeweed tribe
>
> Heliantheae, the sunflower tribe
>
> Senecioneae, the senecio tribe

*Barnadesia arborea*

# COMPOSITAE (ASTERACEAE), *the sunflower or daisy family*

Compositae flowers are aggregations of disk flowers, ray flowers, or both. At first glance, ray flowers look like petals, but a closer look reveals a tiny tube at the base, in some cases with a style inside. Disk flowers have small tubular corollas, typically with five equal points at the top of the tube. The disk flowers are usually bisexual and fertile. A few species have separate male and female flowers. Most ray flowers are either female or sterile, in which case they serve only to attract pollinators. The lettuce tribe has heads composed only of bisexual ray flowers.

The whole inflorescence has an involucre of bracts at its base. These bracts are called phyllaries, and they are often mistaken for sepals. The true sepals in each flower are reduced to bristles, scales, or awns and are called the pappus. The fruit is an achene, which may be crowned by the dried pappus at maturity. Tribes differ in the structure of the phyllaries and in whether there are one or more rows. A few species lack the involucre. The nature of the pappus and whether it is present are important characters for identifying tribes. The heads may be single like sunflowers or grouped together into larger, secondary inflorescences, as seen in goldenrod and yarrow.

*A cross section of the sunflower, Helianthus annuus, left, shows that it is really an inflorescence whose many small flowers sit on a wide receptacle. There are two kinds of flowers in the inflorescence. Ray flowers ring the outside. They look superficially like petals, but each is a flower with a tubular corolla that opens and extends to one side. The centre of the inflorescence is covered with disk flowers. The disk flowers around the periphery bloom first. The central disk flowers are the youngest and last to bloom*

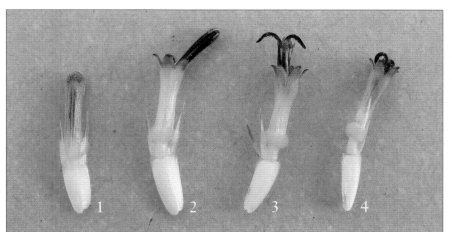

*Individual disk flowers from a sunflower, youngest to oldest shown left to right, each with their white, inferior ovary. 1) The flower in bud. 2) A dark tube of fused anthers protrudes from the corolla. 3) The style has emerged through the anther tube and its two branches have spread apart. 4) The style and anther tube wither as the flower finishes blooming. The corolla will remain on the developing ovary. The two pointed scales on top of each ovary at the base of the corolla are the pappus, the modified sepals*

*An enlargement of the disk flowers of Rudbeckia ampla, the green coneflower (above), shows the black tube formed by the fused anthers of the flowers near the top. Just outside these, on older flowers, the yellow styles project past the anthers, and their two branches have opened (arrow). The stigmas are simply lines on the interior surface of the style branches*

**Eudicots**

**Campanulids**

**Asterales** Lindley

> **Compositae** Giseke (**Asteraceae** Martinov)
>
> **Subfamily Carduoideae** Cassini ex Sweet: **Tribe Cardueae** Cassini
>
>> Genera include:
>>
>> *Arctium* L. (burdock)
>>
>> *Carduus* L. (thistle)
>>
>> *Carthamus* L. (safflower)
>>
>> *Centaurea* L. (cornflower, knapweed)
>>
>> *Cirsium* Miller (thistle)
>>
>> *Cynara* L. (globe artichoke, cardoon)
>>
>> *Onopordum* L. (cotton thistle, Scotch thistle)
>>
>> *Silybum* Vaillant (milk thistle)
>>
>> *Xeranthemum* L. (everlastings, immortelle)

The Carduoideae are dominated by unwanted plants – the thistles of fields and cultivated crops (but important bird food in winter). The tribe also contains many garden ornamentals, such as *Echinops* and some colourful wildflowers, the knapweeds and the cornflower (*Centaurea*). The typical disk flower of this tribe has a deeply lobed corolla and a long style, which makes the heads look very fluffy. Ray flowers are usually absent, although cornflowers have tubular, sterile ray flowers. There are several rows of phyllaries in the involucre. Each phyllary ends in a sharp spine or is edged with teeth. The burdocks, *Arctium*, have phyllaries that end in a long, slender hook. The cornflower almost became extinct in Britain, but as a result of changes in agricultural practice and land disturbance related to road building, is now increasing again and is a treasured arable weed. Of culinary interest is *Cynara scolymus*, the globe or French artichoke, where the swollen succulent bases of the bracts (phyllaries) surrounding the inflorescence are eaten. Leaf extracts of *Silybum marianum* are widely used in Germany in treatments of liver ailments.

# COMPOSITAE: SUBFAMILY CARDUOIDEAE
## *Tribe Cardueae, the thistle tribe*

*Disk flowers of Carduus nutans (nodding thistle), left and above, show their deep corolla lobes and their white pappus, a modified calyx. The pappus remains on the fruit and aids in its dispersal by wind. The style branches of many tribe members are very small and not easily seen without magnification. The style itself projects well past the corolla*

*Cirsium vulgare (spear thistle), far left*

*Arctium minus (common burdock), left. Note the terminal hooks on the phyllaries*

*Centaurea montana (perennial cornflower) is a common garden flower*

*Cynara cardunculus, the cardoon, is an artichoke relative, which is grown as an ornamental and for its edible leaf stalks*

**Eudicots**

**Campanulids**

**Asterales** Lindley

> **Compositae** Giseke (**Asteraceae** Martinov)
>
> **Subfamily Cichorioideae** (Cassini) Chevallier: **Tribe Cichorieae** Lamarck & de Candolle
> Genera include:
>
> *Agoseris* Rafinesque (mountain dandelion)
>
> *Catananche* L. (cupid's-dart)
>
> *Chondrilla* L. (skeletonweed)
>
> *Cichorium* L. (endive, chicory, radicchio)
>
> *Crepis* L. (hawk's beard)
>
> *Hieracium* L. (hawkweed)
>
> *Lactuca* L. (lettuce)
>
> *Sonchus* L. (sow-thistle)
>
> *Taraxacum* Weber ex Wiggers (dandelion)
>
> *Tragopogon* L. (salsify, goat's beard)

The Cichorioideae contains about five tribes, the most familiar being the Cichorieae (Lactuceae), where all the florets are of the ray type as seen in the dandelion and chicory. The dandelions and hawkweeds (*Hieracium*) are interesting botanically because they produce seeds in the absence of gamete fusion (agamospermy-apomixis). This has resulted in a multitude of microspecies that are proving very difficult to classify. *Lactuca sativa* (garden lettuce) has been cultivated for thousands of years. There are many cultivated varieties with different leaf characteristics. The flower heads form on a tall stem that arises from the basal rosette of leaves. Our garden varieties have much less of the bitter latex than wild lettuces. Extracts of *Taraxacum officinale* possess diuretic properties, hence its name 'piss a bed' in Culpepper's Herbal. They also have moderate anti-inflammatory activity for rheumatic conditions.

# COMPOSITAE: SUBFAMILY CICHORIOIDEAE
## *Tribe Cichorieae, the lettuce tribe*

*Heads of the lettuce tribe have only ray flowers; these are bisexual and typically have five tiny points at the end of the corolla. They are called ligulate flowers to distinguish them from other ray flowers in Compositae, which are female or sterile and typically have corollas with three points. The pappus is like a little umbrella that aids in wind dispersal of the achenes. In many species, it is set on a stem-like projection of the seed that is called a beak. Plants of this tribe have milky sap, a type of latex.*

*Tragopogon dubius (yellow salsify), above left, has phyllaries that project beyond its yellow ray flowers. These involucral bracts close back over the developing fruits after the flowers have bloomed. When the fruits are mature, the phyllaries reopen. Each fruit has a long stem-like beak, topped by its fluffy pappus (above right)*

*Cichorium intybus (chicory) is a roadside weed. It is a Mediterranean native that is sometimes cultivated for its roots, which are used as a coffee flavouring. Taraxacum officinale (the common dandelion) is a widespread weed in temperate climates. It produces its abundant seeds asexually*

*The Lactuca species (above left) has blue flowers in contrast to the yellow of L. sativa (garden lettuce) (above right)*

213

**Eudicots**
**Campanulids**
**Asterales** Lindley
    **Compositae** Giseke (**Asteraceae** Martinov)
    **Subfamily Asteroideae** Lindley

The largest subfamily has at least 19 tribes, which are grouped in the garden (Beds 15 and 18) according to their molecular relationships. This arrangement also reflects their geographical distribution. Thus apart from the genus *Inula*, almost all the plants in Bed 18 were originally native to North America and Mexico. Species of *Inula* contain alkaloids widely used in treatment of skin and respiratory problems. Indeed the chemical inulin is now used for treatment of asthma. Many of the remaining taxa are important horticulturally. *Helianthus annuus* is an important source of vegetable oil, while the tubers of *H. tuberosus* (Jerusalem artichoke) are eaten. Of botanical interest are *Senecio* and surprisingly *Chrysanthemum* (*Dendranthema*). For the latter, horticulturalists have exploited laboratory discoveries on growth and reproduction to develop an enormously important industry. For example, it was discovered that chrysanthemum in the wild flowers in autumn. Flowering is initiated on the shortening of days after midsummer and the plant is able to detect very small changes in day length. Thus by manipulating hours of darkness, propagators can now induce flowering at any time of the year. The ragwort genus, *Senecio*, demonstrates evolution in action today. Our newest Welsh species, *Senecio cambrensis* (discovered in Flint in 1948), was produced by hybridisation between *S. squalidus* (the Oxford ragwort) and *S. vulgaris* (groundsel) and has been the subject of research in the Garden. The Oxford ragwort escaped in the early 19th century from the eponymous botanic garden where it had been introduced from Mount Etna a hundred years earlier. It found railway lines an easy route for spreading around the whole of Britain. Our native common ragwort, *S. jacobaea*, is unfortunately poisonous to grazing livestock when consumed in large amounts.

    **Tribe Senecioneae** Cassini
        Genera include:

*Arnoglossum* Rafinesque (Indian plantain)
*Cineraria* L. (cineraria)
*Doronicum* L. (leopard's bane)
*Erechtites* Rafinesque (burnweed)
*Ligularia* Cassini (giant groundsel, ligularia)
*Packera* A. Löve & D. Löve (groundsel, ragwort)

*Pericallis* D. Don (cineraria)
*Petasites* Miller (coltsfoot, butterbur)
*Senecio* L. (senecio, groundsel, ragwort)
*Tussilago* L. (coltsfoot)

The flowers of this tribe have a single row of phyllaries that are all the same length. The involucre is roughly cylindrical and the phyllaries are frequently fused. The heads can have both disk and ray flowers or only disk flowers. The pappus consists of a thatch of fine, white bristles. The genus *Senecio* is quite large, with over a thousand species, but it has recently been divided into a number of smaller genera. Its members are adapted to environments from deserts to alpine slopes.

    **Subfamily Asteroideae** Lindley
    **Tribe Gnaphalieae** Cassini ex Lecoq & Juillet
        Genera include:

*Anaphalis* de Candolle (pearly everlasting, anaphalis)
*Craspedia* G. Forster (drumsticks)
*Filago* L. (cottonrose)
*Gnaphalium* L. (cudweed)

*Leontopodium* R. Brown ex Cassini (edelweiss)
*Pseudognaphalium* Kirpicznikov (cudweed, rabbit-tobacco)
*Xerochrysum* Miller (strawflower)

The heads of the everlasting tribe usually have only disk flowers. The phyllaries of many species are thin, papery and white or brightly coloured. They persist long after the flowers bloom and are the feature for which the everlasting flowers are named. The pappus is typically a tuft of fine bristles. The leaves of this tribe have entire margins.

# COMPOSITAE: SUBFAMILY ASTEROIDEAE
## Tribe Senecioneae, the Senecio tribe

*Senecio integerrimus (lambstongue groundsel), above left, has the typical involucre. Ligularia wilsoniana (Wilson's ligularia), above right. Pericallis hybrida (florist's cineraria), above centre*

*Tussilago farfara (coltsfoot), above far left, is one of our earliest spring flowers. Senecio cambrensis (above centre) the newest Welsh species, with its parents S. vulgaris (groundsel) (above left) and S. squalidus (Oxford ragwort) (above right)*

# COMPOSITAE: SUBFAMILY ASTEROIDEAE
## Tribe Gnaphalieae, the everlasting tribe

*Xerochrysum bracteatum (strawflower), right, is grown for its coloured, papery phyllaries, which are pink in this example. For floral arrangements, its heads are usually picked and dried before the flowers bloom*

*This Anaphalis margaritacea (pearly everlasting), left, has finished blooming and its seeds are maturing in the brown areas. The white structures are its phyllaries*

*Leontopodium nivale subsp. alpinum (edelweiss), right, has a conspicuous whorl of fuzzy white leaves beneath its group of flower heads. The individual disk flowers are quite small*

**Eudicots**
**Campanulids**
**Asterales** Lindley

    **Compositae** Giseke (**Asteraceae** Martinov)
    **Subfamily Asteroideae** Lindley
    **Tribe Astereae** Cassini
        Genera include:
        *Aster* L. (aster, Michaelmas daisy)
        *Bellis* L. (daisy)
        *Boltonia* L'Héritier (fake chamomile)
        *Brachycome* Cassini (Swan River daisy)
        *Callistephus* Cassini (China aster, callistephus)
        *Chrysopsis* (Nuttall) Elliot (golden aster)
        *Conyza* Lessing (horseweed, asthmaweed)
        *Ericameria* Nuttall (goldenbrush, rabbitbrush)
        *Erigeron* L. (erigeron, fleabane)
        *Felicia* Cassini (kingfisher daisy)
        *Grindelia* Willdenow (gumweed)
        *Heterotheca* Cassini (golden aster)
        *Machaeranthera* Nees (tansy aster)
        *Solidago* L. (goldenrod)
        *Townsendia* Hooker (Easter daisy)

The Astereae is a large tribe, with nearly 3000 species. Heads of the aster tribe usually have both ray and disk flowers, although a few members have only disks. There are several rows of phyllaries in the involucre. The typical pappus is a tuft of bristles on the fruit. The genus *Aster* and other large genera have been broken up into smaller genera that better reflect our understanding of their relatedness.

    **Subfamily Asteroideae** Lindley
    **Tribe Anthemideae**
        Genera include:
        *Achillea* L. (milfoil, yarrow)
        *Anacyclus* L. (Atlas daisy)
        *Anthemis* L. (anthemis, golden marguerite)
        *Argyranthemum* Webb ex Schultz-Bipontinus (marguerite)
        *Artemisia* L. (sagebrush, wormwood, tarragon, mugwort)
        *Chamaemelum* Miller (chamomile)
        *Chrysanthemum* (*Dendranthema*) L. (chrysanthemum, marguerite, painted daisy)
        *Leucanthemum* Miller (Shasta daisy, ox-eye daisy)
        *Matricaria* L. (chamomile tea, matricaria, pineapple weed)
        *Santolina* L. (lavender cotton, santoline)
        *Tanacetum* L. (tansy, feverfew, pyrethium)

The heads of the *Anthemis* tribe have ray and disk flowers or disk flowers alone. The leaves are often finely divided and are typically aromatic. There are several rows of phyllaries. The pappus, if it is present, is scaly. The fruits do not bear the bristly pappus found in many other tribes.

# COMPOSITAE: SUBFAMILY ASTEROIDEAE
## Tribe Astereae, the Aster tribe

*Bellis perennis (daisy), above left, one of the most familiar British wildflowers. Heterotheca villosa (hairy golden aster), above centre, has mature fruits with a pappus of bristles. Erigeron speciosus (aspen fleabane), above right, shows the many narrow ray flowers typical of its genus*

*Aster tripolium (sea aster) is common on salt marshes and coastal areas of Britain, above left. Solidago canadensis (goldenrod), above centre, originated in North America but is becoming a weed in Europe. Ericameria nauseosa (rubber rabbitbrush), above right, a shrub of dry, sunny areas in North America has only disk flowers*

# COMPOSITAE: SUBFAMILY ASTEROIDEAE
## Tribe Anthemideae, the Anthemis tribe

*Anthemis tinctoria (golden marguerite), above left, is a common garden flower that has been used as a dye plant. Chrysanthemum morifolium, above centre, is used as cut flowers by the florist industry. They are available in many colours and with many shapes of ray flowers. Achillea millefolium, (yarrow/milfoil), above right. Matricaria discoidea (pineapple weed), right, grows worldwide. If you pick an inflorescence and crush it between your fingers, it releases a strong, pineapple-like fragrance*

**Eudicots**

**Campanulids**

**Asterales** Lindley

> **Compositae** Giseke (**Asteraceae** Martinov)
>
> **Subfamily Asteroideae** Lindley
>
> **Tribe Heliantheae** Cassini
>
>> Genera include:
>>
>> *Ambrosia* L. (ragweed)
>>
>> *Echinacea* Moench (coneflower)
>>
>> *Helianthus* L. (sunflower, Jerusalem artichoke)
>>
>> *Ratibida* Rafinesque (mexican hat, prairie coneflower)
>>
>> *Rudbeckia* L. (black-eyed Susan)
>>
>> *Zinnia* L. (zinnia)

Heads of the sunflower tribe usually have both ray and disk flowers, although some species lack ray flowers. The pappus may be scales, awns, or bristles. The involucre has more than one row of phyllaries. The anthers of this tribe are often black or dark-coloured. In sunflowers, the ray flowers are usually sterile; some genera have female ray flowers. The corollas of the disk flowers remain on the developing fruits of sunflowers. The fruits, which are achenes, are often called sunflower seeds, but the actual seed is inside the thin, brittle hull.

The tribe is best known for its garden plants, although the sunflower itself is grown as a crop plant for its 'seeds'. The coneflower, *Echinacea angustifolia*, has traditionally been used for its antiseptic or antiviral properties in the treatment of septicaemia, tonsilitis, boils and ulcers. It is thought to be an immunostimulant that can be used to combat infection.

> **Subfamily Asteroideae** Lindley
>
> **Tribe Eupatorieae** Cassini
>
>> Genera include:
>>
>> *Ageratina* Spach (snakeroot)
>>
>> *Ageratum* L. (floss flower)
>>
>> *Brickellia* Elliott (brickelbush)
>>
>> *Carphephorus* Cassini (chaffhead, vanilla leaf)
>>
>> *Conoclinium* de Candolle (blue mistflower, thoroughwort)
>>
>> *Eupatorium* L. (agrimony, Joe-Pye weed)
>>
>> *Liatris* Gaertner ex von Schreber (gayfeather, liatris, blazing star)
>>
>> *Mikania* Willdenow (climbing boneset, climbing hempweed)
>>
>> *Stevia* Cavanilles (stevia, candyleaf)

Heads of the gayfeather tribe have only disk flowers. A notable feature of this tribe is the style structure. The two style branches are long and thread-like, which gives the flowers a feathery look. The corollas are white or shades of red to blue, but not yellow. The involucre usually has two or more rows of phyllaries.

*Eupatorium perfoliatum* has traditionally been used for influenza and acute bronchitis, recently supported by the demonstration of immunostimulant activity in its constituents.

# COMPOSITAE: SUBFAMILY ASTEROIDEAE
## *Tribe Heliantheae, the sunflower tribe*

*Helianthus annuus (sunflower) in flower and fruit (above left). Ratibida columnifera (prairie coneflower or Mexican hat), above centre. Rudbeckia sp. (above right). A cultivated Zinnia (Z. elegans) (right) and a North American native, Zinnia grandiflora (plains zinnia), far right*

# COMPOSITAE: SUBFAMILY ASTEROIDEAE
## *Tribe Eupatorieae, the gayfeather tribe*

*Eupatorium maculatum (spotted Joe-pye weed), left, along with several related species, is common in eastern North America*

*Liatris spicata, right. Note the very long feathery styles*

*Ageratum houstonianum (ageratum or floss flower) is a common garden flower; left*

219

**Eudicots**

**Campanulids**

**Asterales** Lindley

    **Compositae** Giseke (**Asteraceae** Martinov)

    **Subfamily Asteroideae** Lindley

    **Tribe Helenieae** Lindley

        Genera include:

        *Baileya* Harvey & A. Gray ex Torrey (desert marigold)

        *Balduina* Nuttall (honeycomb head)

        *Gaillardia* Fougeroux (gaillardia, blanket flower)

        *Helenium* L. (sneezeweed)

        *Hymenoxys* Cassini (bitterweed, rubberweed)

        *Psilostrophe* de Candolle (paperflower)

        *Tetraneuris* Greene (alpine sunflowers, old-man-of-the-mountain)

The sneezeweed tribe can be hard to define on the basis of its flower structures. It has pale anthers, as opposed to the dark ones of the sunflower tribe. The ray flowers are yellow to red, not blue or purple. Their corollas are often wedge-shaped, broader at the apex, and narrow at the base.

    **Subfamily Asteroideae** Lindley

    **Tribe Coreopsideae** Lindley

        Genera include:

        *Bidens* L. (beggar-ticks, bur-marigold, sticktight, Spanish needle)

        *Coreopsis* L. (tickweed)

        *Cosmos* Cavanilles (cosmea, cosmos)

        *Dahlia* Cavanilles (dahlia)

The coreopsis tribe is one of 12 that have been created recently from the former sunflower tribe. The involucre usually has two rows of phyllaries that differ in shape. The inner row lies closely against the ray flowers, whereas the outer row often looks more like leaves and stands out from the stem. The pappus of several tribe members consists of two to four barbed awns that catch on fur or clothing and help in seed dispersal. The common names, tickseed and beggar-ticks, reflect this mode of seed travel.

# COMPOSITAE: SUBFAMILY ASTEROIDEAE
## Tribe Helenieae, the sneezeweed tribe

*Gaillardia x grandiflora (right) (gaillardia or blanket flower) was bred from two species that are native throughout the United States*

*Tetraneuris grandiflora (alpine sunflower or old-man-of-the-mountain) lives in the extreme environment of the alpine tundra in North America*

*The branching styles in this Helenium autumnale (sneezeweed) make a pattern of yellow lines against the darker corollas of the disk flowers*

# COMPOSITAE: SUBFAMILY ASTEROIDEAE
## Tribe Coreopsideae, the Coreopsis tribe

*Many of the Coreopsis tribe are cultivated as ornamentals. These include: Coreopsis verticillata (threadleaf coreopsis) (above) and Cosmos bipinnatus (cosmos), below right. Fruits of Bidens tenuisecta (slimlobe sticktight), top right, each have two barbed awns on the top. When the fruits are mature, they fan out and present their clingy awns to passing animals*

**Eudicots**

**Campanulids**

**Dipsacales** Dumortier

    **Adoxaceae** E. Meyer                      5 genera/225 species

        Genera include:

        *Adoxa* L. (moschatel, townhall clock)

        *Sambucus* L. (elder, elderberry)

        *Viburnum* L. (viburnum, wayfarer's tree, guelder rose)

This family of shrubs and small trees has opposite leaves that are often toothed, and may be compound or simple. The systematic position of its members has been much debated and particularly their relationships with the Caprifoliaceae. The flowers are small, but masses of them form showy, clustered inflorescences. Individual flowers usually have five petals and stamens, although a few have four-fold parts. The pistil is made of three to five carpels, occasionally fewer. The styles are short if they are there at all, and the stigmas are nestled down in the corolla. The ovary is inferior or half-inferior. The fruits are juicy drupes with one or three to five stones, and are usually red or purple. Many of the shrubs are used in landscaping. Of the native Adoxaceae, the unpleasantly smelling elder shrub, *Sambucus nigra*, produces flowers and fruits that are used to produce 'champagne', cordial and wine, while the pith of the stem has long been used by botanists to support specimens in hand-sectioning. Another species, *S. ebulus*, the dwarf elder, exemplifies the herbaceous habit in the Adoxaceae. Whether or not it is a British native or introduced as a herb is uncertain, its alternative common name, dane-wort, may result, not because the plant grew from the blood of Danes killed on the battlefield, but because it induces "the danes" or diarrhoea! Indeed *Sambucus nigra*, itself, has been used as a diuretic and laxative as well as a herbal treatment for influenza, colds, catarrh and sinusitis. Another native herb, *Adoxa moschatellina*, the townhall clock, has a charming inflorescence of five palish green flowers, four pointing away from each other as in a clock tower and the fifth perched above. It is usually pollinated at dusk by insects attracted by its smell of musk and by accumulations of nectar at the base of the flower.

# ADOXACEAE, *the elderberry family*

*Hybrid Viburnum rhytidophylloides (snowball flowers), above left and centre, its ripening fruits. Viburnum plicatum (Japanese snowball), above right, has an adaptation similar to hydrangeas. It has small fertile flowers that are surrounded by larger, showy, sterile flowers*

*Sambucus racemosa (red elderberry) in flower, above left, and fruit, above centre, and S. nigra (black elderberry) above right, show the compound leaves characteristic of this genus. Black elderberries have been used for centuries to make wine, jelly and pies. The fruits are usually cooked before they are eaten because they contain antinutritional substances that are destroyed by heating*

*Viburnum opulus (guelder rose), above*

*Adoxa moschatellina (the town hall clock), left*

*Viburnum carlesii (Korean spice viburnum) is an ornamental known for its fragrance*

**Eudicots**

**Campanulids**

**Dipsacales** Dumortier

    **Caprifoliaceae** Jussieu                     33 genera/900 species

        Genera include:

        *Abelia* R. Brown (abelia)

        *Cephalaria* Schrader ex Roemer & Schultes (giant scabious)

        *Dipelta* Maximowicz (dipelta)

        *Dipsacus* L. (teasel)

        *Heptacodium* Rehder (seven sons flower)

        *Knautia* L. (knautia, field scabious)

        *Kolkwitzia* Graebner (beauty bush)

        *Leycesteria* Wallich (Himalayan honeysuckle, shrimp plant)

        *Linnaea* L. (twin flower)

        *Lonicera* L. (honeysuckle)

        *Scabiosa* L. (scabious)

        *Symphoricarpos* Duhamel (snowberry)

        *Triosteum* L. (wild coffee, fever root)

        *Weigela* Thunberg (weigelia)

Caprifoliaceae, well known for its shrubs and climbers but also containing small trees, occurs in the temperate Northern Hemisphere. It is considered here to include the former families Dipsacaceae, Linnaeaceae and Valerianaceae. Flowers have an inferior ovary. Caprifoliaceae graces both our hedgerows (*Lonicera periclymenium*, honeysuckle) and our gardens (species of *Lonicera*, *Symphoricarpus*). Our native honeysuckle (or woodbine) has sweetly smelling flowers, appreciated best at night when they are pollinated by moths. The exotic *Leycesteria formosa* (Himalayan honeysuckle), although excellent for attracting birds to our gardens with its berries, is beginning to escape and to become an invasive weed.

*Abelia* and *Kolkwitzia* are useful garden shrubs.

*Linnaea* should find a place in any systematic garden because it bears the name of the founder of the system of naming plants with generic and species names (the binominal system). Appropriately Linnaeus would have been very familiar with *Linnaea borealis*, a small mat-forming shrub with delicate bell-shaped, pale pink flowers native to woodlands, heath and tundra of northern Eurasia and North America. The flowers are borne in pairs, hence the name twin flower.

# CAPRIFOLIACEAE, *the honeysuckle family*

*Ornamental honeysuckles include Lonicera heckrottii (goldflame honeysuckle), above left, and Lonicera x brownii (Brown's honeysuckle), above right*

*Abelia sp., above left. Symphoricarpos albus (common snowberry), above right, shows the persistent calyx (arrow) on its developing berries. The white berries are poisonous*

*Leycesteria formosa (the shrimp plant) inflorescence with fruits*

*Linnaea borealis (twin flower)*

# Eudicots

# Campanulids

# Dipsacales Dumortier

## Caprifoliaceae continued

The genera *Cephalaria*, *Dipsacus*, *Knautia* and *Scabiosa*, formerly united in the Dipsacaceae, share many characters with the Compositae; these include an inferior ovary and flowers clustered into dense inflorescences surrounded by bracts, the epicalyx. Unlike the majority of remaining Caprifoliaceae, the fruits are not berries and there are usually just four stamens. The inflorescence may be conical/cylindrical as in *Dipsacus* (the teasel) or flat as in *Scabiosa* (scabious). In *D. sativus* the flower head is covered by small downwardly hooked spines, with special resilient properties that led to its use originally in teasing out wool fibres (carding) and even today in raising a nap on cloth. Field scabious (*Knautia arvensis*) is an attractive native of fields and roadsides normally on calcareous sites, and like many daisies, the petals of flowers on the periphery of the inflorescence are far more pronounced.

# CAPRIFOLIACEAE *continued, the teasels*

*The heads of the former Dipsacaceae have involucres and look much like the Compositae, but the structure of the flowers shows that this is a different family. For example, flowers of the teasels usually have four distinct stamens, although two to three occur in a few members. There is only one type of flower in the heads, although in Scabiosa and related genera, the outer flowers of the head may have much larger corollas than the inner ones (above left). The corollas have four or occasionally five fused petals. The style is unbranched and typically has a single knob-like stigma. The flowers have bracts or an epicalyx at their base. The calyx itself is often reduced to bristles, like in Compositae. It can also be cup-like. The prominent styles with their pinhead-like stigmas of Scabiosa give these flowers the common name, pincushion flower, in the United States. All the flowers mature at about the same time. Fruits of Scabiosa stellata (above right) have bristles that are derived from the calyx as well as a papery epicalyx*

*Dipsacus fullonum, has ovoid heads of small lavender flowers (left). Its dried heads were used by weavers and also in flower arranging (right). The bracts of the involucre are nearly as long as the head. They ring the base of the inflorescence and curve upward around it. Each flower has its own pair of small, spiny bracts that forms an epicalyx at its base. These bracts become woody and remain after the fruits are mature, forming the spiny head*

**Eudicots**

**Campanulids**

**Apiales** Nakai

**Griseliniaceae** Forster & Forster f. ex A. Cunningham          1 genus/7 species

Genus:

*Griselinia* Forster & Forster f. (broad leaf)

The single genus, *Griselinia*, distributed in New Zealand and South America, was originally placed in the Corneaceae but now has its own family. Its members are grown for their evergreen glossy leaves that display a wide range of subtle colours.

**Araliaceae** Jussieu          39 genera/1,425 species

Genera include:

*Aralia* L. (Hercules club, devil's walking stick)

x *Fatshedera* Guillaumin

*Fatsia* Decaisne & Planchon (fatsia, Japanese aralia)

*Hedera* L. (ivy)

*Panax* L. (ginseng)

*Pseudopanax* K. Koch (five finger, lancewood)

*Schefflera* Forster & Forster f. (umbrella plant)

*Tetrapanax* K. Koch (rice paper)

Araliaceae is a widely distributed family in both temperate and tropical regions. Its tropical representatives are shrubs and trees, with many resembling palms, but the most familiar British member is the ivy, *Hedera helix*, which climbs by the production of hundreds of small roots from aerial stems. Ivy flowers are an important source of nectar and pollen to bees in late autumn and the berries that persist until the spring are an important bird food. Its leaves contain saponins and extracts have been used to treat whooping cough. An easily remembered name is *Fatshedera*, an unusual hybrid when *Fatsia*, with its large, glossy, lobed leaves, and globular flower heads, is crossed with ivy. Gingseng is made from the root of a north-east Asian species, *Panax ginseng*. Extracts from the roots of other *Panax* species are thought to possess stimulant properties. They have been used in the long term to improve debilitating and degenerative conditions associated with old age. Indeed the generic name has its roots in the Greek *Panakeia* - universal remedy or panacea. *Tetrapanax papyrifera* is the source of rice paper.

# ARALIACEAE, *the ivy family*

*Hedera helix (ivy) globular inflorescence, above left, and fruit, above right. Compare the shape of the more familiar leaf of the climbing stem, below left, with those associated with flowering stems, above right*

*x Fatshedera lizei, a hybrid between Fatsia and Hedera, above right*

# GRISELINIACEAE, *the griselinia family*

*Schefflera digitata, foliage and inflorescences*

*Griselinia littoralis, evergreen foliage*

229

**Eudicots**
**Campanulids**
**Apiales** Nakai

    **Pittosporaceae** R. Brown                        7 general/250 species
        Genera include:
        *Billardiera* J. E. Smith (purple apple berry)
        *Pittosporum* Banks ex Solander (parchment bark)

This small family of climbers, evergreen shrubs and trees is largely confined to Australia, but the genus *Pittosporum* is also widespread in warmer parts of the Old World. The first introduction to the UK was *P. coriaceam* from Madeira (1783) soon to be followed by species from Australia and New Zealand, including the most hardy *P. tenuifolium* from the latter. All have evergreen leaves and small delicate, often sweetly smelling, flowers. The name comes from resins secreted by the seed coat (pitta = pitch). A second genus, *Billardiera* (once *Sollya*), from Australia contains climbers and pendant shrubs, and is grown for its white to purple, 5-petalled, bell-shaped flowers, and edible blue berries.

    **Apiaceae** Lindley or **Umbelliferae** Jussieu          428 genera/3,500 species
        Genera include:

| | |
|---|---|
| *Aegopodium* L. (bishop's weed, ground elder) | *Eryngium* L. (sea holly) |
| *Anethum* L. (dill) | *Foeniculum* Miller (fennel) |
| *Angelica* L. (angelica) | *Heracleum* L. (hogweed) |
| *Anthriscus* Persoon (chervil, cow parsley) | *Myrrhis* Miller (sweet cicely) |
| *Apium* L. (celery) | *Pastinaca* L. (parsnip) |
| *Carum* L. (caraway) | *Petroselinum* Hill (parsley) |
| *Conium* L. (poison hemlock) | *Pimpinella* L. (anise) |
| *Coriandrum* L. (coriander) | *Sanicula* L. (sanicle) |
| *Crithmum* L. (rock samphire) | *Sium* L. (water parsnip) |
| *Cuminum* L. (cumin) | *Smyrnium* L. (alexanders) |
| *Daucus* L. (carrot) | |

Once called the Umbelliferae, the family has strong culinary connections. The old name refers to the flower head, where numerous, small, usually white flowers are borne on stalks radiating from a central stem so that they form a plate-like inflorescence, the umbel. An exception is the cone-shaped inflorescence of the sea holly (*Eryngium*). The ovary is inferior, composed of two parts, and used in cookery, e.g. caraway (*Carum*). Leaves of most species are once or twice pinnately constructed and they clasp the stem at attachment – a characteristic of the family. The leaves of fennel (*Foeniculum vulgare*), parsley (*Petroselinum crispum*), celery (*Apium graveolens* – the fleshy white structures are petioles or leaf stalks) and coriander (*Coriandrum sativum*) have highly distinctive flavours, produced by oily chemicals, while the roots of parsnip (*Pastinaca sativa*) and carrots (*Daucus carota*) are important vegetables. Stems of *Angelica archangelica* soaked in sugar syrup produce the pretty cake decoration. The poison that killed Socrates derives from the hemlock (*Conium maculatum*) and is a less palatable product resulting in a slow lingering death involving paralysis. Indeed many of the family members are very toxic even in small amounts. Among the many British natives in the Apiaceae is the common hogweed (*Heracleum sphondylium*), the commonest representative along our roads in late summer. A second species *H. mantegazzianum*, the giant hogweed (5 m tall), is introduced, and particularly common in Scotland. It was notorious because sap from its stems and hairs is a severe skin irritant, but similar symptoms can also result from contact with the furocoumarins produced by the common hogweed and the yellow-flowered wild parsnip. Perhaps the most beautiful and ubiquitous roadside umbellifer is *Anthriscus sylvestris*, cow parsley or Queen Anne's lace. Closer to the sea grows alexanders (*Smyrnium olusatrum*). On shingle is found sea holly (*Eryngium maritimum*) and on cliffs and beaches, rock samphire (*Crithmum maritimum*). Far less satisfying has been the Roman introduction of ground elder, *Aegopodium podograria*, the bane of many a gardener's life.

# PITTOSPORACEAE, *the parchment bark family*

*Pittosporum tobira*

*Pittosporum fruits with typical grooves*

# APIACEAE OR UMBELLIFERAE, *the carrot or parsley family*

*The leaves of Petroselinum crispum (parsley), above far left, show the sheathing petiole that is characteristic of Apiaceae. Parsley, like carrots, is a biennial. The first year it is a rosette plant, with little visible stem. The leaf attachment is most easily seen on the second-year, flowering stem, as shown here. Myrrhis odorata (sweet cicely), above left, shows the typical compound leaves of this family. Its developing fruits, above right, retain the gynoecium's two styles. Eryngium (sea holly), above far right, does not look like the typical carrot family member. It has a reduced, cone-shaped inflorescence and thistle-like foliage*

*Foeniculum vulgare (fennel) (above) grows wild in many parts of the world. Its leaf blades are finely divided into many linear segments*

*Anethum graveolens (dill), above, shows the typical form of the inflorescence, the compound umbel*

*The view from underneath an inflorescence of Daucus carota (wild carrot), above, shows the structure of the small umbels that are joined into the large, compound umbel*

# APPENDIX A. EXPANDED OUTLINE OF FLOWERING PLANT FAMILIES

This outline includes families that are illustrated in the main section of this book along with additional families that are not illustrated. For the latter, representative genera and common names are listed. This listing is meant to give a larger view of flowering plant families. The original book "*A Tour of the Flowering Plants*", concentrated on native plants of temperate North America, as well as horticultural and agricultural plants that are grown in North America, but are native to other areas. It also included plants used as food or medicine, but grown outside North America, and plants that are significant in the flowering plant tree of life. Some of these have been replaced in this work by plants from the British flora and non-natives grown in the National Botanic Garden of Wales. The groups, orders and families of this listing are based on the 2009 report from the Angiosperm Phylogeny Group, with additional information from the APG website (see reference section). The common names and genera were added from various resources-see the listing of additional resources in the Selected References section.

## BASAL ANGIOSPERMS

### Basal lineages

Amborellales
>	Amborellaceae (*Amborella*)

Nymphaeales
>	Cabombaceae (fanwort - *Cabomba*)
>	Nymphaeaceae, the water-lily family

Austrobaileyales
>	Schisandraceae, the *Illicium/Kadsura/Schisandra* family

Chloranthales
>	Chloranthaceae, sole family (*Chloranthus*)

### Magnoliids

Canellales
>	Winteraceae, the winter's bark family

Piperales
>	Saururaceae, the lizard's-tail family
>	Piperaceae, the pepper family
>	Aristolochiaceae, the dutchman's-pipe family

Magnoliales
>	Myristicaceae (*Myristica* - nutmeg)
>	Magnoliaceae, the magnolia family
>	Annonaceae (*Annona* - cherimoya, sour sop, sweet sop, pond-apple; *Asimina* - paw-paw;
>		*Deeringothamnus* - Rugel's pawpaw)

Laurales
>	Calycanthaceae (*Calycanthus* - Carolina allspice, California spice bush; *Chimonathus* -
>	wintersweet)
>	Lauraceae, the laurel family

## MONOCOTS

### Basal Monocots

Acorales
>	Acoraceae, the sweet flag family

Alismatales
>	Araceae, the aroids or arum family
>	Alismataceae, the water plantain family

Hydrocharitaceae (*Elodea* - waterweed; *Hydrocharis*; *Limnobium* - frog's-bit; *Vallisneria*-tape grass)
Zosteraceae (*Phyllospadix* - surf-grass; *Zostera* - eelgrass)
Potamogetonaceae (*Potamogeton* - pondweeds)

# LILIOID OR PETALOID MONOCOTS

Dioscoreales
    Nartheciaceae, the bog asphodel family
    Dioscoreaceae, the dioscorea family
Pandanales
    Cyclanthaceae (*Carludovica* - Panama hat plant)
    Pandanaceae (*Pandanus* - screw pine, hala, pandanus)
Liliales
    Melanthiaceae, the death camus family
    Alstroemeriaceae, the alstroemeria family
    Colchicaceae, the colchicum family
    Philesiaceae, the Chilean bell family
    Smilacaceae, the sarsaparilla family
    Liliaceae, the lily family
Asparagales
    Orchidaceae, the orchid family
    Asteliaceae, the astelia family
    Hypoxidaceae, the hypoxis family
    Iridaceae, the iris family
    Xanthorrhoeaceae, the grass tree family
    Amaryllidaceae, the amaryllis or daffodil family
    Asparagaceae, the asparagus family

## Commelinid Monocots

Arecales
    Arecaceae or Palmae, the palm family
Commelinales
    Commelinaceae, the spiderwort family
    Pontederiaceae, the pickerel weed or water hyacinth family
    Haemodoraceae (*Anigozanthos* - kangaroo-paw)
Zingiberales
    Strelitziaceae, the bird-of-paradise family
    Heliconiaceae, the heliconia family
    Musaceae, the banana family
    Cannaceae, the canna family
    Marantaceae, the prayer plant family
    Costaceae (*Costus* - spiral flag, ginger lily)
    Zingiberaceae, the ginger family
Poales
    Typhaceae, the bulrush or bur reed family
    Bromeliaceae, the bromeliad family
    Xyridaceae (*Xyris* - yellow-eyed grass)
    Juncaceae, the rush family
    Cyperaceae, the sedge family
    Restionaceae, the restio family
    Poaceae or Gramineae, the grass family

# EUDICOTS (also called tricolpates, from the three germination openings of the pollen)

## Basal Eudicots

Ceratophyllales
> Ceratophyllaceae, sole family (*Ceratophyllum* - water hornwort)

Ranunculales
> Papaveraceae, the poppy family and bleeding heart family
> Lardizabalaceae, the akebia family
> Menispermaceae (*Anamirta* - fish-berry; *Chondrodendron* - curare; *Cocculus* -Carolina moonseed, coralbeads; *Menispermum* - moonseed)
> Berberidaceae, the barberry family
> Ranunculaceae, the buttercup family

Proteales
> Nelumbonaceae, the lotus family
> Platanaceae, the plane family
> Proteaceae, the protea family

Buxales
> Buxaceae, the box family

Gunnerales
> Gunneraceae, the gunnera family

## Core Eudicots

Saxifragales
> Paeoniaceae, the peony family
> Altingiaceae, the sweet gum family
> Hamamelidaceae, the witch hazel family
> Iteaceae (*Itea* - sweetspire)
> Grossulariaceae, the gooseberry family
> Saxifragaceae, the saxifrage family
> Crassulaceae, the stonecrop family
> Haloragaceae (*Myriophyllum* - water-milfoil)

Vitales
> Vitaceae, the grape family

## Rosids: fabids

Zygophyllales
> Krameriaceae (*Krameria* - rhatany)
> Zygophyllaceae (*Guaiacum* - lignum vitae; *Larrea* - creosote bush; *Tribulus* -puncture vine)

Fabales
> Fabaceae or Leguminosae - the legume family
> Polygalaceae, the milkwort family

Rosales
> Rosaceae, the rose family
> Elaeagnaceae, the sea buckthorn family
> Rhamnaceae, the buckthorn family
> Ulmaceae, the elm family
> Cannabaceae (*Cannabis* - hemp, marihuana; *Celtis* - hackberry tree; *Humulus* -hops)
> Moraceae, the fig and mulberry family
> Urticaceae, the nettle family

Fagales
> Nothofagaceae, the southern beech family

Fagaceae, the oak family
Myricaceae, the bog myrtle family
Juglandaceae, the walnut family
Casuarinaceae, the she-oak family
Betulaceae, the birch and alder family
Cucurbitales
Cucurbitaceae, the squash family
Begoniaceae, the begonia family
Celastrales
Celastraceae (*Celastrus* - bittersweet; *Euonymus*; *Paxistima*)
Oxalidales
Oxalidaceae, the oxalis family
Cunoniaceae, the leatherwood family
Elaeocarpaceae, the elaeocarpus family
Cephalotaceae (*Cephalotus* - Australian pitcher plant)
Malpighiales
Euphorbiaceae, the spurge family
Malpighiaceae (*Malpighia* - Barbados cherry)
Passifloraceae, the passionflower family
Salicaceae, the willow family
Violaceae, the violet and pansy family
Linaceae, the flax family
Hypericaceae, the St. John's wort family

## Rosids: malvids

Geraniales
Geraniaceae, the geranium family
Myrtales
Lythraceae, the loosestrife family
Onagraceae, the evening primrose family
Myrtaceae, the myrtle family
Melastomataceae (*Rhexia* - meadow beauty; most genera are tropical)
Sapindales
Burseraceae (*Bursera* - gumbo-limbo tree, elephant tree)
Anacardiaceae, the sumac family
Sapindaceae, the soapberry, maple, and horse chestnut family
Sapindoideae, the soapberry subfamily
Hippocastanoideae, the horse chestnut and maple subfamily
Rutaceae, the citrus family
Simaroubaceae (*Ailanthus* - tree-of-heaven; *Simarouba* - paradise tree)
Meliaceae (*Melia* - chinaberry tree; *Swietenia* - mahogany)
Malvales
Malvaceae, the mallow family
Thymelaeaceae, the daphne family
Cistaceae, the rockrose family
Brassicales
Tropaeolaceae, the nasturtium family
Caricaceae (*Carica* - papaya)
Limnanthaceae, the poached eggs family
Resedaceae, the mignonette family
Capparaceae (*Capparis* - capers)

Cleomaceae (*Cleome* - spider flower, bee plant)
Brassicaceae or Cruciferae, the mustard family

## Core Eudicots

Santalales
    Santalaceae, the mistletoe and sandalwood family
Caryophyllales
    Tamaricaceae, the tamarix family
    Plumbaginaceae, the leadwort family
    Polygonaceae, the knotweed or dock family
    Droseraceae (*Drosera* - Venus flytrap)
    Nepenthaceae (*Nepenthes* - Asian pitcher plant)
    Simmondsiaceae (*Simmondsia* - jojoba)
    Caryophyllaceae, the pink family Amaranthaceae, the amaranth and goosefoot family. This includes the traditional goosefoot family, Chenopodiaceae, which is no longer recognised as a separate family.
    Aizoaceae, the ice plant family
    Phytolaccaceae (*Phytolacca* - pokeweed; *Rivinia* - rouge plant)
    Nyctaginaceae, the four o'clock family
    Portulacaceae, the purslane family
    Cactaceae (*Opuntia* - prickly pear)

## Asterids

Cornales
    Cornaceae, the dogwood family
    Hydrangeaceae, the hydrangea family
    Loasaceae, the blazingstar or stickleaf family
Ericales
    Balsaminaceae, the impatiens family
    Fouquieriaceae (*Fouquieria* - ocotillo)
    Polemoniaceae, the phlox family
    Lecythidaceae (*Bertholletia* - Brazil nuts; *Couroupita* - cannonball tree)
    Sapotaceae (*Manilkara* - sapodilla or chicle; *Sideroxylon* - bumelia, ironwood)
    Ebenaceae (*Diospyros* - ebony wood, persimmon)
    Primulaceae, the primrose family
    Theaceae, the tea family
    Symplocaceae (*Symplocos* - sapphireberry, sweetleaf)
    Diapensiaceae, the diapensia family
    Styracaceae (*Halesia* - silver bell trees, snowdrop tree; *Styrax* - snowbell)
    Sarraceniaceae (*Sarracenia* - pitcher plant)
    Actinidiaceae, the kiwi fruit family
    Clethraceae (*Clethra* - lily-of-the-valley tree, summersweet, sweet pepperbush)
    Cyrillaceae (*Cliftonia* - buckwheat tree; *Cyrilla* - leatherwood, titi)
    Ericaceae, the heath and heather family

## Lamiids

    Boraginaceae, the borage and waterleaf family. It is not yet placed in an order. This contains the traditional waterleaf family, Hydrophyllaceae, which is no longer recognised as a separate family.
Garryales
    Eucommiaceae (*Eucommia* - gutta pircha tree)
    Garryaceae, the garrya family

Gentianales
    Rubiaceae, the madder family
    Gentianaceae, the gentian family
    Loganiaceae (*Spigelia* - Indian pink, pink root)
    Gelsemiaceae (*Gelsemium* - yellow jessamine, swamp jessamine)
    Apocynaceae, the dogbane and milkweed family. This includes the traditional milkweed family,
    Asclepiaceae, which is no longer recognised as a separate family.
Solanales
    Convolvulaceae, the morning glory family
    Solanaceae, the nightshade or potato family
Lamiales
    Oleaceae, the olive family
    Calceolariaceae (*Calceolaria* - pocket book flower)
    Gesneriaceae (*Achimenes* - hot water plant; *Aeschynanthus* - lipstick plant, zebra vine; *Columnea*;
        *Episcia* - flame violet; *Gesneria* - firecracker; *Saintpaulia* -African violet; *Sinningia* -
        gloxinia; *Streptocarpus* - cape primrose)
    Plantaginaceae, the plantain and snapdragon family
    Scrophulariaceae, the figwort family
    Pedaliaceae (*Sesamum* - sesame)
    Lamiaceae or Labiatae, the mint family
    Phrymaceae (*Mazus; Mimulus* - monkey flower; *Phryma* - lopseed)
    Paulowniaceae, the foxglove tree or empress tree family
    Orobanchaceae (*Orobanche* - broomrape)
    Lentibulariaceae (*Pinguicula* - butterwort; *Utricularia* - bladderwort)
    Acanthaceae, the acanthus family
    Bignoniaceae, the trumpet vine family
    Verbenaceae, the verbena family
    Martyniaceae (*Martynia, Proboscidea* - unicorn plant, devil's claw)

## Campanulids

Aquifoliales
    Aquifoliaceae, the holly family
Asterales
    Campanulaceae, the bellflower and lobelia family
    Menyanthaceae (*Menyanthes* - buckbean, bogbean; *Nymphoides* - floating heart)
    Goodeniaceae (*Scaevola* - fanflower
    Compositae (or Asteraceae) the sunflower family
Dipsacales
    Adoxaceae, the elderberry family
    Caprifoliaceae, the honeysuckle family
    [This family now includes the Diervillaceae, Dipsacaceae, Linnaeaceae and Valerianaceae].
Apiales
    Griseliniaceae, the griselinia family
    Pittosporaceae, the pittosporum family
    Araliaceae, the ivy family
    Apiaceae or Umbelliferae, the carrot and parsley family

# APPENDIX B. GENUS TO COMMON NAME, FAMILY & ORDER LISTING

| GENUS | COMMON NAME | FAMILY | ORDER | PAGE |
|---|---|---|---|---|
| *Abelia* | abelia | Caprifoliaceae | Dipsacales | 224 |
| *Abronia* | sand verbena | Nyctaginaceae | Caryophyllales | 164 |
| *Abutilon* | Chinese lantern | Malvaceae | Malvales | 146 |
| *Acacia* | acacia, mimosa, wattle | Fabaceae | Fabales | 104 |
| *Acaena* | piri-piri, bidibidi | Rosaceae | Rosales | 106 |
| *Acalypha* | chenille plant, Jacob's coat, | Euphorbiaceae | Malpighiales | 126 |
| *Acantholimon* | prickly thrift | Plumbaginaceae | Caryophyllales | 156 |
| *Acanthus* | bear's breech, oyster plant | Acanthaceae | Lamiales | 202 |
| *Acca* | pineapple guava | Myrtaceae | Myrtales | 140 |
| *Acer* | acer, maple | Sapindaceae | Sapindales | 144 |
| *Aceratium* | aceratium, carabeen | Elaeocarpaceae | Oxalidales | 124 |
| *Achillea* | yarrow, milfoil | Compositae | Asterales | 216 |
| *Acleisanthes* | angel trumpets | Nyctaginaceae | Caryophyllales | 164 |
| *Acomastylis* | alpine avens | Rosaceae | Rosales | 106 |
| *Aconitum* | monkshood, wolf's bane | Ranunculaceae | Ranunculales | 82 |
| *Acorus* | calamus, sweet flag | Acoraceae | Acorales | 30 |
| *Actaea* | baneberry | Ranunculaceae | Ranunculales | 82 |
| *Actinidia* | kiwi fruit, Chinese gooseberry | Actinidiaceae | Ericales | 178 |
| *Adlumia* | adlumia | Papaveraceae | Ranunculales | 80 |
| *Adoxa* | moschatel, townhall clock | Adoxaceae | Dipsacales | 222 |
| *Aechmea* | bromeliad | Bromeliaceae | Poales | 68 |
| *Aegopodium* | bishop's weed, ground elder | Apiaceae | Apiales | 230 |
| *Aeonium* | pinwheel, Canary Island rose | Crassulaceae | Saxifragales | 94 |
| *Aesculus* | horse chestnut, buckeye | Sapindaceae | Sapindales | 144 |
| *Agapanthus* | agapanthus, African lily | Agapanthaceae | Asparagales | 50 |
| *Agave* | century plant, sisal | Asparagaceae | Asparagales | 56 |
| *Ageratina* | snakeroot | Compositae | Asterales | 218 |
| *Ageratum* | floss flower | Compositae | Asterales | 218 |
| *Agoseris* | mountain dandelion | Compositae | Asterales | 212 |
| *Agrimonia* | agrimony | Rosaceae | Rosales | 106 |
| *Agrostemma* | corn cockle | Caryophyllaceae | Caryophyllales | 160 |
| *Agrostis* | bent grass | Poaceae | Poales | 72 |
| *Ajuga* | ajuga, bugle | Lamiaceae | Lamiales | 200 |
| *Akebia* | chocolate vine | Lardizabalaceae | Ranunculales | 80 |
| *Alangium* | muskwood | Cornaceae | Cornales | 172 |
| *Albizia* | silk-tree | Fabaceae | Fabales | 104 |
| *Alcantarea* | imperial bromeliad | Bromeliaceae | Poales | 68 |
| *Alcea* | hollyhock | Malvaceae | Malvales | 146 |

| | | | | |
|---|---|---|---|---|
| *Alchemilla* | lady's mantle | Rosaceae | Rosales | 106 |
| *Alisma* | water plantain | Alismataceae | Alismatales | 34 |
| *Allionia* | trailing four o'clock | Nyctaginaceae | Caryophyllales | 164 |
| *Allium* | onion, leek, garlic | Amaryllidaceae | Asparagales | 52 |
| *Alnus* | alder | Betulaceae | Fagales | 118 |
| *Aloe* | aloe | Asphodelaceae | Asparagales | 48 |
| *Aloysia* | lemon verbena | Verbenaceae | Lamiales | 202 |
| *Alpinia* | shell ginger | Zingiberaceae | Zingiberales | 66 |
| *Alstroemeria* | alstroemeria, Peruvian lily | Alstroemeriaceae | Liliales | 38 |
| *Alternanthera* | Jacob's coat | Amaranthaceae | Caryophyllales | 162 |
| *Althaea* | marsh mallow | Malvaceae | Malvales | 146 |
| *Alyogyne* | blue hibiscus | Malvaceae | Malvales | 146 |
| *Alyssum* | alyssum | Brassicaceae | Brassicales | 152 |
| *Amaranthus* | tassel flower, foxtail | Amaranthaceae | Caryophyllales | 162 |
| *Amaryllis* | Cape belladonna, belladonna lily | Amaryllidaceae | Asparagales | 50 |
| *Amborella* | | Amborellaceae | Amborellales | 11 |
| *Ambrosia* | ragweed | Compositae | Asterales | 218 |
| *Amelanchier* | service berry, snowy mespilus | Rosaceae | Rosales | 108 |
| *Ammophila* | marram grass | Poaceae | Poales | 72 |
| *Amorphophallus* | Asian jungle flower | Araceae | Alismatales | 32 |
| *Ampelopsis* | blueberry climber | Vitaceae | Vitales | 100 |
| *Amsonia* | blue star | Apocynaceae | Gentianales | 188 |
| *Anacamptis* | pyramidal orchid | Orchidaceae | Asparagales | 42 |
| *Anacardium* | cashew | Anacardiaceae | Sapindales | 142 |
| *Anacyclus* | Atlas daisy | Compositae | Asterales | 216 |
| *Anagallis* | pimpernel | Primulaceae | Ericales | 176 |
| *Ananas* | pineapple | Bromeliaceae | Poales | 68 |
| *Anaphalis* | pearly everlasting | Compositae | Asterales | 214 |
| *Anchusa* | alkanet | Boraginaceae | not assigned | 182 |
| *Andromeda* | bog rosemary | Ericaceae | Ericales | 180 |
| *Androsace* | rock jasmine | Primulaceae | Ericales | 176 |
| *Anemone* | hepatica, pasque flower, wood anemone | Ranunculaceae | Ranunculales | 82 |
| *Anemopsis* | yerba mansa | Saururaceae | Piperales | 20 |
| *Anethum* | dill | Apiaceae | Apiales | 230 |
| *Angelica* | angelica | Apiaceae | Apiales | 230 |
| *Anthemis* | golden marguerite | Compositae | Asterales | 216 |
| *Anthriscus* | chervil, cow parsley | Apiaceae | Apiales | 230 |
| *Anthurium* | anthurium | Araceae | Alismatales | 32 |
| *Antirrhinum* | snapdragon | Plantaginaceae | Lamiales | 196 |
| *Aphelandra* | zebra plant | Acanthaceae | Lamiales | 202 |
| *Apium* | celery | Apiaceae | Apiales | 230 |

| Apocynum | dogbane | Apocynaceae | Gentianales | 188 |
| --- | --- | --- | --- | --- |
| Apodanthera | melon loco | Cucurbitaceae | Cucurbitales | 120 |
| Aquilegia | columbine | Ranunculaceae | Ranunculales | 82 |
| Arabis | rockcress | Brassicaceae | Brassicales | 152 |
| Arachis | peanut | Fabaceae | Fabales | 102 |
| Aralia | Hercules club, devil's walking stick | Araliaceae | Apiales | 228 |
| Arbutus | madrone, strawberry tree | Ericaceae | Ericales | 180 |
| Arctium | burdock | Compositae | Asterales | 210 |
| Arctostaphylos | bearberry | Ericaceae | Ericales | 180 |
| Ardisia | marlberry | Myrsinaceae | Ericales | 176 |
| Arenaria | sandwort | Primulaceae | Caryophyllales | 160 |
| Arenga | sugar palm | Arecaceae | Arecales | 58 |
| Argemone | prickly poppy | Papaveraceae | Ranunculales | 80 |
| Argyranthemum | marguerite | Compositae | Asterales | 216 |
| Arisaema | arisaema, green dragon | Araceae | Alismatales | 32 |
| Aristolochia | Dutchman's pipe, birthwort | Aristolochiaceae | Piperales | 20 |
| Aristotelia | wineberry | Elaeocarpaceae | Oxalidales | 124 |
| Armeria | sea pink, thrift | Plumbaginaceae | Caryophyllales | 156 |
| Armoracia | horseradish | Brassicaceae | Brassicales | 152 |
| Arnoglossum | Indian plantain | Compositae | Asterales | 214 |
| Aronia | chokeberry | Rosaceae | Rosales | 108 |
| Artemisia | mugwort, sagebrush, wormwood, tarragon | Compositae | Asterales | 216 |
| Artocarpus | breadfruit | Moraceae | Rosales | 112 |
| Arum | cuckoo pint, lords and ladies | Araceae | Alismatales | 32 |
| Aruncus | goat's beard | Rosaceae | Rosales | 108 |
| Asarum | wild ginger | Aristolochiaceae | Piperales | 20 |
| Asclepias | milkweed | Apocynaceae | Gentianales | 188 |
| Asparagus | asparagus, asparagus fern | Asparagaceae | Asparagales | 54 |
| Asphodelus | asphodel | Xanthorrhoeaceae | Asparagales | 48 |
| Astelia | bush flax | Asteliaceae | Asparagales | 44 |
| Aster | aster, Michaelmas daisy | Compositae | Asterales | 216 |
| Astilbe | astilbe, false spirea | Saxifragaceae | Saxifragales | 94 |
| Astragalus | milk vetch, locoweed | Fabaceae | Fabales | 102 |
| Atriplex | salt bush | Amaranthaceae | Caryophyllales | 162 |
| Atropa | belladonna, deadly nightshade | Solanaceae | Solanales | 192 |
| Aubrieta | aubrieta | Brassicaceae | Brassicales | 152 |
| Aucuba | spotted laurel | Garryaceae | Garryales | 184 |
| Avena | oats | Poaceae | Poales | 74 |
| Averrhoa | star fruit | Oxalidaceae | Oxalidales | 124 |
| Avicennia | black mangrove | Acanthaceae | Lamiales | 202 |

| | | | | |
|---|---|---|---|---|
| *Azara* | azara, vanilla tree | Salicaceae | Malpighiales | 130 |
| *Baileya* | desert marigold | Compositae | Asterales | 220 |
| *Balduina* | honeycomb head | Compositae | Asterales | 220 |
| *Bambusa* | bamboo | Poaceae | Poales | 74 |
| *Banksia* | banksia | Proteaceae | Proteales | 86 |
| *Barnadesia* | barnadesia | Compositae | Asterales | 208 |
| *Bauera* | river rose | Cunoniaceae | Oxalidales | 124 |
| *Bauhinia* | orchid tree | Fabaceae | Fabales | 104 |
| *Begonia* | begonia | Begoniaceae | Cucurbitales | 122 |
| *Bellis* | daisy | Compositae | Asterales | 216 |
| *Berberis* | barberry, mahonia | Berberidaceae | Ranunculales | 82 |
| *Bergenia* | bergenia | Saxifragaceae | Saxifragales | 94 |
| *Beta* | beet, chard | Amaranthaceae | Caryophyllales | 162 |
| *Betula* | birch | Betulaceae | Fagales | 118 |
| *Bidens* | bur-marigold | Compositae | Asterales | 220 |
| *Bignonia* | crossvine | Bignoniaceae | Lamiales | 202 |
| *Billia* | billia | Sapindaceae | Sapindales | 144 |
| *Billardiera* | purple apple-berry | Pittosporaceae | Apiales | 230 |
| *Bistorta* | bistort | Polygonaceae | Caryophyllales | 158 |
| *Bletilla* | ground orchid, urn orchid | Orchidaceae | Asparagales | 42 |
| *Boehmeria* | ramie, China grass | Urticaceae | Rosales | 112 |
| *Boltonia* | boltonia, false chamomile | Compositae | Asterales | 216 |
| *Bomarea* | climbing alstroemeria | Alstroemeriaceae | Liliales | 38 |
| *Borago* | borage | Boraginaceae | not assigned | 182 |
| *Boronia* | boronia | Rutaceae | Sapindales | 142 |
| *Bougainvillea* | bougainvillea | Nyctaginaceae | Caryophyllales | 164 |
| *Bouvardia* | bouvardia, firecracker bush | Rubiaceae | Gentianales | 186 |
| *Boykinia* | boykinia | Saxifragaceae | Saxifragales | 94 |
| *Brabejum* | wild almond, wild chestnut | Proteaceae | Proteales | 86 |
| *Brachycome* | Swan River daisy | Compositae | Asterales | 216 |
| *Brachypodium* | false brome grass | Poaceae | Poales | 72 |
| *Brassica* | cabbage, broccoli, cauliflower, kale, kohlrabi, canola, turnip, Brussels sprouts, mustard weed | Brassicaceae | Brassicales | 152 |
| *Brickellia* | brickelbush | Compositae | Asterales | 218 |
| *Briza* | quaking grass | Poaceae | Poales | 72 |
| *Bromelia* | tank plant | Bromeliaceae | Poales | 68 |
| *Bromus* | brome grass | Poaceae | Poales | 72 |
| *Broussonetia* | paper mulberry | Moraceae | Rosales | 112 |
| *Brugmansia* | angel's trumpet | Solanaceae | Solanales | 192 |
| *Brunfelsia* | yesterday-today-and-tomorrow | Solanaceae | Solanales | 192 |
| *Bryonia* | bryony | Cucurbitaceae | Cucurbitales | 120 |

| Buddleja | butterfly bush | Scrophulariaceae | Lamiales | 198 |
|---|---|---|---|---|
| Bulbine | onionweed | Xanthorrhoeaceae | Asperagales | 48 |
| Buxus | box | Buxaceae | Buxales | 88 |
| Caesalpinia | bird-of-paradise | Fabaceae | Fabales | 104 |
| Caladium | Indian kale | Araceae | Alismatales | 32 |
| Calamagrostis | small-reed | Poaceae | Poales | 72 |
| Calamus | rattan palm | Arecaceae | Arecales | 58 |
| Calanthe | calanthe | Orchidaceae | Asparagales | 42 |
| Calathea | peacock plant | Marantaceae | Zingiberales | 66 |
| Calliandra | powderpuff | Fabaceae | Fabales | 104 |
| Callicarpa | beautyberry | Lamiaceae | Lamiales | 200 |
| Callirhoe | buffalo rose, poppy mallow | Malvaceae | Malvales | 146 |
| Callisia | inch plant, basket plant | Commelinaceae | Commelinales | 60 |
| Callistemon | bottlebrush | Myrtaceae | Myrtales | 140 |
| Callistephus | China aster | Compositae | Asterales | 216 |
| Callitriche | water star-wort | Plantaginaceae | Lamiales | 196 |
| Calluna | heather, ling | Ericaceae | Ericales | 180 |
| Caltha | marsh marigold, king cup | Ranunculaceae | Ranunculales | 82 |
| Camassia | camass | Asparagaceae | Asparagales | 56 |
| Camellia | camellia, tea | Theaceae | Ericales | 178 |
| Camissonia | evening primrose, suncup | Onagraceae | Myrtales | 138 |
| Campanula | bellflower, Canterbury bells, harebell, bluebell of Scotland | Campanulaceae | Asterales | 206 |
| Campsis | trumpet creeper or vine | Bignoniaceae | Lamiales | 202 |
| Canna | canna, Indian shot | Cannaceae | Zingiberales | 64 |
| Capsella | shepherd's purse | Brassicaceae | Brassicales | 152 |
| Capsicum | bell pepper, chili pepper, pimento, paprika | Solanaceae | Solanales | 192 |
| Cardamine | milkmaids, cuckoo flower, lady's smock | Brassicaceae | Brassicales | 152 |
| Cardiocrinum | giant lily | Liliaceae | Liliales | 40 |
| Carduus | thistle | Compositae | Asterales | 210 |
| Carex | sedge | Cyperaceae | Poales | 70 |
| Carphephorus | chaffhead, vanilla leaf | Compositae | Asterales | 218 |
| Carpinus | hornbeam | Betulaceae | Fagales | 118 |
| Carpobrotus | Hottentot fig | Aizoaceae | Caryophyllales | 162 |
| Carthamus | safflower | Compositae | Asterales | 210 |
| Carum | caraway | Apiaceae | Apiales | 230 |
| Carya | pecan, hickory nut | Juglandaceae | Fagales | 116 |
| Caryota | fishtail palm | Arecaceae | Arecales | 58 |
| Cassia | golden shower tree | Fabaceae | Fabales | 104 |
| Cassiope | white mountain heather | Ericaceae | Ericales | 180 |
| Castanea | chestnut | Fagaceae | Fagales | 114 |

| | | | | |
|---|---|---|---|---|
| *Castanopsis* | golden chestnut | Fagaceae | Fagales | 114 |
| *Casuarina* | she-oak, iron wood | Casuarinaceae | Fagales | 118 |
| *Catalpa* | Indian bean tree | Bignoniaceae | Lamiales | 202 |
| *Catananche* | cupid's dart | Compositae | Asterales | 212 |
| *Catharanthus* | Madagascar periwinkle | Apocynaceae | Gentianales | 188 |
| *Cattleya* | cattleya orchid | Orchidaceae | Asparagales | 42 |
| *Ceanothus* | California lilac | Rhamnaceae | Rosales | 110 |
| *Celosia* | cockscomb | Amaranthaceae | Caryophyllales | 162 |
| *Centaurea* | cornflower, knapweed | Compositae | Asterales | 210 |
| *Centaurium* | centaury | Gentianaceae | Gentianales | 186 |
| *Cephalanthus* | buttonbush | Rubiaceae | Gentianales | 186 |
| *Cephalaria* | giant scabious | Dipsacaceae | Dipsacales | 224 |
| *Cerastium* | chickweed, snow-in-summer | Caryophyllaceae | Caryophyllales | 160 |
| *Ceratonia* | carob, lotus bean | Fabaceae | Fabales | 104 |
| *Ceratostigma* | plumbago | Plumbaginaceae | Caryophyllales | 156 |
| *Cercis* | redbud, Judas tree | Fabaceae | Fabales | 104 |
| *Cercocarpus* | mountain mahogany | Rosaceae | Rosales | 106 |
| *Ceropegia* | rosary vine, string of hearts | Acanthaceae | Gentianales | 188 |
| *Ceroxylon* | wax palm | Arecaceae | Arecales | 58 |
| *Cestrum* | night jasmine | Solanaceae | Solanales | 192 |
| *Chaenomeles* | quince, japonica | Rosaceae | Rosales | 108 |
| *Chamaemelum* | chamomile | Compositae | Asterales | 216 |
| *Chamaerops* | dwarf fan palm | Arecaceae | Arecales | 58 |
| *Chamelaucium* | waxflower | Myrtaceae | Myrtales | 140 |
| *Chamerion* | rose bay willow herb, fire weed | Onagraceae | Myrtales | 138 |
| *Chelidonium* | greater celandine | Papaveraceae | Ranunculales | 80 |
| *Chelone* | turtle head, shell flower | Plantaginaceae | Lamiales | 196 |
| *Chenopodium* | goosefoot, fat-hen | Amaranthaceae | Caryophyllales | 162 |
| *Chionanthus* | fringe tree | Oleaceae | Lamiales | 194 |
| *Choisya* | Mexican orange | Rutaceae | Sapindales | 142 |
| *Chondrilla* | skeleton weed | Compositae | Asterales | 212 |
| *Chrysanthemum* | chrysanthemum, marguerite | Compositae | Asterales | 216 |
| *Chrysopsis* | golden aster | Compositae | Asterales | 216 |
| *Chrysosplenium* | golden saxifrage | Saxifragaceae | Saxifragales | 94 |
| *Cichorium* | chicory, endive, radicchio | Compositae | Asterales | 212 |
| *Cinchona* | quinine | Rubiaceae | Gentianales | 186 |
| *Cineraria* | cineraria | Compositae | Asterales | 214 |
| *Cinnamomum* | cinnamon, camphor tree | Lauraceae | Laurales | 24 |
| *Circaea* | enchanter's nightshade | Onagraceae | Myrtales | 138 |
| *Cirsium* | thistle | Compositae | Asterales | 210 |
| *Cissus* | grape ivy, kangaroo vine | Vitaceae | Vitales | 100 |

| *Cistus* | rock rose | Cistaceae | Malvales | 148 |
|---|---|---|---|---|
| *Citrullus* | watermelon | Cucurbitaceae | Cucurbitales | 120 |
| *Citrus* | orange, lemon, lime, grapefruit | Rutaceae | Sapindales | 142 |
| *Cladium* | saw edge sedge | Cyperaceae | Poales | 70 |
| *Clarkia* | clarkia | Onagraceae | Myrtales | 138 |
| *Claytonia* | spring beauty, winter purslane | Portulacaceae | Caryophyllales | 164 |
| *Clematis* | clematis, old man's beard, traveller's joy | Ranunculaceae | Ranunculales | 82 |
| *Clerodendrum* | bleeding heart vine, glorybower | Lamiaceae | Lamiales | 200 |
| *Clintonia* | bluebead lily, wood lily | Liliaceae | Liliales | 40 |
| *Clivia* | clivia, kaffir lily | Amaryllidaceae | Asparagales | 50 |
| *Cneorum* | cneorum | Rutaceae | Sapindales | 142 |
| *Cobaea* | cup-and-saucer vine | Polemoniaceae | Ericales | 174 |
| *Cocos* | coconut palm | Arecaceae | Arecales | 58 |
| *Codiaeum* | croton | Euphorbiaceae | Malphighiales | 126 |
| *Codonopsis* | bonnet bellflower | Campanulaceae | Asterales | 206 |
| *Coffea* | coffee | Rubiaceae | Gentianales | 186 |
| *Colchicum* | autumn crocus, meadow saffron | Colchicaceae | Liliales | 38 |
| *Collomia* | collomia, tiny trumpet | Polemoniaceae | Ericales | 174 |
| *Colocasia* | taro, elephant's ear | Araceae | Alismatales | 32 |
| *Commelina* | dayflower | Commelinaceae | Commelinales | 60 |
| *Conium* | hemlock | Apiaceae | Apiales | 230 |
| *Conoclinium* | blue mist flower, thoroughwort | Compositae | Asterales | 218 |
| *Convallaria* | lily-of-the-valley | Asparagaceae | Asparagales | 54 |
| *Convolvulus* | bindweed, morning glory | Convolvulaceae | Solanales | 190 |
| *Conyza* | horseweed, asthma weed | Compositae | Asterales | 216 |
| *Copernicia* | wax or carnuba wax palm | Arecaceae | Arecales | 58 |
| *Coreopsis* | coreopsis, tickweed | Compositae | Asterales | 220 |
| *Coriandrum* | coriander | Apiaceae | Apiales | 230 |
| *Cornus* | dogwood, cornel | Cornaceae | Cornales | 172 |
| *Correa* | Australian fuchsia | Rutaceae | Sapindales | 142 |
| *Corydalis* | corydalis, fumewort | Papaveraceae | Ranunculales | 80 |
| *Corylopsis* | corylopsis | Hamamelidaceae | Saxifragales | 90 |
| *Corylus* | hazelnut, filbert | Betulaceae | Fagales | 118 |
| *Cosmos* | cosmos, cosmea | Compositae | Asterales | 220 |
| *Cotinus* | smoke bush | Anacardiaceae | Sapindales | 142 |
| *Cotoneaster* | cotoneaster | Rosaceae | Rosales | 108 |
| *Crambe* | sea kale | Brassicaceae | Brassicales | 152 |
| *Craspedia* | drumsticks | Compositae | Asterales | 214 |
| *Crassula* | jade plant, crassula | Crassulaceae | Saxifragales | 94 |
| *Crataegus* | hawthorn, may | Rosaceae | Rosales | 108 |
| *Crepis* | hawk's beard | Compositae | Asterales | 212 |

| *Crescentia* | calabash | Bignoniaceae | Lamiales | 202 |
|---|---|---|---|---|
| *Crinodendron* | lantern tree | Elaeocarpaceae | Oxalidales | 124 |
| *Crinum* | swamp lily, Cape lily | Amaryllidaceae | Asparagales | 50 |
| *Crithmum* | rock samphire | Apiaceae | Apiales | 230 |
| *Crocosmia* | crocosmia | Iridaceae | Asparagales | 44 |
| *Crocus* | crocus | Iridaceae | Asparagales | 44 |
| *Croton* | croton | Euphorbiaceae | Malphighiales | 126 |
| *Cryptantha* | hidden flower | Boraginaceae | not assigned | 182 |
| *Ctenanthe* | ctenanthe | Marantaceae | Zingiberales | 66 |
| *Cucumis* | cucumber, marrow | Cucurbitaceae | Cucurbitales | 120 |
| *Cucurbita* | squash, pumpkin, gourd, buffalo gourd, marrow | Cucurbitaceae | Cucurbitales | 120 |
| *Cuminum* | cumin | Apiaceae | Apiales | 230 |
| *Cunonia* | butterspoons | Cunoniaceae | Oxalidales | 124 |
| *Cuphea* | cuphea, cigar plant | Lythraceae | Myrtales | 136 |
| *Curcuma* | turmeric | Zingiberaceae | Zingiberales | 66 |
| *Cuscuta* | dodder | Convolvulaceae | Solanales | 190 |
| *Cyclamen* | cyclamen | Primulaceae | Ericales | 176 |
| *Cydonia* | quince | Rosaceae | Rosales | 108 |
| *Cynara* | globe artichoke, cardoon | Compositae | Asterales | 210 |
| *Cynoglossum* | hound's tongue | Boraginaceae | not assigned | 182 |
| *Cyperus* | papyrus | Cyperaceae | Poales | 70 |
| *Cypripedium* | lady's slipper orchid | Orchidaceae | Asparagales | 42 |
| *Cytisus* | broom | Fabaceae | Fabales | 102 |
| *Daboecia* | St. Daboc's heath | Ericaceae | Ericales | 180 |
| *Dactylis* | cock's foot | Poaceae | Poales | 72 |
| *Dactylorhiza* | marsh orchid, common spotted orchid | Orchidaceae | Asparagales | 42 |
| *Dahlia* | dahlia | Compositae | Asterales | 220 |
| *Daphne* | daphne, mezereon, spurge laurel | Thymelaeaceae | Malvales | 148 |
| *Daphnopsis* | daphnopsis | Thymelaeaceae | Malvales | 148 |
| *Darmera* | umbrella plant | Saxifragaceae | Saxifragales | 94 |
| *Datura* | thorn apple | Solanaceae | Solanales | 192 |
| *Daucus* | carrot | Apiaceae | Apiales | 230 |
| *Decaisnea* | decaisnea | Lardizabalaceae | Ranunculales | 80 |
| *Decodon* | swamp loosestrife | Lythraceae | Myrtales | 136 |
| *Decumaria* | climbing hydrangea | Hydrangeaceae | Cornales | 172 |
| *Delosperma* | ice plant | Aizoaceae | Caryophyllales | 162 |
| *Delphinium* | delphinium, larkspur | Ranunculaceae | Ranunculales | 82 |
| *Dendrobium* | dendrobium | Orchidaceae | Asparagales | 42 |
| *Deschampsia* | hair grass | Poaceae | Poales | 72 |
| *Deutzia* | deutzia | Hydrangeaceae | Cornales | 172 |

| | | | | |
|---|---|---|---|---|
| *Dianella* | flax lily | Hemerocallidaceae | Asparagales | 46 |
| *Dianthus* | carnation, sweet William, pink | Caryophyllaceae | Caryophyllales | 160 |
| *Diapensia* | diapensia, pincushion plant | Diapensiaceae | Ericales | 178 |
| *Diascia* | diascia | Scrophulariaceae | Lamiales | 198 |
| *Dicentra* | bleeding heart, Dutchman's breeches | Papaveraceae | Ranunculales | 80 |
| *Dichondra* | dichondra | Convolvulaceae | Solanales | 190 |
| *Dictamnus* | burning bush, gas plant | Rutaceae | Sapindales | 142 |
| *Dieffenbachia* | dieffenbachia | Araceae | Alismatales | 32 |
| *Dierama* | Venus' fishing rod, fairy wand, wandflower | Iridaceae | Asparagales | 44 |
| *Digitalis* | foxglove | Plantaginaceae | Lamiales | 196 |
| *Dioscorea* | yam | Dioscoreaceae | Dioscoreales | 36 |
| *Dipelta* | dipelta | Caprifoliaceae | Dipsacales | 224 |
| *Dipsacus* | teasel | Caprifoliaceae | Dipsacales | 224 |
| *Dirca* | leatherwood | Thymelaeaceae | Malvales | 148 |
| *Dodecatheon* | shooting star | Primulaceae | Ericales | 176 |
| *Doronicum* | leopard's bane | Compositae | Asterales | 214 |
| *Draba* | draba, whitlow grass | Brassicaceae | Brassicales | 152 |
| *Dracaena* | dracaena, dragon's blood | Asparagaceae | Asparagales | 54 |
| *Dracophyllum* | dracophyllum | Ericaceae | Ericales | 180 |
| *Dracunculus* | dragon arum | Araceae | Alismatales | 32 |
| *Drimys* | winter's bark | Winteraceae | Canellales | 18 |
| *Dryas* | mountain avens | Rosaceae | Rosales | 106 |
| *Dudleya* | cliff lettuce, dudleya | Crassulaceae | Saxifragales | 94 |
| *Duranta* | golden dewdrop | Verbenaceae | Lamiales | 202 |
| *Ecballium* | squirting cucumber | Cucurbitaceae | Cucurbitales | 120 |
| *Echeveria* | hen and chickens | Crassulaceae | Saxifragales | 94 |
| *Echinacea* | coneflower | Compositae | Asterales | 218 |
| *Echinocystis* | bur cucumber, wild cucumber | Cucurbitaceae | Cucurbitales | 120 |
| *Echium* | viper's bugloss | Boraginaceae | not assigned | 182 |
| *Edgeworthia* | paper bush | Thymelaeaceae | Malvales | 148 |
| *Eichhornia* | water hyacinth | Pontederiaceae | Commelinales | 60 |
| *Elaeagnus* | oleaster, Russian olive, silver berry | Elaeagnaceae | Rosales | 110 |
| *Elaeis* | oil palm | Arecaceae | Arecales | 58 |
| *Elaeocarpus* | blueberry ash, Indian bead tree | Elaeocarpaceae | Oxalidales | 124 |
| *Elegia* | restio | Restionaceae | Poales | 70 |
| *Eleocharis* | spike rush, Chinese water chestnut | Cyperaceae | Poales | 70 |
| *Elettaria* | cardamom | Zingiberaceae | Zingiberales | 66 |
| *Elymus* | wheatgrass, wild rye | Poaceae | Poales | 72 |
| *Embothrium* | Chilean flame tree | Proteaceae | Proteales | 86 |

| *Empetrum* | crowberry | Ericaceae | Ericales | 180 |
|---|---|---|---|---|
| *Engelhardtia* | engelhardtia, cheo tia | Juglandaceae | Fagales | 116 |
| *Enkianthus* | Chinese bell flower | Ericaceae | Ericales | 180 |
| *Ensete* | Abyssian banana | Musaceae | Zingiberales | 64 |
| *Epacris* | Australian fuchsia | Ericaceae | Ericales | 180 |
| *Epidendrum* | star orchid | Orchidaceae | Asparagales | 42 |
| *Epilobium* | willow herb | Onagraceae | Myrtales | 138 |
| *Epimedium* | bishop's hat, barrenwort | Berberidaceae | Ranunculales | 82 |
| *Epipactis* | heleborines | Orchidaceae | Asparagales | 42 |
| *Eranthis* | winter aconite | Ranunculaceae | Ranunculales | 82 |
| *Erechtites* | burnweed | Compositae | Asterales | 214 |
| *Eremurus* | foxtail lily | Xanthorrhoeaceae | Asparagales | 48 |
| *Erica* | heath, heather | Ericaceae | Ericales | 180 |
| *Ericameria* | rabbitbrush, golden brush | Compositae | Asterales | 216 |
| *Erigeron* | fleabane | Compositae | Asterales | 216 |
| *Eriogonum* | sulfur flower | Polygonaceae | Caryophyllales | 158 |
| *Eriophorum* | cotton grass | Cyperaceae | Poales | 70 |
| *Erodium* | heronsbill, storksbill | Geraniaceae | Geraniales | 134 |
| *Eryngium* | sea holly | Apiaceae | Apiales | 230 |
| *Erysimum* | wallflower | Brassicaceae | Brassicales | 152 |
| *Erythrina* | coral tree | Fabaceae | Fabales | 102 |
| *Erythronium* | trout lily, dog-tooth violet | Liliaceae | Liliales | 40 |
| *Eschscholzia* | California poppy | Papaveraceae | Ranunculales | 80 |
| *Etlingera* | torch lily | Zingiberaceae | Zingiberales | 66 |
| *Eucalyptus* | gum tree | Myrtaceae | Myrtales | 140 |
| *Eucnide* | rock nettle, sting bush | Loasaceae | Cornales | 172 |
| *Eucomis* | pineapple lily | Asparagaceae | Asparagales | 56 |
| *Eucryphia* | leatherwood | Cunoniaceae | Oxalidales | 124 |
| *Eugenia* | Australian bush cherry, Surinam cherry | Myrtaceae | Myrtales | 140 |
| *Eupatorium* | Joe-pye weed, agrimony | Compositae | Asterales | 218 |
| *Euphorbia* | poinsettia, spurge | Euphorbiaceae | Malpighiales | 126 |
| *Eustoma* | lisianthus, prairie gentian | Gentianaceae | Gentianales | 186 |
| *Exacum* | Persian violet | Gentianaceae | Gentianales | 186 |
| *Exochorda* | pearl bush | Rosaceae | Rosales | 108 |
| *Exothea* | inkwood | Sapindaceae | Sapindales | 144 |
| *Fagopyrum* | buckwheat | Polygonaceae | Caryophyllales | 158 |
| *Fagus* | beech | Fagaceae | Fagales | 114 |
| *Fallopia* | Japanese knotweed, Russian vine | Polygonaceae | Caryophyllales | 158 |
| *Fatshedera* | fatshedera | Araliaceae | Apiales | 228 |
| *Fatsia* | fatsia, Japanese aralia | Araliaceae | Apiales | 228 |
| *Felicia* | kingfisher daisy | Compositae | Asterales | 216 |

| | | | | |
|---|---|---|---|---|
| *Fenestraria* | baby toes | Aizoaceae | Caryophyllales | 162 |
| *Festuca* | fescue grass | Poaceae | Poales | 72 |
| *Ficus* | figs, banyan tree | Moraceae | Rosales | 112 |
| *Filago* | cottonrose | Compositae | Asterales | 214 |
| *Filipendula* | meadowsweet, dropwort | Rosaceae | Rosales | 108 |
| *Floerkea* | false mermaid | Limnanthaceae | Brassicales | 150 |
| *Foeniculum* | fennel | Apiaceae | Apiales | 230 |
| *Forestiera* | swamp privet | Oleaceae | Lamiales | 194 |
| *Forsythia* | forsythia | Oleaceae | Lamiales | 194 |
| *Fothergilla* | fothergilla | Hamamelidaceae | Saxifragales | 90 |
| *Frangula* | alder buckthorn | Rhamnaceae | Rosales | 110 |
| *Franklinia* | Franklin tree | Theaceae | Ericales | 178 |
| *Frasera* | green gentian | Gentianaceae | Gentianales | 186 |
| *Fraxinus* | ash | Oleaceae | Lamiales | 194 |
| *Freesia* | freesia | Iridaceae | Asparagales | 44 |
| *Fritillaria* | fritillary, snake's head lily | Liliaceae | Liliales | 40 |
| *Fuchsia* | fuchsia | Onagraceae | Myrtales | 138 |
| *Fumaria* | fumitory | Papaveraceae | Ranunculales | 80 |
| *Gaillardia* | blanket flower | Compositae | Asterales | 220 |
| *Galanthus* | snowdrop | Amaryllidaceae | Asparagales | 50 |
| *Galax* | galax, beetleweed | Diapensiaceae | Ericales | 178 |
| *Galium* | bedstraw, sweet woodruff, goose grass, cleavers | Rubiaceae | Gentianales | 186 |
| *Galtonia* | summer hyacinth, Galton lily | Asparagaceae | Asparagales | 56 |
| *Gardenia* | gardenia | Rubiaceae | Gentianales | 186 |
| *Garrya* | garrya, silktassel | Garryaceae | Garryales | 184 |
| *Gaultheria* | wintergreen, snowberry, tea berry | Ericaceae | Ericales | 180 |
| *Genista* | broom, greenwood | Fabaceae | Fabales | 102 |
| *Gentiana* | gentian | Gentianaceae | Gentianales | 186 |
| *Gentianella* | dwarf gentian, felwort | Gentianaceae | Gentianales | 186 |
| *Gentianopsis* | fringed gentian | Gentianaceae | Gentianales | 186 |
| *Geranium* | wild and hardy geranium, cranesbill, herb Robert | Geraniaceae | Geraniales | 134 |
| *Gerbera* | gerbera | Compositae | Asterales | 208 |
| *Geum* | geum, avens, herb bennet | Rosaceae | Rosales | 106 |
| *Gilia* | blue bowls, thimble flower | Polemoniaceae | Ericales | 174 |
| *Gladiolus* | gladiolus | Iridaceae | Asparagales | 44 |
| *Glandularia* | mock vervain | Verbenaceae | Lamiales | 202 |
| *Glaucium* | horned poppy | Papaveraceae | Ranunculales | 80 |
| *Glechoma* | ground ivy | Lamiaceae | Lamiales | 200 |
| *Gleditsia* | honey locust | Fabaceae | Fabales | 104 |
| *Gloriosa* | gloriosa lily | Colchicaceae | Liliales | 38 |

| *Glottiphyllum* | tongue leaf plant | Aizoaceae | Caryophyllales | 162 |
|---|---|---|---|---|
| *Glycine* | soybean | Fabaceae | Fabales | 102 |
| *Glycyrrhiza* | liquorice | Fabaceae | Fabales | 102 |
| *Gnaphalium* | cudweed | Compositae | Asterales | 214 |
| *Gordonia* | loblolly bay | Theaceae | Ericales | 178 |
| *Gomphrena* | globe amaranth | Amaranthaceae | Caryophyllales | 162 |
| *Gossypium* | cotton | Malvaceae | Malvales | 146 |
| *Grevillea* | silky oak | Proteaceae | Proteales | 86 |
| *Grindelia* | gumweed | Compositae | Asterales | 216 |
| *Griselinia* | broad leaf | Araliaceae | Apiales | 228 |
| *Gunnera* | gunnera | Gunneraceae | Gunnerales | 88 |
| *Gymnocladus* | coffee tree | Fabaceae | Fabales | 104 |
| *Gypsophila* | baby's breath, gypsophila | Caryophyllaceae | Caryophyllales | 160 |
| *Hakea* | pincushion flower | Proteaceae | Proteales | 86 |
| x *Halimiocistus* | halimiocistus | Cistaceae | Malvales | 148 |
| *Halimium* | halimium | Cistaceae | Malvales | 148 |
| *Hamamelis* | witch hazel | Hamamelidaceae | Saxifragales | 90 |
| *Haworthia* | haworthia | Asphodelaceae | Asparagales | 48 |
| *Hedera* | ivy | Araliaceae | Apiales | 228 |
| *Hedychium* | ginger lily | Zingiberaceae | Zingiberales | 66 |
| *Helenium* | sneezeweed | Compositae | Asterales | 220 |
| *Helianthemum* | rock rose | Cistaceae | Malvales | 148 |
| *Helianthus* | sunflower, Jerusalem artichoke | Compositae | Asterales | 218 |
| *Heliconia* | lobster claw, heliconia, parrot flower | Heliconiaceae | Zingiberales | 62 |
| *Heliophila* | heliophila | Brassicaceae | Brassicales | 152 |
| *Heliotropium* | heliotrope | Boraginaceae | not assigned | 182 |
| *Helleborus* | Christmas or Lenten rose | Ranunculaceae | Ranunculales | 82 |
| *Hemerocallis* | daylily | Hemerocallidaceae | Asparagales | 46 |
| *Hemiphylacus* | hemiphylacus | Asparagaceae | Asparagales | 54 |
| *Heptacodium* | seven sons flower | Caprifoliaceae | Dipsacales | 224 |
| *Heracleum* | hog weed | Apiaceae | Apiales | 230 |
| *Hesperis* | dame's violet, rocket | Brassicaceae | Brassicales | 152 |
| *Hesperocallis* | desert lily | Asparagaceae | Asparagales | 56 |
| *Heteranthera* | mudplantain | Pontederiaceae | Commelinales | 60 |
| *Heterotheca* | golden aster | Compositae | Asterales | 216 |
| *Heuchera* | coral bells | Saxifragaceae | Saxifragales | 94 |
| *Hevea* | rubber tree | Euphorbiaceae | Malpighiales | 126 |
| *Hibiscus* | hibiscus, rose mallow | Malvaceae | Malvales | 146 |
| *Hieracium* | hawkweed | Compositae | Asterales | 212 |
| *Hillebrandia* | Hawaiian begonia | Begoniaceae | Cucurbitales | 122 |
| *Hippeastrum* | amaryllis | Amaryllidaceae | Asparagales | 50 |

| | | | | |
|---|---|---|---|---|
| *Hippophae* | sea buckthorn | Eleagnaceae | Rosales | 110 |
| *Hippuris* | mare's tail | Plantaginaceae | Lamiales | 196 |
| *Hoffmannseggia* | hog potato, Indian rush pea | Fabaceae | Fabales | 104 |
| *Holboellia* | holboellia | Lardizabalaceae | Ranunculales | 80 |
| *Hordeum* | barley | Poaceae | Poales | 74 |
| *Hosta* | hosta, plantain lily | Agavaceae | Asparagales | 56 |
| *Hottonia* | featherfoil, water violet | Primulaceae | Ericales | 176 |
| *Houttuynia* | houttuynia | Saururaceae | Piperales | 20 |
| *Hoya* | waxplant, waxflower | Apocynaceae | Gentianales | 188 |
| *Hudsonia* | beach heather | Cistaceae | Malvales | 148 |
| *Hyacinthoides* | bluebell, wood hyacinth | Hyacinthaceae | Asparagales | 56 |
| *Hyacinthus* | hyacinth | Hyacinthaceae | Asparagales | 56 |
| *Hybanthus* | green violet | Violaceae | Malpighiales | 130 |
| *Hydrangea* | hydrangea | Hydrangeaceae | Cornales | 172 |
| *Hymenocallis* | spider lily | Amaryllidaceae | Asparagales | 50 |
| *Hymenoxys* | rubber sunflower | Compositae | Asterales | 220 |
| *Hyoscyamus* | henbane | Solanaceae | Solanales | 192 |
| *Hypericum* | St. John's wort, rose of Sharon | Hypericaceae | Malpighiales | 132 |
| *Hypoestes* | polka-dot plant | Acanthaceae | Lamiales | 202 |
| *Hypoxis* | hypoxis | Hypoxidaceae | Asperagales | 44 |
| *Hyssopus* | hyssop | Lamiaceae | Lamiales | 200 |
| *Iberis* | candytuft | Brassicaceae | Brassicales | 152 |
| *Idesia* | idesia, wonder tree | Salicaceae | Malpighiales | 130 |
| *Ilex* | holly, yerba maté | Aquifoliaceae | Aquifoliales | 204 |
| *Illicium* | star anise, anise tree | Schisandraceae | Austrobaileyales | 11 |
| *Impatiens* | impatiens, busy lizzie, touch-me-not, balsam | Balsaminaceae | Ericales | 174 |
| *Imperata* | Japanese blood grass | Poaceae | Poales | 72 |
| *Incarvillea* | hardy gloxinia | Bignoniaceae | Lamiales | 202 |
| *Indigofera* | indigo | Fabaceae | Fabales | 102 |
| *Ipheion* | spring star flower | Amaryllidaceae | Asparagales | 52 |
| *Ipomoea* | morning glory, sweet potato | Convolvulaceae | Solanales | 190 |
| *Iris* | iris | Iridaceae | Asparagales | 44 |
| *Isatis* | woad | Brassicaceae | Brassicales | 152 |
| *Ixia* | African corn lily | Iridaceae | Asparagales | 44 |
| *Jacaranda* | jacaranda | Bignoniaceae | Lamiales | 202 |
| *Jacquemontia* | clustervine | Convolvulaceae | Solanales | 190 |
| *Jamesia* | waxflower | Hydrangeaceae | Cornales | 172 |
| *Jasione* | sheep's bit | Campanulaceae | Asterales | 206 |
| *Jasminum* | jasmine | Oleaceae | Lamiales | 194 |
| *Jatropha* | coral plant, physic nut | Euphorbiaceae | Malpighiales | 126 |
| *Juglans* | walnut | Juglandaceae | Fagales | 116 |

| | | | | |
|---|---|---|---|---|
| *Juncus* | rush | Juncaceae | Poales | 70 |
| *Justicia* | shrimp plant | Acanthaceae | Lamiales | 202 |
| *Kadsura* | kadsura | Schisandraceae | Austrobaileyales | 11 |
| *Kaempferia* | peacock ginger | Zingiberaceae | Zingiberales | 66 |
| *Kalanchoe* | kalanchoe, maternity felt or panda plant | Crassulaceae | Saxifragales | 94 |
| *Kalmia* | mountain laurel, alpine laurel, calico bush | Ericaceae | Ericales | 180 |
| *Kalmiopsis* | kalmiopsis | Ericaceae | Ericales | 180 |
| *Kerria* | Jew's mallow | Rosaceae | Rosales | 108 |
| *Kerriodoxa* | white elephant palm | Arecaceae | Arecales | 58 |
| *Kigelia* | sausage tree | Bignoniaceae | Lamiales | 202 |
| *Kissenia* | kissenia, sandpaper bush | Loasaceae | Cornales | 172 |
| *Knautia* | field scabious | Caprifoliaceae | Dipsacales | 224 |
| *Kniphofia* | red-hot poker, torch lily | Xanthorrhoeaceae | Asparagales | 48 |
| *Koelreuteria* | goldenrain tree | Sapindaceae | Sapindales | 144 |
| *Kolkwitzia* | beauty bush | Caprifoliaceae | Dipsacales | 224 |
| *Krugiodendron* | leadwood | Rhamnaceae | Rosales | 110 |
| *Lablab* | hyacinth bean | Fabaceae | Fabales | 102 |
| *Laburnum* | golden chain | Fabaceae | Fabales | 102 |
| *Lactuca* | lettuce | Compositae | Asterales | 212 |
| *Lagenaria* | bottle gourd, calabash | Cucurbitaceae | Cucurbitales | 120 |
| *Lagerstroemia* | crepe myrtle | Lythraceae | Myrtales | 136 |
| *Lamium* | dead nettle, yellow archangel | Lamiaceae | Lamiales | 200 |
| *Lampranthus* | ice plant | Aizoaceae | Caryophyllales | 162 |
| *Lantana* | lantana, shrub verbena | Verbenaceae | Lamiales | 202 |
| *Lapageria* | Chilean bell flower | Philesiaceae | Liliales | 40 |
| *Laportea* | wood nettle | Urticaceae | Rosales | 112 |
| *Lathyrus* | everlasting pea, sweet pea | Fabaceae | Fabales | 102 |
| *Laurus* | bay laurel, sweet bay | Lauraceae | Laurales | 24 |
| *Lavandula* | lavender | Lamiaceae | Lamiales | 200 |
| *Lavatera* | tree mallow | Malvaceae | Malvales | 146 |
| *Lawsonia* | henna | Lythraceae | Myrtales | 136 |
| *Lemna* | duckweed | Araceae | Alismatales | 32 |
| *Lens* | lentil | Fabaceae | Fabales | 102 |
| *Leontopodium* | edelweiss | Compositae | Asterales | 214 |
| *Lepidium* | garden cress, pepperwort | Brassicaceae | Brassicales | 152 |
| *Leptospermum* | tea tree | Myrtaceae | Myrtales | 140 |
| *Leucadendron* | silver tree | Proteaceae | Proteales | 86 |
| *Leucanthemum* | Shasta daisy, ox-eye daisy | Compositae | Asterales | 216 |
| *Leucojum* | snowflake | Amaryllidaceae | Asparagales | 50 |
| *Leucophyllum* | silverleaf, Texas ranger | Scrophulariaceae | Lamiales | 198 |

| | | | | |
|---|---|---|---|---|
| *Leucopogon* | Australian currant | Ericaceae | Ericales | 180 |
| *Leucospermum* | pincushion shrub | Proteaceae | Proteales | 86 |
| *Leucothoe* | pearl flower | Ericaceae | Ericales | 180 |
| *Lewisia* | bitterroot, lewisia | Portulacaceae | Caryophyllales | 164 |
| *Leycesteria* | Himalayan honeysuckle, shrimp plant | Caprifoliaceae | Dipsacales | 224 |
| *Liatris* | gayfeather, blazing star | Compositae | Asterales | 218 |
| *Ligularia* | ligularia, giant groundsel | Compositae | Asterales | 214 |
| *Ligustrum* | privet | Oleaceae | Lamiales | 194 |
| *Lilium* | lily, tiger lily, Easter lily | Liliaceae | Liliales | 40 |
| *Limnanthes* | poached egg flower | Limnanthaceae | Brassicales | 150 |
| *Limonium* | statice, sea lavender | Plumbaginaceae | Caryophyllales | 156 |
| *Linaria* | toadflax | Plantaginaceae | Lamiales | 196 |
| *Lindera* | spice bush, wild allspice | Lauraceae | Laurales | 24 |
| *Linnaea* | twinflower | Caprifoliaceae | Dipsacales | 224 |
| *Linum* | flax, linseed | Linaceae | Malpighiales | 132 |
| *Lippia* | lemon verbena | Verbenaceae | Lamiales | 202 |
| *Liquidambar* | sweet gum tree | Altingiaceae | Saxifragales | 92 |
| *Liriodendron* | tulip tree | Magnoliaceae | Magnoliales | 22 |
| *Liriope* | lily turf | Asparagaceae | Asparagales | 54 |
| *Litchi* | lychee | Sapindaceae | Sapindales | 144 |
| *Lithocarpus* | tanbark oak | Fagaceae | Fagales | 114 |
| *Lithops* | living stones | Aizoaceae | Caryophyllales | 162 |
| *Lithospermum* | gromwell | Boraginaceae | not assigned | 182 |
| *Loasa* | loasa | Loasaceae | Cornales | 172 |
| *Lobelia* | lobelia, cardinal flower | Campanulaceae | Asterales | 206 |
| *Lolium* | rye grass | Poaceae | Poales | 72 |
| *Lonicera* | honeysuckle | Caprifoliaceae | Dipsacales | 224 |
| *Loropetalum* | Chinese witch hazel | Hamamelidaceae | Saxifragales | 90 |
| *Ludwigia* | seedbox | Onagraceae | Myrtales | 138 |
| *Luffa* | loofah, vegetable sponge | Cucurbitaceae | Cucurbitales | 120 |
| *Luma* | myrtle | Myrtaceae | Myrtales | 140 |
| *Lunaria* | honesty, money plant | Brassicaceae | Brassicales | 152 |
| *Lupinus* | lupin | Fabaceae | Fabales | 102 |
| *Luzula* | wood rush | Juncaceae | Poales | 70 |
| *Lycium* | Duke of Argyll's tea tree, desert thorn, wolfberry | Solanaceae | Solanales | 192 |
| *Lysichiton* | skunk cabbage | Araceae | Alismatales | 32 |
| *Lysimachia* | yellow loosestrife, creeping Jenny | Primulaceae | Ericales | 176 |
| *Lythrum* | purple loosestrife | Lythraceae | Myrtales | 136 |
| *Macadamia* | macadamia nut | Proteaceae | Proteales | 86 |
| *Machaeranthera* | tansy aster | Compositae | Asterales | 216 |

| | | | | |
|---|---|---|---|---|
| *Maclura* | Osage orange | Moraceae | Rosales | 112 |
| *Magnolia* | magnolia | Magnoliaceae | Magnoliales | 22 |
| *Malephora* | ice plant | Aizoaceae | Caryophyllales | 162 |
| *Malus* | apple, crab-apple | Rosaceae | Rosales | 108 |
| *Malva* | mallow | Malvaceae | Malvales | 146 |
| *Mandragora* | mandrake | Solanaceae | Solanales | 192 |
| *Mangifera* | mango | Anacardiaceae | Sapindales | 142 |
| *Manihot* | tapioca, cassava | Euphorbiaceae | Malpighiales | 126 |
| *Maranta* | prayer plant, arrowroot | Marantaceae | Zingiberales | 66 |
| *Marrubium* | horehound mint | Lamiaceae | Lamiales | 200 |
| *Marsdenia* | Madagascar jasmine | Apocynaceae | Gentianales | 188 |
| *Matelea* | milkvine | Apocynaceae | Gentianales | 188 |
| *Matricaria* | pineapple weed, chamomile | Compositae | Asterales | 216 |
| *Matthiola* | stock | Brassicaceae | Brassicales | 152 |
| *Meconopsis* | Himalayan poppy, Welsh poppy | Papaveraceae | Ranunculales | 80 |
| *Medicago* | alfalfa, lucerne | Fabaceae | Fabales | 102 |
| *Melissa* | lemon balm | Lamiaceae | Lamiales | 200 |
| *Mentha* | mint, peppermint, spearmint | Lamiaceae | Lamiales | 200 |
| *Mentzelia* | blazing star, stick leaf | Loasaceae | Cornales | 172 |
| *Mercurialis* | dog's mercury | Euphorbiacae | Malpighiales | 126 |
| *Merremia* | Hawaiian wood rose | Convolvulaceae | Solanales | 190 |
| *Mertensia* | mertensia, oyster plant | Boraginaceae | not assigned | 182 |
| *Mesembryanthemum* | ice plant, Livingstone daisy | Aizoaceae | Caryophyllales | 162 |
| *Metopium* | Florida poisonwood | Anacardiaceae | Sapindales | 142 |
| *Metrosideros* | New Zealand Christmas tree | Myrtaceae | Myrtales | 140 |
| *Metroxylon* | sago palm | Arecaceae | Arecales | 58 |
| *Mikania* | climbing boneset, climbing hempweed | Compositae | Asterales | 218 |
| *Milligania* | | Asteliaceae | Asparagales | 44 |
| *Mimosa* | mimosa, sensitive plant | Fabaceae | Fabales | 104 |
| *Minuartia* | sandwort | Caryophyllaceae | Caryophyllales | 160 |
| *Mirabilis* | four o'clock plant, marvel of Peru | Nyctaginaceae | Caryophyllales | 164 |
| *Miscanthus* | eulalia | Poaceae | Poales | 72 |
| *Molinia* | moor grass | Poaceae | Poales | 72 |
| *Moluccella* | bells of Ireland, shell flower | Lamiaceae | Lamiales | 200 |
| *Monarda* | bee balm, bergamot, horsemint | Lamiaceae | Lamiales | 200 |
| *Monstera* | split leaf philodendron, Swiss cheese plant | Araceae | Alismatales | 32 |
| *Morella* | bayberry, wax myrtle | Myricaceae | Fagales | 116 |
| *Morus* | mulberry | Moraceae | Rosales | 112 |
| *Muhlenbergia* | hair grass | Poaceae | Poales | 72 |
| *Musa* | banana, plantain | Musaceae | Zingiberales | 64 |

| *Muscari* | grape hyacinth | Hyacinthaceae | Asparagales | 56 |
|---|---|---|---|---|
| *Myosotis* | forget-me-not | Boraginaceae | not assigned | 182 |
| *Myrica* | bog myrtle, sweet gale | Myricaceae | Fagales | 116 |
| *Myristica* | nutmeg, mace | Myristicaceae | Magnoliales | 22 |
| *Myrrhis* | sweet cicely | Apiaceae | Apiales | 230 |
| *Myrsine* | Cape beech | Myrsinaceae | Ericales | 176 |
| *Myrtus* | myrtle | Myrtaceae | Myrtales | 140 |
| *Nandina* | heavenly bamboo, sacred bamboo | Berberidaceae | Ranunculales | 82 |
| *Narcissus* | daffodil, jonquil | Amaryllidaceae | Asparagales | 50 |
| *Narthecium* | bog asphodel | Nartheciaceae | Dioscoreales | 36 |
| *Nelumbo* | lotus | Nelumbonaceae | Proteales | 84 |
| *Nemacladus* | threadstem | Campanulaceae | Asterales | 206 |
| *Nemesia* | nemesia | Scrophulariaceae | Lamiales | 198 |
| *Neoregelia* | heart of flame, blushing bromeliad | Bromeliaceae | Poales | 68 |
| *Nepeta* | catnip, catmint | Lamiaceae | Lamiales | 200 |
| *Nerium* | oleander | Apocynaceae | Gentianales | 188 |
| *Nicotiana* | tobacco, tree tobacco | Solanaceae | Solanales | 192 |
| *Nierembergia* | cup flower | Solanaceae | Solanales | 192 |
| *Nigella* | love-in-a-mist | Ranunculaceae | Ranunculales | 82 |
| *Nolana* | little bells | Solanaceae | Solanales | 192 |
| *Nomocharis* | nomocharis | Liliaceae | Liliales | 40 |
| *Nothofagus* | southern beech | Nothofagaceae | Fagales | 114 |
| *Nothoscordum* | false garlic, crow poison | Amaryllidaceae | Asparagales | 52 |
| *Nuphar* | brandy balls, yellow water-lily | Nymphaeaceae | Nymphaeales | 14 |
| *Nyctaginia* | devil's bouquet | Nyctaginaceae | Caryophyllales | 164 |
| *Nymphaea* | water-lily | Nymphaeaceae | Nymphaeales | 14 |
| *Ocimum* | basil | Lamiaceae | Lamiales | 200 |
| *Oenothera* | evening primrose | Onagraceae | Myrtales | 138 |
| *Olea* | olive | Oleaceae | Lamiales | 194 |
| *Onopordum* | Scotch thistle, cotton thistle | Compositae | Asterales | 210 |
| *Ophrys* | bee orchid, fly orchid | Orchidaceae | Asparagales | 42 |
| *Origanum* | oregano, marjoram | Lamiaceae | Lamiales | 200 |
| *Ornithogalum* | star of Bethlehem | Asparagaceae | Asparagales | 56 |
| *Oryza* | rice | Poaceae | Poales | 74 |
| *Osmanthus* | osmanthus | Oleaceae | Lamiales | 194 |
| *Ostrya* | hop hornbeam | Betulaceae | Fagales | 118 |
| *Oxalis* | oxalis, wood sorrel, shamrock | Oxalidaceae | Oxalidales | 124 |
| *Pachyphragma* | pennycress | Brassicaceae | Brassicales | 152 |
| *Pachysandra* | Japanese spurge | Buxaceae | Buxales | 88 |

| *Packera* | groundsel, ragwort | Compositae | Asterales | 214 |
|---|---|---|---|---|
| *Paeonia* | peony | Paeoniaceae | Saxifragales | 90 |
| *Panax* | ginseng | Araliaceae | Apiales | 228 |
| *Panicum* | common millet | Poaceae | Poales | 72 |
| *Papaver* | poppy | Papaveraceae | Ranunculales | 80 |
| *Paphiopedilum* | slipper orchid | Orchidaceae | Asparagales | 42 |
| *Parietaria* | pellitory of the wall | Urticaceae | Rosales | 112 |
| *Paris* | herb paris | Melanthiaceae | Lilales | 38 |
| *Parkinsonia* | palo verde, Jerusalem thorn | Fabaceae | Fabales | 104 |
| *Parrotia* | parrotia, ironwood | Hamamelidaceae | Saxifragales | 90 |
| *Parthenocissus* | Virginia creeper, Boston ivy | Vitaceae | Vitales | 100 |
| *Passiflora* | passion flower | Passifloraceae | Malpighiales | 128 |
| *Pastinaca* | parsnip | Apiaceae | Apiales | 230 |
| *Paulownia* | foxglove tree, empress tree | Paulowniaceae | Lamiales | 198 |
| *Pelargonium* | geranium | Geraniaceae | Geraniales | 134 |
| *Penstemon* | penstemon | Plantaginaceae | Lamiales | 196 |
| *Pentachondra* | beard-heath | Ericaceae | Ericales | 180 |
| *Pentas* | pentas | Rubiaceae | Gentianales | 186 |
| *Peperomia* | peperomia | Piperaceae | Piperales | 20 |
| *Pericallis* | cineraria | Compositae | Apiales | 214 |
| *Perovskia* | Russian sage | Lamiaceae | Lamiales | 200 |
| *Persea* | avocado, red bay tree, silk bay tree | Lauraceae | Laurales | 24 |
| *Persicaria* | knotweed | Polygonaceae | Caryophyllales | 158 |
| *Petalonyx* | sandpaper plant | Loasaceae | Cornales | 172 |
| *Petasites* | butterbur, coltsfoot | Compositae | Asterales | 214 |
| *Petrea* | purple wreath | Verbenaceae | Lamiales | 202 |
| *Petroselinum* | parsley | Apiaceae | Apiales | 230 |
| *Petunia* | petunia | Solanaceae | Solanales | 192 |
| *Phacelia* | phacelia, scorpion weed | Boraginaceae | not assigned | 182 |
| *Phalaenopsis* | moth orchid | Orchidaceae | Asparagales | 42 |
| *Phalaris* | reed grass | Poaceae | Poales | 72 |
| *Phaseolus* | bean | Fabaceae | Fabales | 102 |
| *Phenakospermum* | phenakospermum | Strelitziaceae | Zingiberales | 62 |
| *Philadelphus* | mock orange, syringa | Hydrangeaceae | Cornales | 172 |
| *Philodendron* | philodendron | Araceae | Alismatales | 32 |
| *Philesia* | philesia | Philesiaceae | Liliales | 40 |
| *Phleum* | timothy grass | Poaceae | Poales | 72 |
| *Phlomis* | Jerusalem sage | Lamiaceae | Lamiales | 200 |
| *Phlox* | phlox | Polemoniaceae | Ericales | 174 |
| *Phoenix* | date palm | Arecaceae | Arecales | 58 |

| *Phoradendron* | Christmas and desert mistletoe, big leaf | Santalaceae | Santalales | 154 |
|---|---|---|---|---|
| *Phormium* | New Zealand flax | Xanthorrhoeaceae | Asparagales | 46 |
| *Phragmites* | reeds, giant reed | Poaceae | Poales | 72 |
| *Phyla* | wedgeleaf, frogfruit | Verbenaceae | Lamiales | 202 |
| *Phyllostachys* | hardy bamboo | Poaceae | Poales | 74 |
| *Physalis* | Cape gooseberry, Chinese lantern | Solanaceae | Solanales | 192 |
| *Physocarpus* | ninebark | Rosaceae | Rosales | 108 |
| *Physostegia* | obedient plant | Lamiaceae | Lamiales | 200 |
| *Pieris* | pieris, lily-of-the-valley bush | Ericaceae | Ericales | 180 |
| *Pilea* | aluminum plant | Urticaceae | Rosales | 112 |
| *Pimenta* | allspice | Myrtaceae | Myrtales | 140 |
| *Pimpinella* | anise | Apiaceae | Apiales | 230 |
| *Piper* | black pepper | Piperaceae | Piperales | 20 |
| *Pistacia* | pistachio nut | Anacardiaceae | Sapindales | 142 |
| *Pistia* | water lettuce | Araceae | Alismatales | 32 |
| *Pisum* | pea | Fabaceae | Fabales | 102 |
| *Pittosporum* | pittosporum, parchment bark | Pittosporaceae | Apiales | 230 |
| *Planera* | planer tree | Ulmaceae | Rosales | 110 |
| *Plantago* | plantain | Plantaginaceae | Lamiales | 196 |
| *Platanthera* | fringed orchid, green orchid | Orchidaceae | Asparagales | 42 |
| *Platanus* | plane tree | Platanaceae | Proteales | 86 |
| *Platycodon* | balloon flower | Campanulaceae | Asterales | 206 |
| *Plectranthus* | coleus | Lamiaceae | Lamiales | 200 |
| *Plumbago* | Cape plumbago, leadwort | Plumbaginaceae | Caryophyllales | 156 |
| *Plumeria* | frangipani | Apocynaceae | Gentianales | 188 |
| *Poa* | meadow grass | Poaceae | Poales | 72 |
| *Podophyllum* | May apple, American mandrake | Berberidaceae | Ranunculales | 82 |
| *Polemonium* | Jacob's ladder | Polemoniaceae | Ericales | 174 |
| *Polygala* | milkwort | Polygalaceae | Fabales | 102 |
| *Polygonatum* | Solomon's seal | Ruscaceae | Asparagales | 54 |
| *Polygonum* | knotweed, bistort | Polygonaceae | Caryophyllales | 158 |
| *Pontederia* | pickerel weed | Pontederiaceae | Commelinales | 60 |
| *Populus* | aspen, poplar | Salicaceae | Malpighiales | 130 |
| *Portulaca* | portulaca, purslane | Portulacaceae | Caryophyllales | 164 |
| *Potentilla* | cinquefoil, strawberry | Rosaceae | Rosales | 106 |
| *Primula* | primrose, cowslip, oxlip polyanthus | Primulaceae | Ericales | 176 |
| *Prionium* | prionium | Juncaceae | Poales | 70 |
| *Prosopis* | mesquite | Fabaceae | Fabales | 104 |
| *Protea* | protea | Proteaceae | Proteales | 86 |
| *Prunella* | self-heal | Lamiaceae | Lamiales | 200 |

| | | | | |
|---|---|---|---|---|
| *Prunus* | plum, cherry, apricot, peach, nectarine, almond, cherry laurel | Rosaceae | Rosales | 108 |
| *Pseudognaphalium* | cud weed, rabbit-tobacco | Compositae | Asterales | 214 |
| *Pseudopanax* | lancewood, five finger | Araliaceae | Apiales | 228 |
| *Pseudowintera* | pepper tree | Winteraceae | Canellales | 18 |
| *Psidium* | guava | Myrtaceae | Myrtales | 140 |
| *Psilostrophe* | paperflower | Compositae | Asterales | 220 |
| *Psychotria* | ipecac | Rubiaceae | Gentianales | 186 |
| *Pterocarya* | wingnut | Juglandaceae | Fagales | 116 |
| *Ptilotus* | pussy tail | Amarynthaceae | Caryophyllales | 162 |
| *Pulmonaria* | lungwort | Boraginaceae | not assigned | 182 |
| *Punica* | pomegranate | Lythraceae | Myrtales | 136 |
| *Purshia* | cliff rose | Rosaceae | Rosales | 106 |
| *Puschkinia* | puschkinia | Asparagaceae | Asparagales | 56 |
| *Puya* | puya | Bromeliaceae | Poales | 68 |
| *Pyracantha* | firethorn, pyracantha | Rosaceae | Rosales | 108 |
| *Pyrola* | wintergreen | Ericaceae | Ericales | 180 |
| *Pyrus* | pear | Rosaceae | Rosales | 108 |
| *Quercus* | oak | Fagaceae | Fagales | 114 |
| *Quincula* | Chinese lantern, purple ground cherry | Solanaceae | Solanales | 192 |
| *Ranunculus* | buttercup, lesser celandine | Ranunculaceae | Ranunculales | 82 |
| *Raphanus* | radish | Brassicaceae | Brassicales | 152 |
| *Raphia* | raffia palm | Arecaceae | Arecales | 58 |
| *Ratibida* | Mexican hat, prairie cornflower | Compositae | Asterales | 218 |
| *Ravenala* | traveler's palm | Strelitziaceae | Zingiberales | 62 |
| *Reinwardtia* | yellow flax | Linaceae | Malpighiales | 132 |
| *Reseda* | mignonette, dyer's weed | Resedaceae | Brassicales | 150 |
| *Restio* | restio | Restionaceae | Poales | 70 |
| *Rhamnus* | buckthorn, cascara sagrada | Rhamnaceae | Rosales | 110 |
| *Rheum* | rhubarb | Polygonaceae | Caryophyllales | 158 |
| *Rhodocoma* | restio | Restionaceae | Poales | 70 |
| *Rhododendron* | azalea, rhododendron | Ericaceae | Ericales | 180 |
| *Rhodohypoxis* | rhodohypoxis | Hypoxidaceae | Asparagales | 44 |
| *Rhus* | sumac, poison ivy | Anacardiaceae | Sapindales | 142 |
| *Ribes* | gooseberry, currant | Grossulariaceae | Saxifragales | 92 |
| *Richea* | pandani | Ericaceae | Ericales | 180 |
| *Ricinus* | castor oil plant | Euphorbiaceae | Malpighiales | 126 |
| *Robinia* | locust tree, black locust | Fabaceae | Fabales | 102 |
| *Rodgersia* | rodgersia | Saxifragaceae | Saxifragales | 94 |
| *Romneya* | California tree poppy | Papaveraceae | Ranunculales | 80 |
| *Rosa* | rose | Rosaceae | Rosales | 106 |

| | | | | |
|---|---|---|---|---|
| *Roscoea* | roscoea | Zingiberaceae | Zingiberales | 66 |
| *Rosmarinus* | rosemary | Lamiaceae | Lamiales | 200 |
| *Rubia* | madder | Rubiaceae | Gentianales | 186 |
| *Rubus* | blackberry, raspberry, bramble, boysenberry, dewberry, cloud-berry, loganberry | Rosaceae | Rosales | 106 |
| *Rudbeckia* | black-eyed Susan | Compositae | Asterales | 218 |
| *Ruellia* | ruellia, wild petunia | Acanthaceae | Lamiales | 202 |
| *Rumex* | sorrel, dock | Polygonaceae | Caryophyllales | 158 |
| *Rupicapnos* | rupicapnos | Papaveraceae | Ranunculales | 80 |
| *Ruscus* | butcher's broom | Asparagaceae | Asparagales | 54 |
| *Ruta* | rue | Rutaceae | Sapindales | 142 |
| *Sabal* | palmetto palm | Arecaceae | Arecales | 58 |
| *Saccharum* | sugar cane | Poaceae | Poales | 74 |
| *Sagina* | pearlwort | Caryophyllaceae | Caryophyllales | 160 |
| *Sagittaria* | arrowhead, wapato | Alismataceae | Alismatales | 34 |
| *Salicornia* | glasswort, samphire, saltwort | Amaranthaceae | Caryophyllales | 162 |
| *Salix* | willow, sallow | Salicaceae | Malpighiales | 130 |
| *Salpiglossis* | painted tongue | Solanaceae | Solanales | 192 |
| *Salsola* | tumbleweed, Russian thistle | Amaranthaceae | Caryophyllales | 162 |
| *Salvia* | sage, salvia | Lamiaceae | Lamiales | 200 |
| *Sambucus* | elder, elderberry | Adoxaceae | Dipsacales | 222 |
| *Sandersonia* | Christmas bell | Colchicaceae | Liliales | 38 |
| *Sanguinaria* | bloodroot | Papaveraceae | Ranunculales | 80 |
| *Sanguisorba* | burnet | Rosaceae | Rosales | 106 |
| *Sanicula* | sanicle | Apiaceae | Apiales | 230 |
| *Sansevieria* | mother-in-law's tongue | Asparagaceae | Asparagales | 54 |
| *Santalum* | sandalwood | Santalaceae | Santalales | 154 |
| *Santolina* | lavender cotton, santolina | Compositae | Asterales | 216 |
| *Sapindus* | soapberry | Sapindaceae | Sapindales | 144 |
| *Saponaria* | soapwort | Caryophyllaceae | Caryophyllales | 160 |
| *Sarcocapnos* | sarcocapnos | Papaveraceae | Ranunculales | 80 |
| *Sarcococca* | sweet or Christmas box | Buxaceae | Buxales | 88 |
| *Sassafras* | sassafras | Lauraceae | Laurales | 24 |
| *Saururus* | lizard tail | Saururaceae | Piperales | 20 |
| *Saxifraga* | saxifrage | Saxifragaceae | Saxifragales | 94 |
| *Scabiosa* | scabious | Caprifoliaceae | Dipsacales | 224 |
| *Schefflera* | umbrella plant | Araliaceae | Apiales | 228 |
| *Schima* | schima | Theaceae | Ericales | 178 |
| *Schinus* | peppertree | Anacardiaceae | Sapindales | 142 |
| *Schisandra* | | Schisandraceae | Austrobaileyales | 11 |
| *Schizanthus* | butterfly flower | Solanaceae | Solanales | 192 |

| *Schoenoplectus* | bulrush | Cyperaceae | Poales | 70 |
| *Scilla* | squill | Asparagaceae | Asparagales | 56 |
| *Scirpus* | bulrush | Cyperaceae | Poales | 70 |
| *Scrophularia* | figwort | Scrophulariaceae | Lamiales | 198 |
| *Scutellaria* | skullcap | Lamiaceae | Lamiales | 200 |
| *Secale* | rye | Poaceae | Poales | 74 |
| *Sedum* | stonecrop, sedum | Crassulaceae | Saxifragales | 94 |
| *Semiarundinaria* | bamboo | Poaceae | Poales | 74 |
| *Sempervivum* | houseleek, hen and chickens | Crassulaceae | Saxifragales | 94 |
| *Senecio* | senecio, groundsel, ragwort | Compositae | Asterales | 214 |
| *Senegalia* | acacia, gum arabic | Fabaceae | Fabales | 104 |
| *Senna* | senna | Fabaceae | Fabales | 104 |
| *Shepherdia* | buffalo berry | Elaeagnaceae | Rosales | 110 |
| *Shortia* | oconee bells, fringe bells | Diapensiaceae | Ericales | 178 |
| *Sidalcea* | miniature hollyhock | Malvaceae | Malvales | 146 |
| *Silene* | campion, catchfly, silene | Caryophyllaceae | Caryophyllales | 160 |
| *Silybum* | milk thistle | Compositae | Asterales | 210 |
| *Sinofranchetia* | sinofranchetia | Lardizabalaceae | Ranunculales | 80 |
| *Sisymbrium* | hedge mustard, rocket | Brassicaceae | Brassicales | 152 |
| *Sisyrinchium* | blue-eyed grass | Iridaceae | Asparagales | 44 |
| *Sium* | water parsnip | Apiaceae | Apiales | 230 |
| *Skimmia* | skimmia | Rutaceae | Sapindales | 142 |
| *Smilax* | greenbrier, sarsaparilla | Smilacaceae | Liliales | 40 |
| *Smyrnium* | alexanders | Apiaceae | Apiales | 230 |
| *Solanum* | aubergine, tomato, potato, eggplant, nightshade, bittersweet | Solanaceae | Solanales | 192 |
| *Soldanella* | shooting star | Primulaceae | Ericales | 176 |
| *Soleirolia* | mind-your-own-business, mother-of-thousand | Urticaceae | Rosales | 112 |
| *Solidago* | goldenrod | Compositae | Asterales | 216 |
| *Sonchus* | sow-thistle | Compositae | Asterales | 212 |
| *Sophora* | pagoda tree, kowhai | Fabaceae | Fabales | 102 |
| *Sorbaria* | false spirea | Rosaceae | Rosales | 108 |
| *Sorbus* | white beam, mountain ash | Rosaceae | Rosales | 108 |
| *Sorghum* | sorghum, Johnson grass | Poaceae | Poales | 74 |
| *Sparaxis* | harlequin flower | Iridaceae | Asparagales | 44 |
| *Sparganium* | bur reed | Typhaceae | Poales | 68 |
| *Spathodea* | flame tree | Bignoniaceae | Lamiales | 202 |
| *Spinacia* | spinach | Amaranthaceae | Caryophyllales | 162 |
| *Spiraea* | spirea, bridal wreath | Rosaceae | Rosales | 108 |
| *Spiranthes* | lady's tresses | Orchidaceae | Asparagales | 42 |
| *Sprekelia* | Aztec lily, Jacobean lily | Amaryllidaceae | Asparagales | 50 |

| | | | | |
|---|---|---|---|---|
| *Stachys* | lamb's ears, betony | Lamiaceae | Lamiales | 200 |
| *Stapelia* | carrion or starfish flower | Apocynaceae | Gentianales | 188 |
| *Stellaria* | chickweed, stitchwort | Caryophyllaceae | Caryophyllales | 160 |
| *Stevia* | stevia, candyleaf | Compositae | Asterales | 218 |
| *Stewartia* | stewartia | Theaceae | Ericales | 178 |
| *Stipa* | feathergrass needle, needle grass | Poaceae | Poales | 72 |
| *Strelitzia* | bird-of-paradise | Strelitziaceae | Zingiberales | 62 |
| *Strobilanthes* | | Acanthaceae | Lamiales | 202 |
| *Stromanthe* | stromanthe, red rain | Marantaceae | Zingiberales | 66 |
| *Strophanthus* | climbing oleander, corkscrew flower | Apocynaceae | Gentianales | 188 |
| *Strychnos* | monkey apple | Loganiaceae | Gentianales | 188 |
| *Swertia* | star gentian | Gentianaceae | Gentianales | 186 |
| *Symphoricarpos* | snowberry | Caprifoliaceae | Dipsacales | 224 |
| *Symphytum* | comfrey | Boraginaceae | not assigned | 182 |
| *Symplocarpus* | skunk cabbage | Araceae | Alismatales | 32 |
| *Syringa* | lilac | Oleaceae | Lamiales | 194 |
| *Syzygium* | clove, mace | Myrtaceae | Myrtales | 140 |
| *Tacca* | bat-flower, arrowroot | Dioscoreaceae | Dioscoreales | 36 |
| *Tamarindus* | tamarind | Fabaceae | Fabales | 104 |
| *Tamarix* | salt cedar, tamarix | Tamaricaceae | Caryophyllales | 156 |
| *Tanacetum* | tansy, feverfew, pyrethrum | Compositae | Asterales | 216 |
| *Taraxacum* | dandelion | Compositae | Asterales | 212 |
| *Tasmannia* | mountain pepper | Winteraceae | Canellales | 18 |
| *Tecoma* | Cape honeysuckle | Bignoniaceae | Lamiales | 202 |
| *Tectona* | teak | Lamiaceae | Lamiales | 200 |
| *Tellima* | fringe-cup | Saxifragaceae | Saxifragales | 94 |
| *Telopea* | waratah | Proteaceae | Proteales | 86 |
| *Tetraneuris* | alpine sunflower | Compositae | Asterales | 220 |
| *Tetrapanax* | rice paper plant | Araliaceae | Apiales | 228 |
| *Tetrastigma* | chestnut vine | Vitaceae | Vitales | 100 |
| *Teucrium* | germander | Lamiaceae | Lamiales | 200 |
| *Thalia* | water canna | Marantaceae | Zingiberales | 66 |
| *Thalictrum* | meadow rue | Ranunculaceae | Ranunculales | 82 |
| *Thlaspi* | pennycress | Brassicaceae | Brassicales | 152 |
| *Thunbergia* | black-eyed Susan | Acanthaceae | Lamiales | 202 |
| *Thymus* | thyme | Lamiaceae | Lamiales | 200 |
| *Tiarella* | foamflower | Saxifragaceae | Saxifragales | 94 |
| *Tigridia* | tiger flower | Iridaceae | Asparagales | 44 |
| *Tilia* | linden tree, lime, basswood | Malvaceae | Malvales | 146 |
| *Tillandsia* | Spanish moss | Bromeliaceae | Poales | 68 |
| *Townsendia* | Easter daisy, townsendia | Compositae | Asterales | 216 |

| | | | | |
|---|---|---|---|---|
| *Trachelium* | throatwort | Campanulaceae | Asterales | 206 |
| *Trachycarpus* | chusan palm | Arecaceae | Arecales | 58 |
| *Tradescantia* | spiderwort, wandering Jew | Commelinaceae | Commelinales | 60 |
| *Tragopogon* | salsify, goat's beard | Compositae | Asterales | 212 |
| *Tricyrtis* | toad lily | Liliaceae | Liliales | 40 |
| *Trientalis* | chickweed wintergreen | Primulaceae | Ericales | 176 |
| *Trifolium* | clover | Fabaceae | Fabales | 102 |
| *Trillium* | wake Robin, trillium | Melanthiaceae | Liliales | 38 |
| *Triosteum* | wild coffee, fever root | Caprifoliaceae | Dipsacales | 224 |
| *Triticum* | wheat, spelt | Poaceae | Poales | 74 |
| *Trochocarpa* | pink berry, cheese bery | Ericaceae | Ericales | 180 |
| *Trollius* | globeflower | Ranunculaceae | Ranunculales | 82 |
| *Tropaeolum* | nasturtium, canary creeper | Tropaeolaceae | Brassicales | 150 |
| *Tulbaghia* | society garlic | Amaryllidaceae | Asparagales | 52 |
| *Tulipa* | tulip | Liliaceae | Liliales | 40 |
| *Tussilago* | coltsfoot | Compositae | Asterales | 214 |
| *Typha* | cattail, bulrush | Typhaceae | Poales | 68 |
| *Ulex* | gorse | Fabaceae | Fabales | 102 |
| *Ulmus* | elm | Ulmaceae | Rosales | 110 |
| *Umbilicus* | pennywort | Crassulaceae | Saxifragales | 94 |
| *Urtica* | stinging nettle | Urticaceae | Rosales | 112 |
| *Vaccinium* | blueberry, huckleberry, cranberry | Ericaceae | Ericales | 180 |
| *Vanda* | lei orchid | Orchidaceae | Asparagales | 42 |
| *Vanilla* | vanilla orchid | Orchidaceae | Asparagales | 42 |
| *Verbascum* | mullein | Scrophulariaceae | Lamiales | 198 |
| *Verbena* | verbena, vervain | Verbenaceae | Lamiales | 202 |
| *Veronica* | speedwell, veronica, brooklime | Plantaginaceae | Lamiales | 196 |
| *Viburnum* | guelder rose, viburnum, wayfarer's tree | Adoxaceae | Dipsacales | 222 |
| *Vicia* | vetch | Fabaceae | Fabales | 102 |
| *Victoria* | giant water-lily, Victorian water-lily | Nymphaeaceae | Nymphaeales | 14 |
| *Vinca* | periwinkle | Apocynaceae | Gentianales | 188 |
| *Viola* | violet, viola, pansy, heartsease | Violaceae | Malpighiales | 130 |
| *Viscum* | mistletoe | Santalaceae | Santalales | 154 |
| *Vitis* | grape vine | Vitaceae | Vitales | 100 |
| *Wahlenbergia* | ivy-leaved bellflower, royal bluebell | Campanulaceae | Asterales | 206 |
| *Washingtonia* | California fan palm, Mexican fan palm | Arecaceae | Arecales | 58 |
| *Weigela* | weigela | Caprifoliaceae | Dipsacales | 224 |
| *Weinmannia* | towai, kamahi | Cunoniaceae | Oxalidales | 124 |
| *Wisteria* | wisteria | Fabaceae | Fabales | 102 |

| | | | | |
|---|---|---|---|---|
| *Wolffia* | water meal | Araceae | Alismatales | 32 |
| *Xanthoceras* | yellow horn | Sapindaceae | Sapindales | 144 |
| *Xanthorrhoea* | grass tree | Xanthorrhoeaceae | Asparagales | 46 |
| *Xanthosoma* | tannia, yautia | Araceae | Alismatales | 32 |
| *Xeranthemum* | overlastings, immortelle | Compositae | Asterales | 210 |
| *Xerochrysum* | strawflower | Compositae | Asterales | 214 |
| *Yucca* | yucca, Joshua tree | Asparagaceae | Asparagales | 56 |
| *Zantedeschia* | calla lily, arum lily | Araceae | Alismatales | 32 |
| *Zea* | corn, popcorn, sweet corn, maize | Poaceae | Poales | 74 |
| *Zelkova* | zelkova | Ulmaceae | Rosales | 110 |
| *Zephyranthes* | zephyr lily, atamasco lily | Amaryllidaceae | Asparagales | 50 |
| *Zingiber* | ginger | Zingiberaceae | Zingiberales | 66 |
| *Zinnia* | zinnia | Compositae | Asterales | 218 |
| *Ziziphus* | Chinese jujube | Rhamnaceae | Rosales | 110 |

# APPENDIX C. ACKNOWLEDGEMENTS FOR ILLUSTRATIONS

The majority of the photographs in this book were taken by Priscilla Spears. The use of the remainder is very gratefully acknowledged here;

*First Nature (Sue Parker & Pat O'Reilly)*

Frontispiece; viii; p.15, Nymphaeaceae; p.33, *Arum*; p.37, *Dioscorea communis* berries, *Narthecium*; p.41, *Fritillaria*; p.43, orchids except *Paphiopedilum*, *Phalaeonopsis* and *Vanilla*; p.51, Tenby daffodil; p.53, *Allium ursinum*; p.55, *Polygonatum*; p.57, *Scilla*, *Hyacinthoides*; p.69, *Sparganium*; p.71, *Luzula*, *Carex*; p.81, *Akebia*; p.102, *Polygala*; p.103, *Vicia*; p.106, *Dryas*; p.109, *Filipendula*; p.121, *Bryonia*; p.125, *Oxalis*; p.131, *Viola riviniana*; p.133, *Linum*; p.135, *Geranium pratense*; p.137, *Lythrum*; p.145, *Aesculus hippocastanum*; p.149, *Helianthemum*; p.151, *Reseda luteola*; p.155, *Viscum album* overview; p.161, *Silene dioica*; p.175, *Impatiens*; p.179, *Camellia* R.L. Wheeler; p.181, *Vaccinium*; p.187, *Gentiana*; p.191, *Convolvulus soldanella*; p.199, *Scrophularia*; p.208, *Barnadesia*; p.211, *Cirsium*; p.217, *Bellis*, *Achillea*, *Aster*; p.223, *Adoxa*; p.225, *Leycesteria*; Back cover.

*Laura Davies and staff at the National Botanic Garden of Wales*

Front Cover; p.x; pp.8,9; p.11, *Schisandra*; p.19; p.23, *Magnolia (Michelia) alba*; p.29, overviews; p.37, *Dioscorea* leaves, *Tacca*; p.39, *Bomarea*, *Colchicum*, *Gloriosa*; p.41, *Lapageria*; p.45, *Astelia*, Hypoxidaceae; p.47, *Xanthorrhoea*; p.49; p.50; p.51, Derwydd daffodil; p.53, *Tulbaghia*; p.55, *Convallaria*; p.59, *Trachycarpus*; p.71, restios; p.73, ornamental grasses; p.75, *Avena*; p.79, Crassulaceae and Paeoniaceae; p.87, *Banksia*, *Hakea*, *Leucadendron*, *Protea*; p.89, except *Sarcococca*; p.91, *Fothergilla* sp.; p.93, *Ribes rubrum*; p.99, eudicot borders, Fabales; p.109, *Sorbus*, *Spiraea*; p.111, *Eleagnus*; p.117, *Morella faya*; p.119, *Casuarina*; p.127, *Euphorbia* sp.; p.133, all Hypericaceae except *Hypericum calycinum*; p.149, *Cistus*; p.151, *Tropaeolum tricolor*, *T. majus*; *Limnanthus*; p.159, *Rheum* leaf bases; p.169, asterids, Cornales; p.170, Apiales; p.171, Solanales; p.179, *Camellia* Cornish snow; p.181, *Epacris*; p.211, *Centauria*; p.229, *Hedera* flowers, *Fatshedera*.

*Chris Berry/Alan Channing*

p.25, *Laurus*; p.55, *Ruscus* berry; p.71, *Juncus*; p.73, d; p.89, *Sarcococca*; p.91, *Corylopsis*; p.109, *Chaenomeles*; p.115, *Fagus* fruit; p.149, *Daphne odora*; p.151, close ups of *Reseda*; p.157, *Tamarix*; p.173, *Cornus mas*; p.177, *Primula vulgaris*, *Lysimachia*, *Cyclamen*; p.185, *Garrya*, *Aucuba*; p.225, *Abelia*; p.229, *Hedera* leaf and fruits.

*General*

p.11, Sangtae Kim, University of Florida, *Amborella*; Daniel Mosquin, *Kadsura*; Cajsa Anderson, *Illicium*; pp.12,13, Pat Gensel, whole pages; p.37, National Museum of Wales (NMW), *Dioscorea communis* flowers; p.39, Royal Botanic Garden Edinburgh, *Trillium*; Tim Rich, *Paris*; p.43, Patricia and Jeff Harding, *Vanilla*; p.47, Ralph Laby, *Dianella*; p.49, NMW, *Asphodelus lusitanicus*; p.75, IGER, a-c, e-f; p.79, Pat Gensel, Ranunculales, Saxafragales; p.87, D. Siveter, bark; P. Ladd, *Grevillea*; H. Sauquet, *Embothrium*; p.93, P. Ladd, *Ribes uva-crispa*; p.105, *Acacia*; p. 113, *Urtica dioica* (close-up); p.117, S.A.Crutchley, Royal Botanic Garden Edinburgh, *Myrica gale*; p.125, P. Ladd, *Crinodendron*; J. & G. Ettershank, *Eucrypha*; p.133, Cajsa Anderson *Hypericum calycinum*; p.141, P. Ladd, *Callistemon* flowers; p.149, NMW, *Daphne mezereum*, *D. laureola*; p.155, P. Ladd, *Viscum album* fruit; p.179, Royal Botanic Garden Edinburgh, *Diapensia lapponica*; D. Siveter, *Actinidia* sp. p.199, J. Tims, *Paulownia*; p.213, H. Sass, *Lactuca sativa*; p.215, Richard Abbott, *Senecio cambrensis*; p.223, T. Rich, *Viburnum opulus*; p.225, Sandy Knapp, *Linnaea*.

# GLOSSARY

**achene**: a closed, dry fruit with one seed; the seed attaches to the relatively thin hull at one point. Example: sunflower seed.

**anther**: the part of a stamen where the pollen develops and is released. It is attached to the top of the filament.

**aromatic**: fragrant, having a marked, usually pleasant smell.

**asymmetric**: shaped such that it cannot be divided into two equal halves.

**berry**: a simple, fleshy fruit that usually has several seeds and develops from a single pistil. Examples: watermelon, blueberry.

**bilateral**: having two equal sides; can be divided into two equal parts with a cut in only one place. Example: snapdragon flower.

**bisexual**: having both stamens and carpels (pistils) - the most common structure for flowers.

**bract**: a modified leaf that is usually smaller than the normal leaves and is often found on the floral shoot.

**bulb**: an underground bud with thickened, fleshy modified leaves.

**calyx**: all of thc sepals together; thc outermost whorl of flower parts and of the perianth.

**capsule**: a dry fruit that forms from a pistil with two or more carpels and that splits open when it is mature.

**carpel**: a simple pistil; the unit of compound pistils; the ovule-bearing unit of the flower, consisting of the ovary, style, and stigma.

**carpellate**: term used to tell how many units make up a pistil. Example: the three-carpellate pistil of a lily is made of three carpels fused together.

**carpellate flower**: a flower that has one or more carpels, but no stamens. Also called a pistillate flower; casually called a fcmale flower.

**claw**: the markedly narrowed base portion of a petal. A clawed petal is one that has a claw. Example: carnation petal.

**cladophyll**: a stem that has the form and function of a leaf.

**compound**: composed of two or more similar units.

**compound leaf**: a leaf that has two or more blades; it is rarely found outside the eudicots.

**contractile roots**: modified roots that pull the shoot or bulb deeper into the ground.

**cordate**: heart-shaped. Usually describes the shape of leaves.

**corm**: a modified stem that is short, fleshy, and underground. Example: gladiolus corm.

**corolla**: all of the petals of a flower taken together; the inner whorl of the perianth.

**corona**: an outgrowth of the corolla or stamens, usually showy. Example: daffodil trumpet.

**cotyledon**: a seed leaf, the first leaf or leaves of the embryo plant.

**cyathium**: a specialised inflorescence composed of unisexual flowers enclosed in a cup-like structure with nectar glands; characteristic of the Euphorbiaceae. (plural-cyathia)

**dioecious**: literally, "in two houses"; a species that has unisexual flowers with the sexes on separate plants. Example: holly.

**disk flower**: a radially symmetrical flower that makes up part or all of the head inflorescence of the family Compositae (Asteraceae).

**distinct**: separate, not joined to a like part, not fused.

**drupe**: a simple, fleshy fruit that has a stony pit. Examples: peach, cherry.

**endocarp**: the inner layer of the pericarp, usually in a fleshy fruit. The pit of a peach and the gel-like layer around tomato seeds are endocarps.

**epicalyx**: bracts that lie beneath the true calyx.

**ethereal oils**: aromatic, oily compounds made by plants and often found in glands or dots on the leaves.

**exocarp**: the outer layer of a pericarp, usually in a fleshy fruit, like the skin of a peach.

**filament**: the stalk of the stamen, which supports the anther.

**floral shoot**: a branch on which one or more flowers grow.

**floral cup**: a cup-like structure formed from the fusion of the perianth and stamen parts. Example: the base of a rose. Also called a hypanthium.

**floral tube**: a tube formed from the fusion of perianth and stamen parts. Example: section between the ovary and calyx of evening primrose. Also called a hypanthium.

**follicle**: a dry fruit that develops from a single carpel and splits open along one side when it is mature.

**fruit**: the mature, ripened ovary of a pistil. Fruits can be dry seed pods or fleshy and juicy.

**fused**: grown as if the parts were melted together.

**haustoria**: roots that are modified to grow into another plant and remove water and nutrients. (singular haustorium)

**head**: an inflorescence composed of small flowers attached directly to a short, broad, often disk-like receptacle.

**inferior ovary**: an ovary that is positioned beneath the perianth and stamens. Examples: squash, daffodil.

**inflorescence**: two or more flowers on one flower-bearing stem or floral shoot.

**internode**: the part of a stem that is between two nodes.

**involucre**: many, closely set bracts that grow beneath a flower or inflorescence. Found in Compositae (Asteraceae) and other families, and often mistaken for a calyx.

**legume**: a dry fruit that develops from a superior ovary and splits into two halves with seeds on both halves in alternating positions. Example: pea pod.

**lobed leaf**: a leaf with large, rounded projections from the margin. Example: classic oak leaf.

**locule**: a chamber or compartment within the ovary, in which the ovules attach. Anthers also have locules, in which the pollen forms.

**margin**: the outer edge of a plant structure, such as the edge of a leaf blade.

**mesocarp**: the middle layer of a pericarp, usually developed in a fleshy fruit. Example: the flesh of a peach.

**monoecious**: literally, "in one house"; a species that has unisexual flowers with both sexes on one plant. Example: squash.

**multiple fruit**: a fruit formed by the fusion of the separate ovaries from many flowers. Examples: pineapple, mulberry.

**mycorrhizae**: mutually beneficial partnership between fungi and the roots or other underground parts of a plant. Probably the most widespread symbiosis on Earth.

**nectary**: the location in which nectar is produced and presented to pollinators.

**node**: the place on a stem where a leaf or lateral stem attaches.

**numerous**: more than about 15 of a part; for stamens, more than twice the number of petals.

**nut**: a dry fruit that forms from a single carpel and does not split open at maturity. It usually has a thick, woody shell. Example: acorn.

**odd-pinnately compound**: a compound leaf that has an odd number of leaflets and ends with a single leaflet.

**ovary**: the part of the pistil or carpel that holds the ovules and develops into the fruit.

**ovule**: an immature seed. It can become the seed after it is fertilised by cells from pollen.

**palmate**: radiating out from a single point or area. It can describe leaflets in a compound leaf or a venation pattern.

**pappus**: the modified sepals of the family Compositae (Asteraceae), which are bristles, scales, hairs, or fibres.

**perennial**: a plant that lives for more than two years.

**perianth**: the two whorls of flower parts beneath the stamens and pistil; the term for the calyx and corolla together.

**pericarp**: the wall of a fruit. It forms from the wall of the ovary and consists of everything from the seed(s) to the outside of the fruit. See also endocarp, mesocarp, and exocarp.

**persistent**: remaining attached after its function has been served; refers to sepals or petals that stay on the flower after it has bloomed.

**petiole**: the stalk of a leaf.

**phyllary**: one of the bracts that make the involucre of Compositae (Asteraceae) flowers. Example: the leaf-like part we pull off from an artichoke when we eat it.

**pinnate**: with one central stem or vessel and many side branches, like a feather or the teeth of a comb. It can describe leaflets of a compound leaf or a venation pattern. "Bipinnate" describes a compound leaf whose side branches have their own side branches.

**pistil**: the ovule-bearing part of the flower that consists of one carpel, or two or more fused carpels.

**pistillate**: a flower with only a pistil or whose only functional reproductive part is a pistil; casually called a female flower.

**pome:** a fruit of the rose family whose fleshy part is derived from the wall of the receptacle cup. Examples: apple, pear, quince.

**raceme:** an inflorescence that has a single, elongated stem and in which the flowers each have a short stem and mature from the bottom up.

**radial symmetry:** structured such that it can be cut in two equal halves in several planes. Example: a petunia flower.

**ray flower:** a flower of the Compositae (Asteraceae) that has an elongated, strap-like corolla. It can occur around the outside of disk flowers or be the only component of a head. It is often mistaken for petals.

**receptacle:** the end of the flower-bearing stem where the flower parts attach. It is often broader than the stem.

**rhizome:** an underground stem that grows horizontally and often functions as storage for food or water.

**root nodules:** swelling or small knob on a root in which nitrogen-fixing bacteria live. These structures are common in the family Fabaceae, but also are found in other families.

**rosette:** a dense, rounded cluster of leaves that grows at ground level.

**samara:** a closed, dry fruit with a wing-like structure that helps it blow away on the wind.

**scape:** an erect stem that has no leaves and ends in a flower or inflorescence.

**schizocarp:** a dry fruit from a pistil that has two or more carpels; it breaks into two or more one-seeded, closed segments at maturity. Examples: hollyhock, maple.

**serrate leaf:** a leaf with forward-pointing teeth on its margin. Biserrate leaves have coarse teeth that are covered with fine teeth.

**sessile:** literally, "sitting upon"; a stem that is so short it cannot be seen; a leaf that has no petiole.

**sheathing leaf:** a leaf whose petiole base wraps around the stem.

**simple leaf:** a leaf with only one blade; not divided into leaflets.

**solitary:** one at a time; describes single flowers on a floral shoot versus inflorescences

**spike:** an inflorescence with a single, elongated stem to which the flowers are directly attached. Flowers mature from the bottom upward.

**spikelet:** a small spike composed of one or more flowers with two bracts beneath them; the basic inflorescence unit of grasses and sedges.

**spine:** a modified leaf or stipule that is sharp and pointy.

**stamen:** the pollen-bearing part of the flower, consisting of a filament and an anther.

**staminate:** a flower with only stamens or whose only functional reproductive parts are stamens.

**stigma:** the surface at the end of the pistil to which the pollen sticks.

**stipule:** usually one of a pair of leaf blade-like structures that grow either at the base of the petiole or on the internode; may also be single.

**style:** the long, narrow part that connects the carpel's or pistil's ovary to its stigma.

**succulent:** thick and juicy.

**superior ovary:** an ovary that is positioned on top of the perianth and stamens.

**tendril:** a modified leaf or stem that is long and thin and that supports a climbing plant by wrapping around structures.

**tepal:** a perianth segment that is neither petal or sepal; a perianth segment that looks much like all the other segments and serves the same function.

**tuber:** a short, thick, underground stem that is modified to store food. Example: potato.

**umbel:** an inflorescence with many branches that are about the same length and that each end in a flower. In compound umbels, the branches end in another smaller umbel.

**unisexual:** a flower that has either stamens or pistils, but not both.

**vascular bundles:** groups of xylem and phloem tubes.

**venation:** the pattern of veins in a leaf. Venation may be pinnate, palmate, or parallel.

**whorl:** three or more parts of the same kind that are attached at one level around the stem.

# SELECTED REFERENCES

The following references were either consulted in the preparation of this book or will provide additional information.

## Principal resources:

Stevens, P. F. (2001 onwards). Angiosperm Phylogeny Website. Version 6, May 2005 [and more or less continuously updated since]. Available at: http://www.mobot.org/MOBOT/research/APweb/. Accessed January 6, 2006.

Angiosperm Phylogeny Group. 2009. An update of the Angiosperm Phylogeny Group classification for the orders and families of flowering plants: APG III. Bot. J. Linn. Soc. 161: 105-121.

Bremer, K. Bremer, B. Thulin, M. 2003. Introduction to phylogeny and systematics of flowering plants. Acta Universitatis Uspaliensis Symbolae Botanicae Upsalienses 33(2):1-102. [ISSN 0082-0644 ISBN 91-554-5828-9]

Chase, M.W., Reveal, J.L. & Fay, M.F. 2009. A subfamilial classification for the expanded asparagalean families Amaryllidaceae, Asparagaceae and Xanthorrhoeaceae. Bot. J. Linn. Soc. 161: 132-136.

Funk, V. A, Bayer, R. J., Keeley, S., Chan, R., Watson, L., Gemeinholzer, B., Schilling, E., Panero, J. L., Baldwin, B. G., Garcia-Jacas, N., Susanna, A. & Jansen, R. K. 2005. Everywhere but Antarctica: Using a supertree to understand the diversity and distribution of the Compositae. Biol. Skr. 55: 343-374.

Haston, E., Richardson, J.W., Stevens, P.F., Chase, M.W. & Harris, D.J. 2009. The linear Angiosperm Phylogeny Group (LAPG) III: a linear sequence of the families in APG III. Bot. J. Linn. Soc. 161, 128-131.

Judd, W. S., Campbell, C., Kellogg, E. A., Stevens, P. F. & Donoghue, M. J. 2002. Plant systematics: A phylogenetic approach. Sinauer Associates, Sunderland, Massachusetts. [ISBN 0-87893-403-0]

Judd, W. S. & Olmstead, R. G. 2004. A survey of tricolpate (eudicot) phylogenetic relationships. Amer. J. Bot. 91: 1627-1644.

Mabberley, D. J. 2008. Mabberley's plant-book: A portable dictionary of plants, their classification and uses. 3rd edition. Cambridge Univ. Press, Cambridge. [ISBN 978-0-521-82071-4]

Mabey, R. Flora Britannica. The definitive new guide to wild flowers, plants and trees. Sinclair-Stevenson, London [ISBN 1-85619-377-2]

Potter, D., Eriksson, T., Evans, R. C., Oh, S., Smedmark, J. E. E., Morgan, D. R., Kerr, M., Robertson, K. R., Arsenault, M., Dickinson, T. A. & Campbell, C. S. 2007. Phylogeny and classification of Rosaceae. Pl. Syst. Evol. 266: 5-43.

Soltis, P. S. & Soltis, D. E. 2004. The origin and diversification of the angiosperms. Amer. J. Bot. 91: 1614-1626.

Soltis, D. K, Soltis, P. S., Endress, P. K. & Chase, M. W. 2005. Phylogeny and evolution of the angiosperms. Sinauer Associates, Sunderland, Massachusetts. [ISBN 0-87893-817-6]

Zomlefer, W. 1994. Guide to the flowering plant families. Univ. of North Carolina Press, Chapel Hill. [ISBN 0-8078-4470-5]

## Additional resources:

Angiosperm Phylogeny Group. 1998. An ordinal classification for the families of flowering plants. Ann. Missouri Bot. Gard. 85: 531-553.

Blainey, M., Fitter, R. & Fitter, A. 2003. Wild flowers of Britain and Ireland. A. & C. Black, London. [ISBN 0-7136-5944-0]

Bremer, K. 1994. Asteraceae: cladistics & classification. Timber Press, Portland, Oregon. [ISBN 0-88192-275-7]

Brickell, C. (Ed.). 2006. RHS Encyclopedia of plants & flowers. Dorling Kindersley, London. [ISBN 9781405314541]

Bryant, G., Rodd, T. & von Berg, G. (editors). 1999. Botanica's annuals and perennials. Laurel Glenn Publishing, San Diego, California. [ISBN *-57*45-648-*]

Ellis, R. G. 1983. Flowering plants of Wales. 3rd edition. National Museum of Wales, Cardiff. [ISBN 0720002710]

Evans, T. G. 2007. Flora of Monmouthshire. Chepstow Society, Chepstow. [ISBN 0900278495]

Heywood, V.H., Brummitt, R.K., Culham, A. & Seberg, O. 2007. Flowering plant families of the world. Royal Botanic Gardens, Kew. [ISBN-13 978 1 84246 165 5; ISBN-10 1 84246 165 6]

Hubbard, C. E. 1984. Grasses. Penguin Books, 3rd edition. London. [ISBN 0-14-013227-9]

Integrated Taxonomic Information System (ITIS). Available at: http://www.itis.usda.govf. Accessed December 29, 2005.

International Plant Names Index (2004). Available at: http://V\TWV\T.ipnLorg/index.html. Accessed January 6, 2006.

Lippert, W. & Podlech D. 1994. Wild flowers of Britain and Europe. Harper Collins. London [ISBN 0-00-219996-3]

Marren, P. 2005. Britain's rare flowers. A & C Black, London. [ISBN 9780713671629]

McGee, H. 2004. On food and cooking: The science and lore of the kitchen. Revised edition. Scribner, New York. [ISBN 0-684-80001-2]

McHoy, P. 1995. The complete houseplant book. Smithmark Books, New York. [ISBN 0-8317-1175-2]

O'Reilly, P. & Parker, S. 2005. Wonderful wildflowers of Wales, vol. 1. Woodland and waysides. First Nature, Rhydlewis. [ISBN 0-9549554-1-2]

O'Reilly, P. & Parker, S. 2005. Wonderful wildflowers of Wales, vol. 2. Seashores and coastal cliffs. First Nature, Rhydlewis. [ISBN 0-9549554-2-0]

O'Reilly, P. & Parker, S. 2006. Wonderful wildflowers of Wales, vol. 3. Mountains, moorland and meadows. First Nature, Rhydlewis. [ISBN 0-9549554-3-9]

O'Reilly, P. & Parker, S. 2006. Wonderful wildflowers of Wales, vol. 4. Waterside and wetland. First Nature, Rhydlewis. [ISBN 0-9549554-4-7]

Parker, S. 2006. Wild orchids in Wales. First Nature, Rhydlewis. [ISBN 0-9549554-6-3]

Pavord A. 2005. The naming of names: the search for order in the world of plants. Bloomsbury publishing plc. [ISBN 0-7475-7952-0; ISBN-13 9780747579526]

Phillips, R. 1977. Wild flowers of Britain. Pan Books Ltd., London. [ISBN 0-320-25183-X]

Phillips, R. 1978. Trees in Britain, Europe and North America. Pan Books Ltd., London. [ISBN 0-330-25480-4]

Preston, C. D., Pearman, D. A. & Dines, T. D. 2002. New atlas of the British and Irish flora. Oxford University Press, Oxford. [ISBN 0198510675]

RHS plant finder. 2008-9. Dorling Kindersley, London. [ISBN 978-1-4053-3190-6]

Richards, A. J. 1997. Plant breeding systems. Chapman & Hall, London. [ISBN 0-412-57440-3 (Hb), 0-412-57450-0 (Pb)]

Rose, F. & O'Reilly, C. 2006. The wild flower key. Frederick Warne, London. [ISBN 0723251754]

Stace, C. 2010. New Flora of the British Isles. 23rd edition, Cambridge, Cambridge University Press. [ISBN -13:9780521707725]

Vaughan, J. G. & Geissler, C. A. 1997. The new Oxford book of food plants. Oxford Univ. Press, Oxford. [ISBN 0-19850567-1]

W3TROPICOS website. Available at: http://mobot.mobot.org/W3T/Search/vast.html. Accessed Jannary 6,2006.

Wasson, E. (editor). 2003. The complete encyclopedia of trees and shrubs. Thunder Bay Press, San Diego, California. [ISBN 1-59223-055-5]

White, J., White, J. & Walters, S. M. 2005. Trees – a field guide to the trees of Britain and Northern Europe. Oxford University Press. [ISBN-0-19-851874].

Wigginton, M. J. (ed.). 1999. British red data books. 1. Vascular plants. 3rd edition. Joint Nature Conservation Committee, Peterborough. [ISBN 1861074514]

# INDEX OF FLOWERING PLANT FAMILIES *(entries in blue are illustrated)*